ELLIOT FINE

MOVES & GROOVES FOR DRUM SET

I dedicate this book to my wife Agnes, and to Chuck Elledge, whose constant prodding brought this book to its conclusion.

E. F.

Dear Friends in Percussion,

Elliot Fine's contribution to percussion education is unrivaled. His commitment to his students is unceasing and inspiring. In the following pages, you will find a wealth of material by Mr. Fine which will enrich your skills and creativity, regardless of your level of advancement. It is with admiration and respect that this book is brought to you.

Best of luck in all your music endeavors!

Chuck Elledge
Editor

ISBN 0-8497-5503-4

TABLE OF CONTENTS

ABOUT THE BOOK

The main body of MOVES & GROOVES (pages 8–134) contains two different types of studies: those relating to fill development, and those relating to groove development (hence the title "Moves and Grooves"). However, differentiation between grooves and fills is, in many ways, academic. Many grooves can also function as subtle fills, or vice versa, depending on the context.

Although the studies are organized sequentially according to the rhythms used in each study, they may be explored in any order which best fits the objectives of the player. While some players may wish to approach the studies sequentially, others may prefer to "skip around" the book, using the Table of Contents on pages 2–3 as a guide and checklist.

Additional groove and fill development material may be found in the Appendices (pages 135–149). A Feet Pattern Library, referred to frequently throughout the book, appears on pages 150–151.

Exploring the Studies

After mastering the patterns* in each MOVES & GROOVES study "as written," further explore each study by applying the **Practice Options** and **Variations** provided:

Practice Options give basic suggestions for creative interpretation of each study.

Variations provide more advanced technical alternatives for each study, taking you beyond the printed page.

You are encouraged to apply this material imaginatively. In many cases, **Practice Options** and **Variations** may be combined to create even more practice possibilities. With a bit of adapting, many can even be applied to other classic drum set and snare drum texts.

In addition, when practicing, apply these general suggestions as appropriate:

- ☐ Practice the patterns in each study at a variety of tempos, using a metronome or drum machine during a portion of your practice session. At first, always practice a pattern as slowly as necessary to achieve accurate performance. Once you have mastered the pattern, practice it at both slow and fast tempos.
- ☐ Play each pattern at a variety of dynamic levels, ranging from ***pp*** to ***ff***.
- ☐ Whenever possible, play each pattern using brushes. This will develop your overall control, especially in your wrists and fingers.
- ☐ Play the patterns within each study consecutively, one after another. This will develop your improvisational skills, and ability to create long phrases and extended solos.

NOTE: Examples provided with **Practice Options** and **Variations** are identified by a number and/or letter combination which appears in parentheses after the word "Example." This number and/or letter refers to the specific exercise in each study which has been modified for the sake of demonstration.

*In this book, the grooves and fill patterns in each study are often referred to simply as "patterns."

Notation

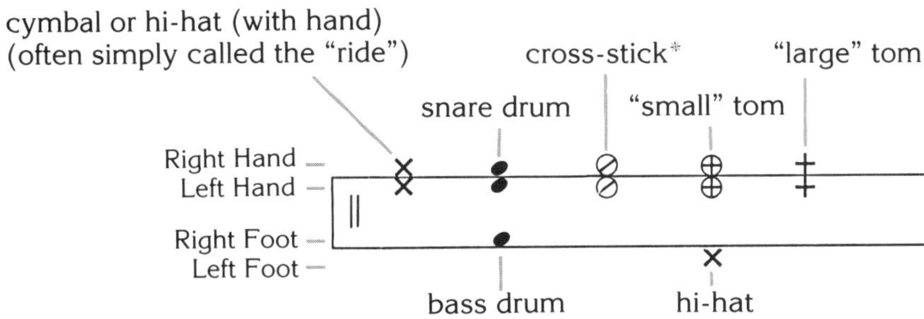

As you use MOVES & GROOVES, keep the following in mind regarding the notation:

- ☐ In general, play notes and symbols written above the top line with your right hand, and notes and symbols written below the top line with your left hand. For additional practice, play patterns with your left hand playing the "right hand part" (part above the top line), and your right hand playing the "left hand part" (part below the top line). Modify the patterns as necessary to allow this hand "role reversal."†

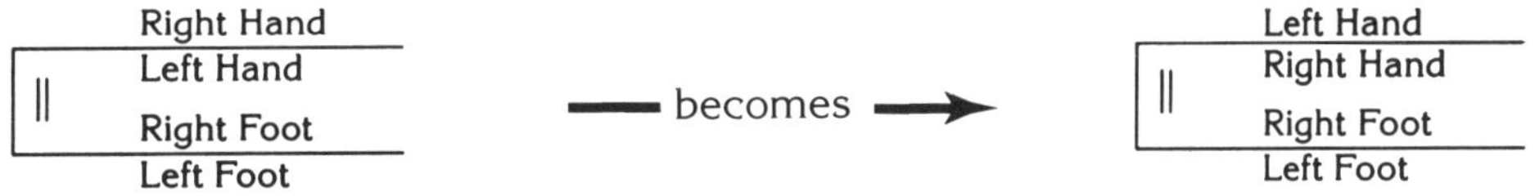

- ☐ When an "X" appears above or below the top line, it is referring to a cymbal or hi-hat. It is suggested that you ride on a cymbal when first learning a pattern, unless the pattern is specifically designed to utilize the hi-hat. When playing jazz grooves, it is usually stylistically most appropriate to ride on a cymbal.

- ☐ In some studies, the symbols "+" and "o" are used as specific indications to close and open the hi-hat with the foot. When this is the case, the hi-hat should be open only on notes with an "o" above them. The hi-hat should close on any "+" and remain closed until the next "o" appears. Use the hi-hat as the primary riding surface for both your right and left hands in these studies.

- ☐ To provide maximum flexibility, only two tom symbols are used in this book: one for "small" tom (⊕) and one for "large" tom (+). At first, follow these symbols literally, using only one mounted ("small"/high-pitched) tom and one floor ("large"/low-pitched) tom. Once you have mastered the basic movements, you are encouraged to adapt each study to your particular drum kit, interpreting the notation in a more general way. For example:

  — play any of your high-pitched or mounted toms when you see the "small tom" symbol (⊕).
  — play any of your low-pitched or floor toms when you see the "large tom" symbol (+).

---

* To play a cross-stick:
1. Lay the stick across the drum, with the bead resting on the drum head and the butt end extending over the rim.
2. Using the bead as a pivot point, raise the stick with your index finger and thumb.
3. Strike the rim with the shaft of the stick. Make sure that the bead remains on the head for the entire stroke.

† In many studies, the roles of the *feet* may also be reversed (bass drum part being played on the hi-hat, and hi-hat part being played on the bass drum). It is even possible, in some studies, to exchange the roles of the hands and feet (hand parts being played by the feet and feet parts being played by the hands). You are encouraged to experiment with the various combinations and apply what best fits *your* practicing and performing goals!

More about Fill ("Move") Studies

A piece of music is made up of short musical ideas called phrases. A phrase is often four or eight measures in a popular song. A fill is a rhythmic figure most often played at the end of a phrase, leading into a new phrase. If musically appropriate in a given arrangement, fills may also be played at other points in a phrase.

With these points in mind, practice each fill pattern in this book in the following three ways:

1) Repeatedly alone, to capture the feel of the fill, and to master it technically.
2) Alternating with a groove pattern of the same length and in an appropriate style. (In this context, the groove pattern is referred to as "time" or "rhythm ahead".) When the fill pattern is no more than two beats, alternate the groove pattern with the fill repeated twice.
3) In the context of a four or eight measure phrase, with the fill coming at the end of the phrase. (The "time" followed by the fill should add up to four or eight total measures).

Below are some basic grooves you can use as "time" when practicing fills. Use them only as a starting point. You may also use many of the simpler grooves found throughout this book.*

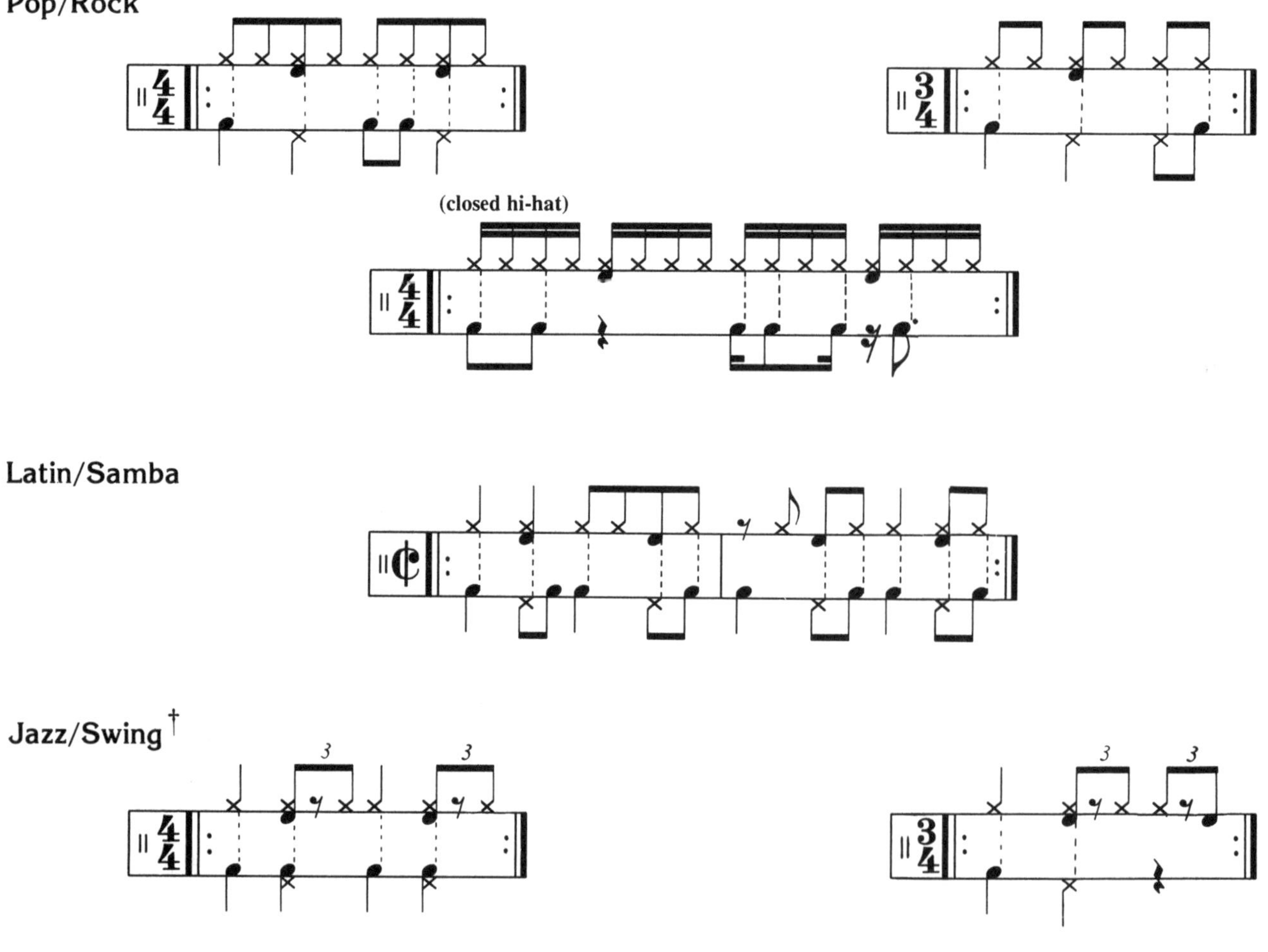

---

* Whenever necessary, omit the first note of the ride part in a groove pattern to eliminate awkward sticking between the end of a fill and the beginning of the time. Also, to help maintain continuity, keep the hi-hat part constant between the time and the fill. This may require you to adjust the fill's written hi-hat part, depending on the "time pattern" you choose.

† While the bass drum is often shown on every beat in written jazz grooves or charts, it is generally not played on every beat in contemporary jazz settings. In such cases, feel free to break away from this pattern and play more sparsely. However, "four to the floor" is often the appropriate technique in big band and traditional jazz settings, and therefore should not be overlooked.

Similarly, the snare drum is often shown on beats 2 and 4 in written parts, even though it is generally not to be played strictly on those beats in contemporary jazz. Once again, however, a 2 and 4 back-beat can be extremely effective in many big band or traditional jazz settings.

More about Groove Studies

While playing fills is an important part of drumming, most drumming involves playing "time"—also known as playing "beats," or "grooves." Many styles of popular music are determined in large part by the groove supplied by the drummer. The groove studies in this book cover many of the most important styles.

In many cases, the groove studies are presented in $\frac{2}{4}$ or even $\frac{1}{4}$ time! This does not mean that they are designed only for music in $\frac{2}{4}$ or $\frac{1}{4}$ time, but rather that they are patterns one or two beats in length which can be combined to create longer grooves. Remember, a $\frac{2}{4}$ groove played twice results in a $\frac{4}{4}$ groove (or a $\frac{5}{4}$ groove if played two and a half times!)

Also remember that many patterns in this book classified as grooves can also be used in a fill context. Often, only slightly changing the groove in a phrase is enough to provide a "fill effect." When practicing groove studies, try playing one pattern for three or seven measures, then complete the phrase with another pattern from the same study. You'll notice how the subtle groove change really makes the phrase ending come alive.

In groove studies where the parts are the same from pattern to pattern for three of the limbs, you are encouraged to practice improvising the variable part while continuously repeating the constants. (For example, in study #6 on page 18, improvise the ride part while continuously repeating the snare and feet parts.) This will further develop your improvisational skills and your ability to create long phrases. As with the use of the **Practice Options** and **Variations** (see page 4), explore the improvisational possibilities of grooves only after mastering the patterns "as written."

1 *Eighth Note Grooves I*

Each of the five sections ("A."-"E.") features a different hand pattern, with the bass drum part changing from exercise to exercise.

Practice Options

- ☐ Play the ride part on a closed hi-hat (omit the left foot part).
- ☐ Combine any two patterns.
- ☐ Combine any two, three, or four patterns, interpreting each pattern as four sixteenth notes.
- ☐ Swing the eighth notes (♫ = ♩³♪).
- ☐ Substitute various appropriate hi-hat patterns (see p. 151)

Variations

hands

- ☐ Combine any two patterns, playing the snare drum on beat 3 only.

Example
(#B3 and #C4 combined)

or as sixteenth notes with snare drum on beat 2 only (notice hi-hat)

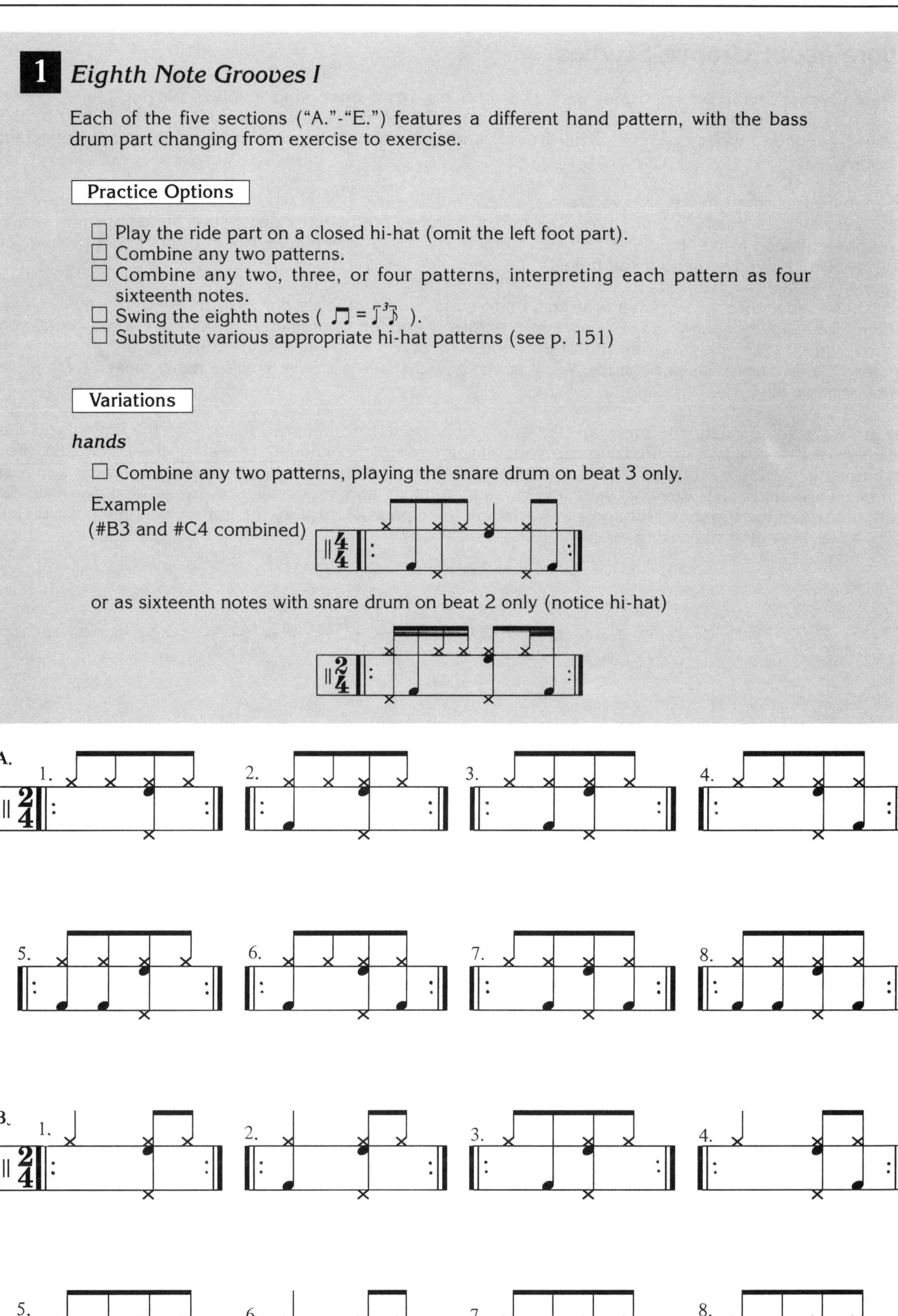

C.
1.
2.
3.
4.
5.
6.
7.
8.
D.
1.
2.
3.
4.
5.
6.
7.
8.
E.
1.
2.
3.
4.
5.
6.
7.
8.

2 *Eighth Note Fill Patterns I*

These fills (beginning on p. 12) are based on various sticking patterns spread around the drum set. (See p. 5 for information on sticking notation.)

Practice Options

- ☐ Play each fill in the context of time (see p. 6).
- ☐ Combine the first half of any pattern ("a.") with the second half of any other pattern ("b.").
- ☐ Combine any two patterns.
- ☐ Swing the eighth notes (♫ = ♩♪).
- ☐ Substitute various appropriate hi-hat and feet patterns (see pp. 150–151).

Variations

hands

☐ Following the indicated sticking, play each fill using various surface combinations:
- — both right and left hand on snare drum.
- — right hand stationary on one tom, left hand on snare.
- — right hand on cymbal bell or special effects cymbal, left hand on snare.
- — right hand moving from surface to surface, *ad lib.*; left hand stationary on snare or hi-hat.
- — left hand moving from surface to surface, *ad lib.*; right hand stationary on snare, cymbal bell, or special effects cymbal.
- — both hands moving from surface to surface, *ad lib.*

☐ Play each pattern two times. The first time, play the right hand part on the hi-hat (loosely closed) and the left hand part on the snare drum. The second time, play the left hand part on the hi-hat (loosely closed) and the right hand part on the snare drum.

Example (#B9)*

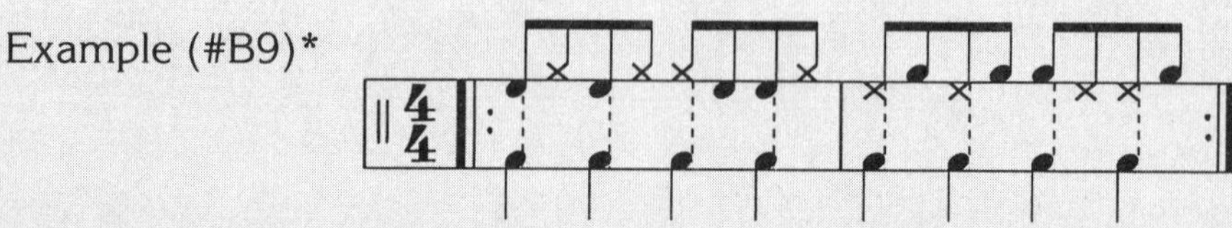

hands and feet

☐ Play the right hand part on a cymbal bell and the left hand part on the snare drum. Double the right hand part with the bass drum and play the hi-hat on all four beats.

Example (#B5)

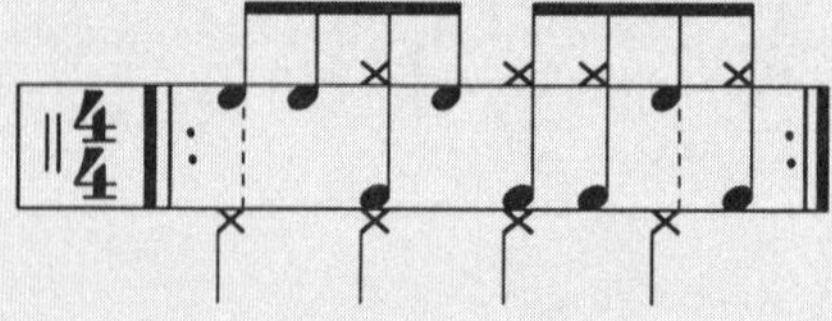

Play the right hand part on the snare drum and the left hand part on the hi-hat (loosely closed). Double the left hand part with the bass drum.

Example (#B5)

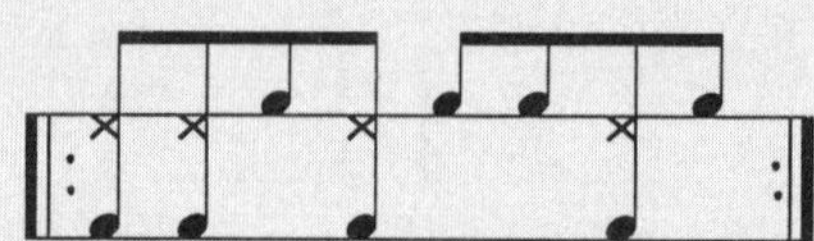

---

*See p. 4 for an explanation of Example identification in MOVES & GROOVES.

☐Replace the snare drum notes with the bass drum. (Omit the written bass drum part when using this variation.)

Example (#A10)

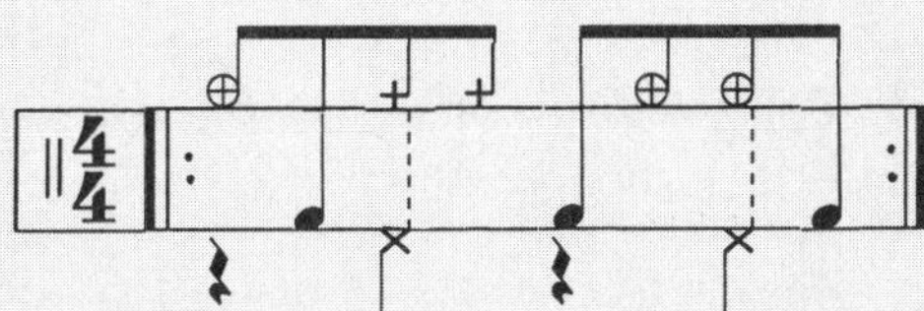

Following a similar approach, replace the small tom notes with the bass drum. (Omit the written bass drum part when using this variation.)

Example (#A10)

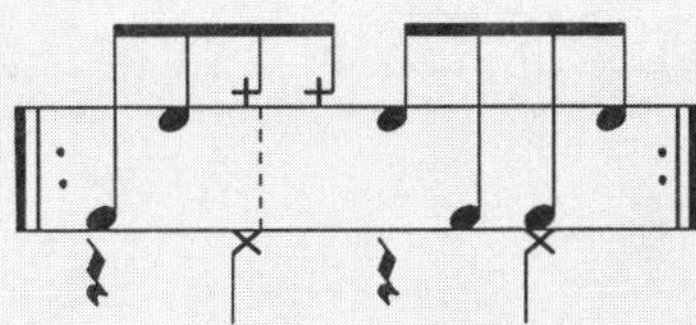

Following a similar approach, replace the large tom notes with the bass drum. (Omit the written bass drum part when using this variation.)

Example (#A10)

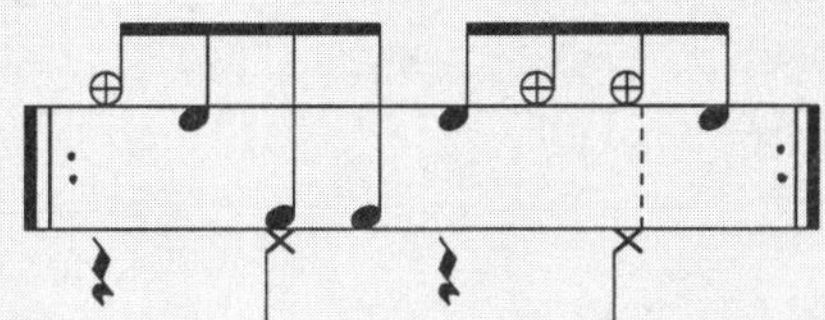

☐At the end of each pattern, repeat beats 1 and 2 of that same pattern. Interpret the combination as a two measure 3/4 fill. Use any appropriate feet pattern (see p. 151).

Example (#B14)

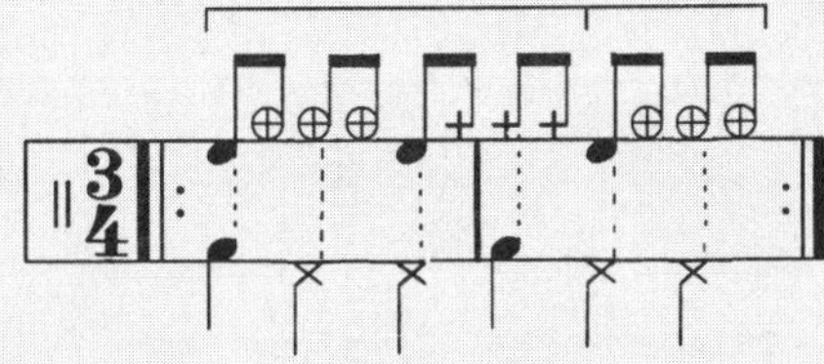

☐At the end of each pattern, repeat beats 1 and 2 of that same pattern. Interpret each combination as a one measure 4/4 fill by playing each group of three eighth notes as a triplet.

Example (#B14)

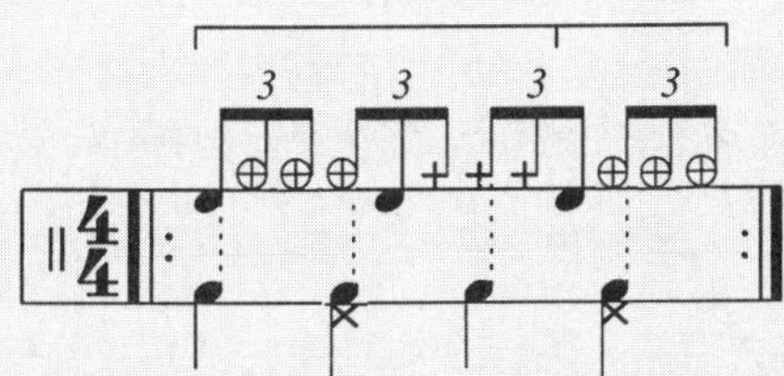

Following a similar approach, play each pattern three complete times. Interpret each combination as a two measure 4/4 fill by playing each group of three eighth notes as a triplet.

A.
a.
b.
1.
2.
3.
4.
5.
6.
7.
8.
9.
10.
11.
12.
13.
14.
15.
16.
17.
18.

a.
b.
B.
1.
2.
3.
4.
5.
6.
7.
8.
9.
10.
11.
12.
13.
14.
15.
16.
17.
18.

3 *Eighth Note Grooves II*

Each groove incorporates a constant ride on an opening and closing hi-hat to create a slightly syncopated feel. Ride on the edge of the hi-hat cymbals with the shoulder of your stick to increase the opening and closing effect.

Practice Options

- ☐ Omit the ride when the hi-hat closes (In other words, do not strike the hi-hat with your stick when you are closing it with your foot.)
- ☐ Repeatedly alternate pattern #1 with any other pattern.
- ☐ Combine any two patterns.
- ☐ Swing the eighth notes (♫ = ♩♪).

Variations

feet

- ☐ Play the bass drum when the hi-hat is open only.

Example (#11)

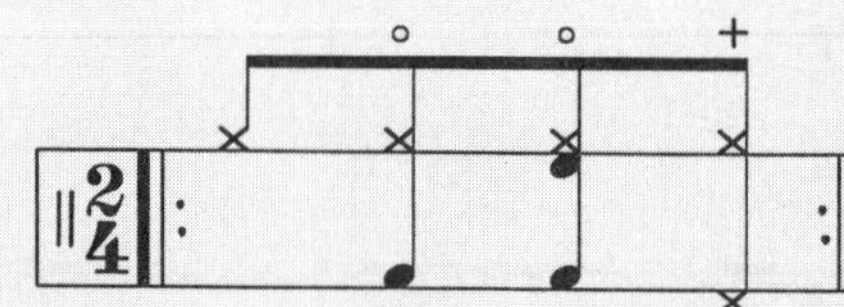

hands and feet

- ☐ Combine any two patterns and play the eighth notes as sixteenth notes. Play the bass drum on beat 1 only and the snare drum on beat 2 only.

Example (#2 and #5 combined)

(Note the interpretation of the "o" and "+" indications.)

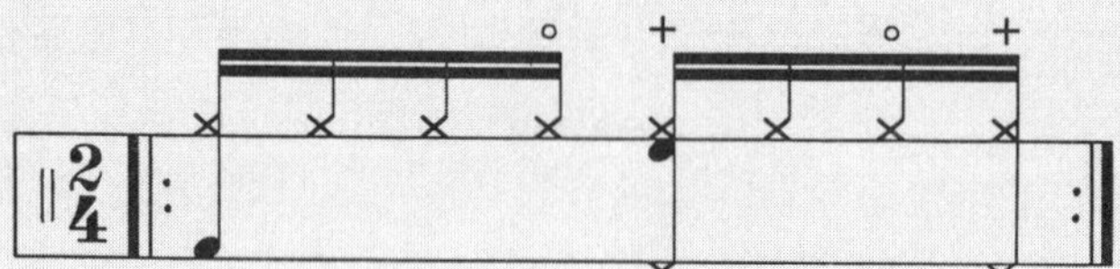

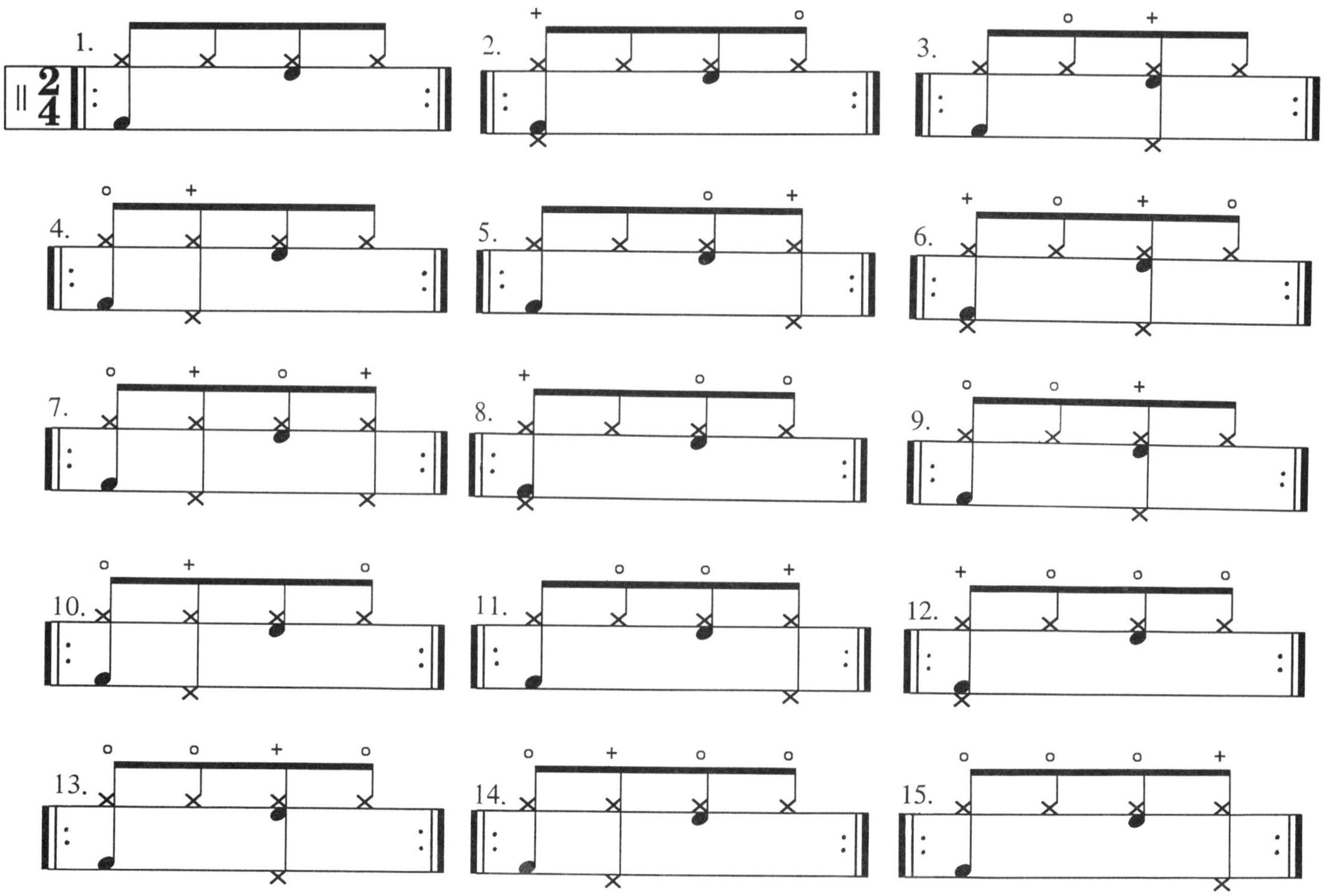

4 *Eighth Note Grooves III*

Each groove combines an alternating hand pattern between the hi-hat and snare drum with an opening and closing hi-hat. Play on the edge of the hi-hat cymbals with the shoulder of your stick.

Practice Options

- ☐ Play the snare drum part on a tom, cymbal bell, or "special effect" cymbal with a fast decay.
- ☐ Omit the hi-hat part played by the hands when the hi-hat closes. (In other words, do not strike the hi-hat with your stick when you are closing it with your foot.)
- ☐ Repeatedly alternate pattern #1 with any other pattern.
- ☐ Combine any two patterns.
- ☐ Swing the eighth notes (♫ = ♩♪).

Variations

feet

- ☐ Play the bass drum when the hi-hat is open only.

Example (#5)

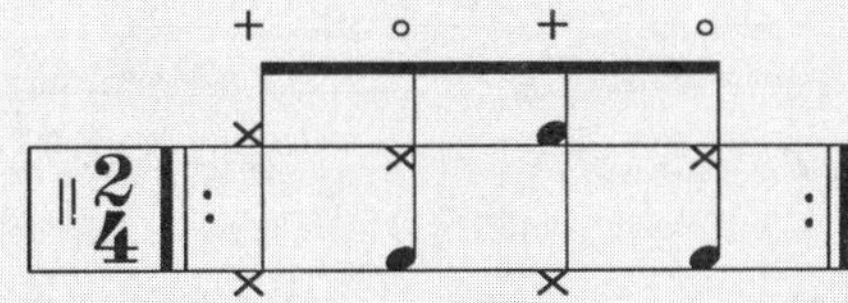

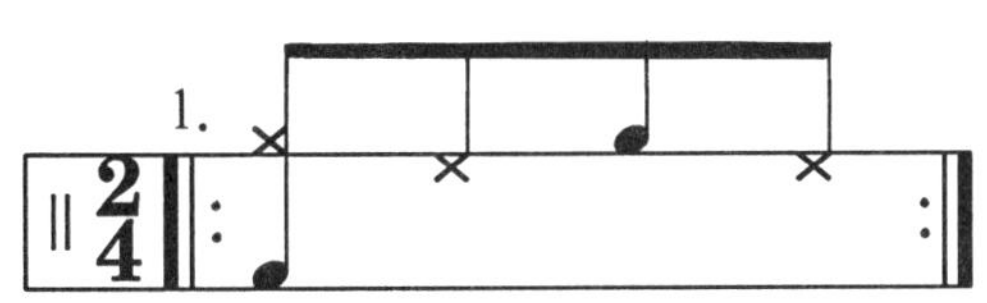

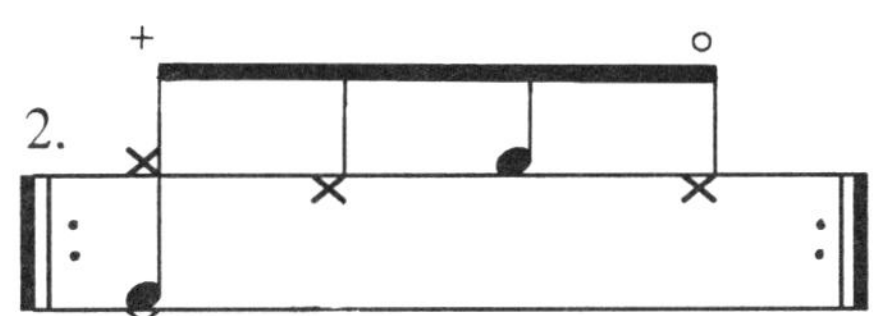

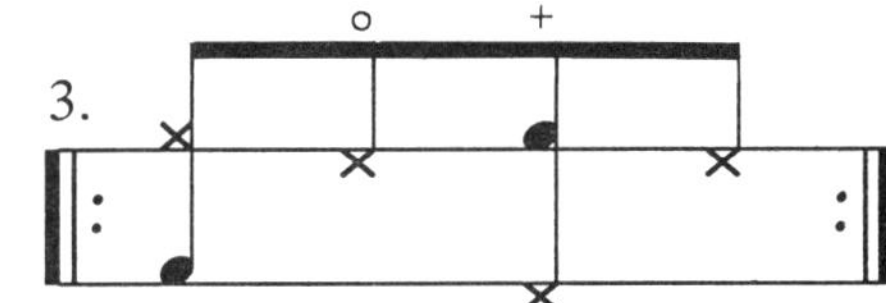

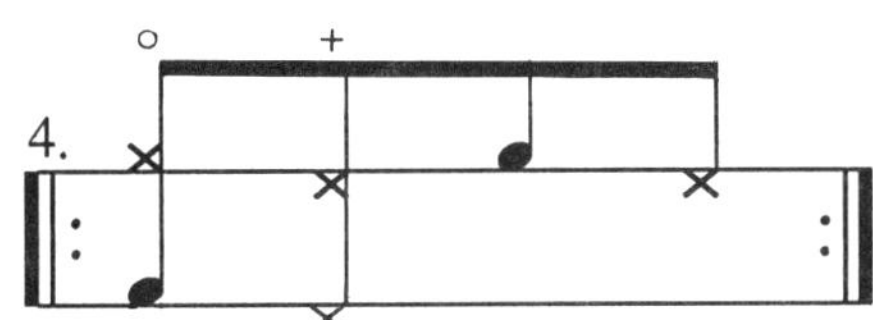

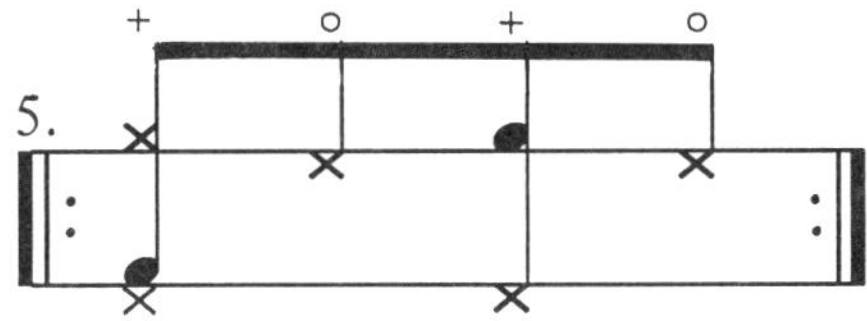

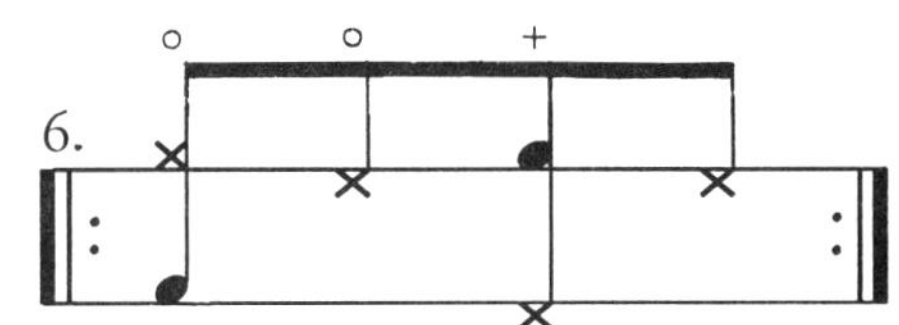

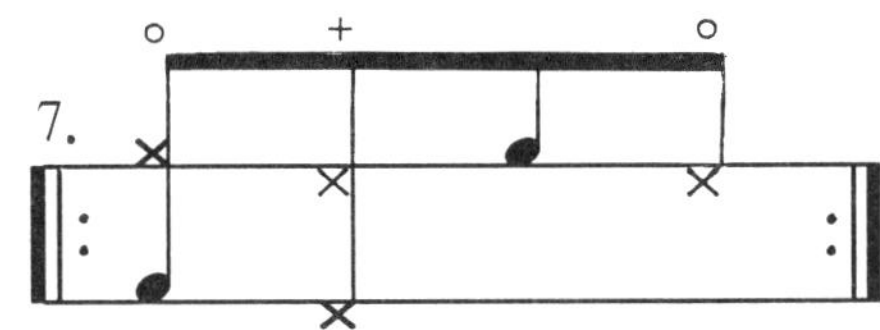

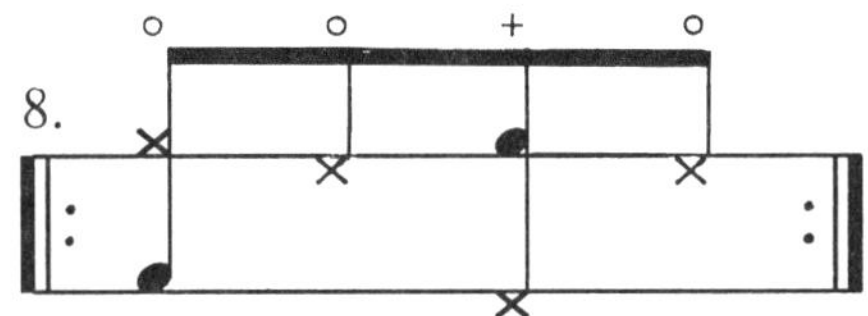

5 *Eighth Note Latin Grooves*

These grooves are derived from several significant styles of Latin American music.

Practice Options

- ☐ Play the ride part on a cymbal bell, cowbell, closed hi-hat (omit the left foot part), or shell of a tom.
- ☐ Substitute various appropriate hi-hat and feet patterns (see pp. 150–151).

A. Bossa - Nova

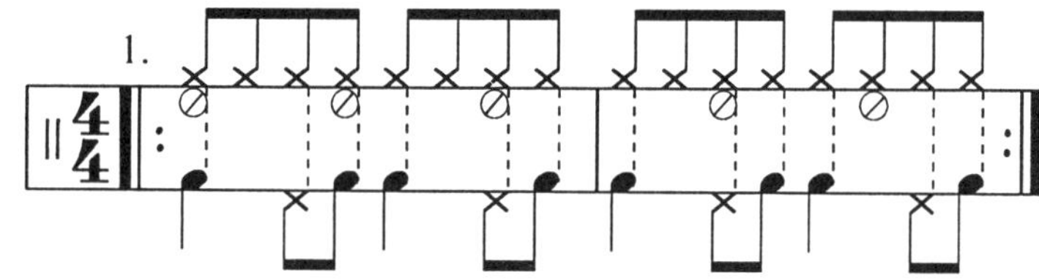

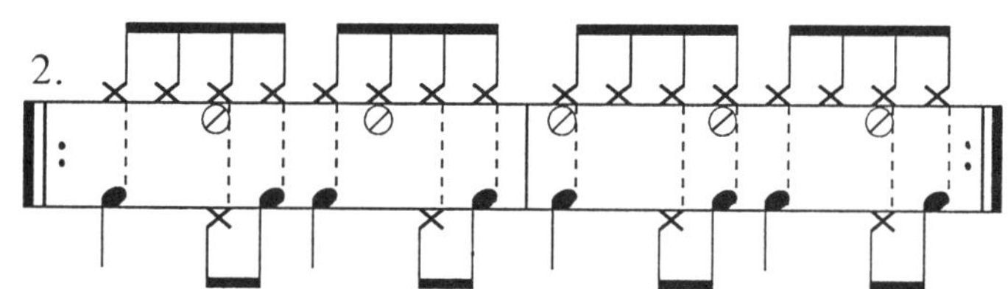

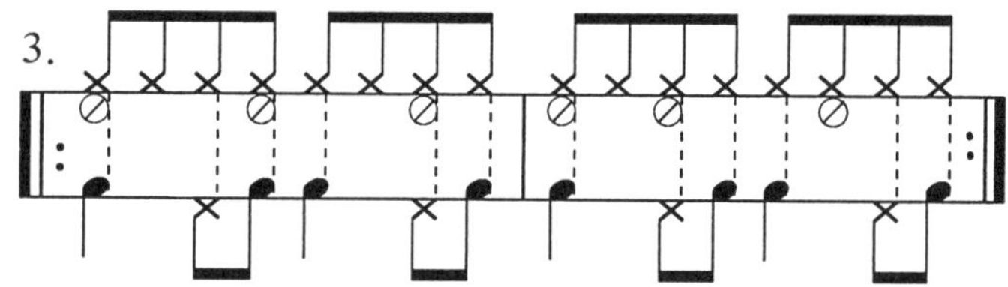

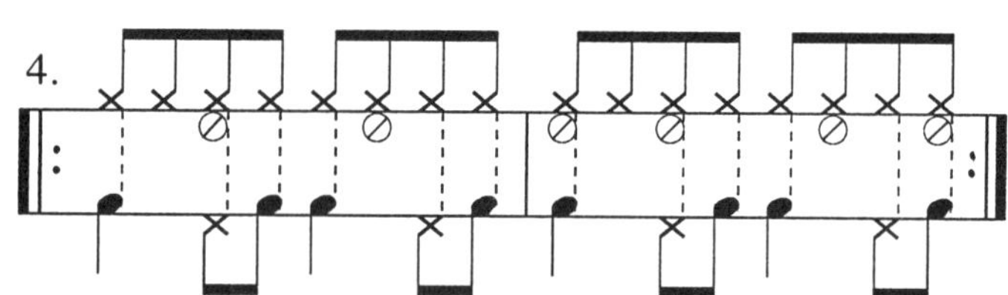

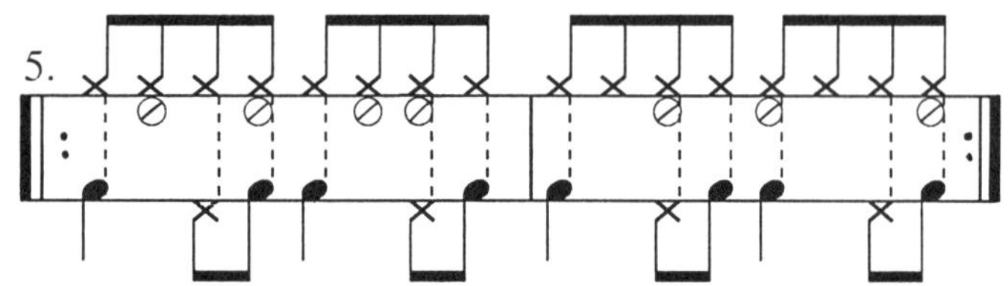

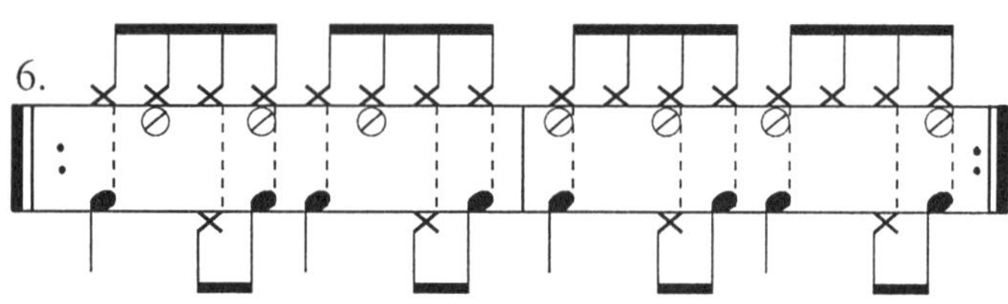

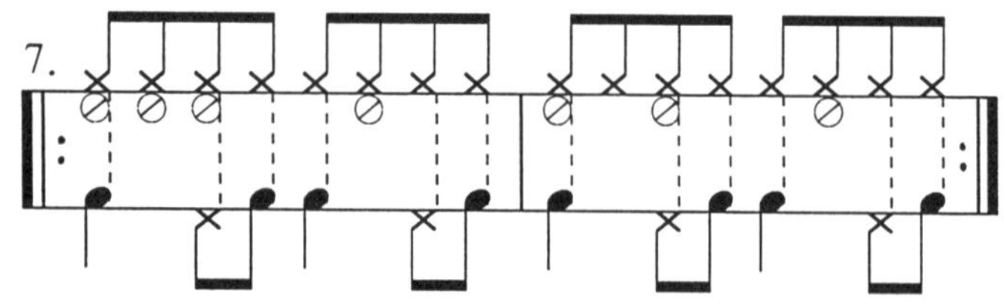

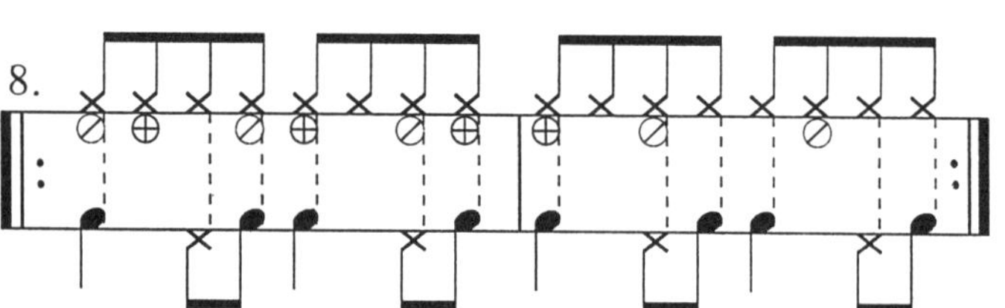

B. Cha - Cha

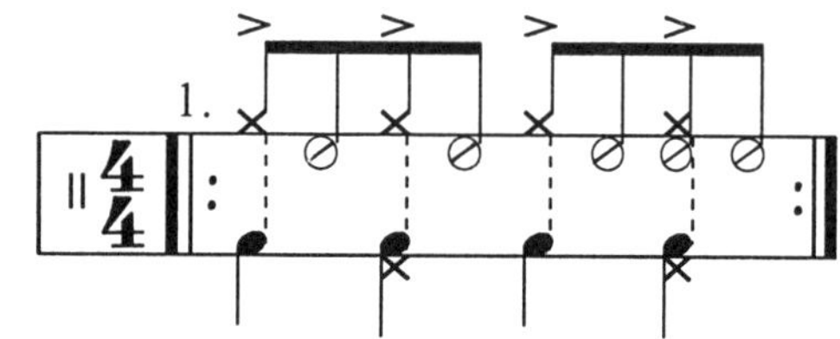

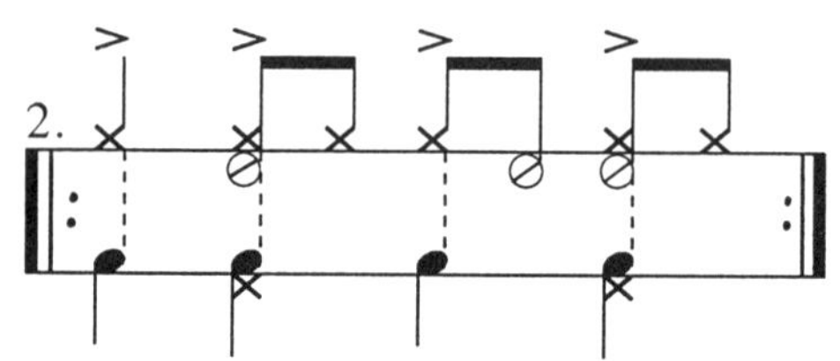

C. Bembe´

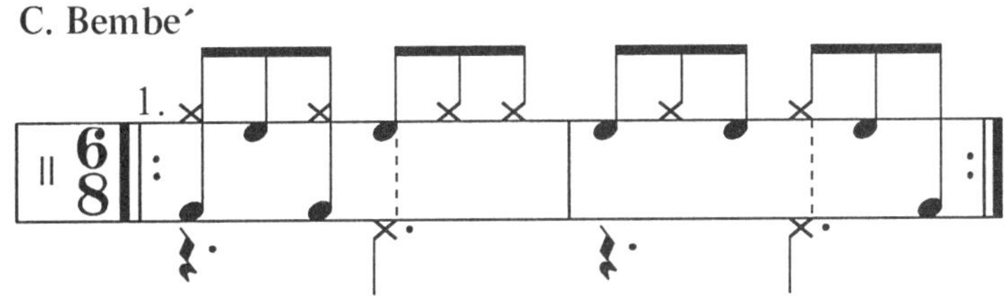

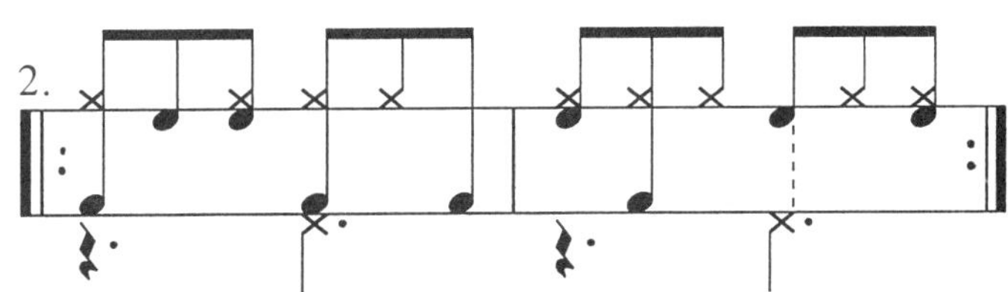

D. Nañigo

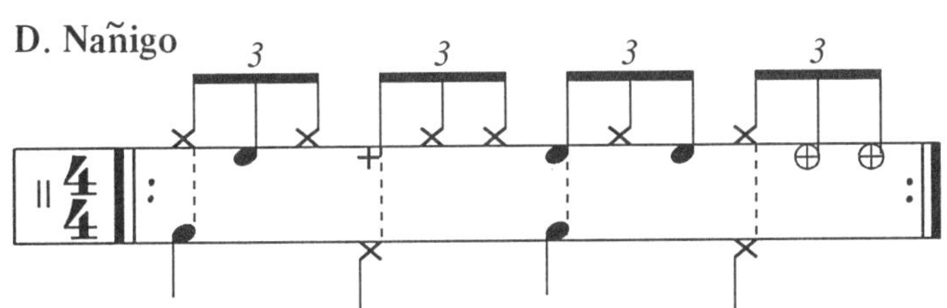

E. Songo

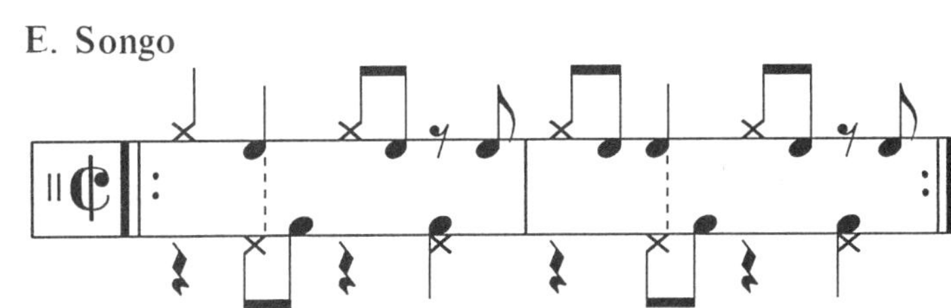

F. Baion

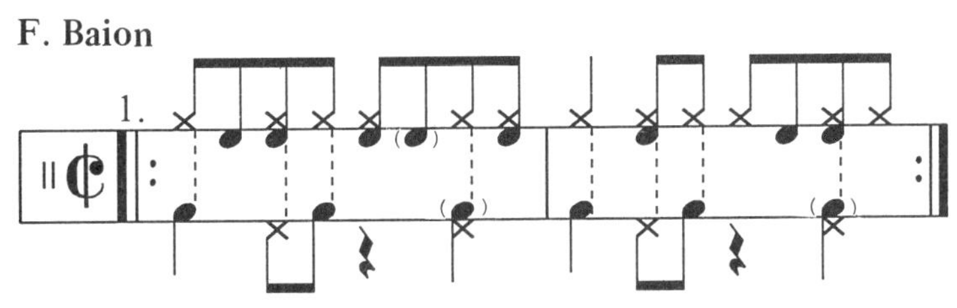

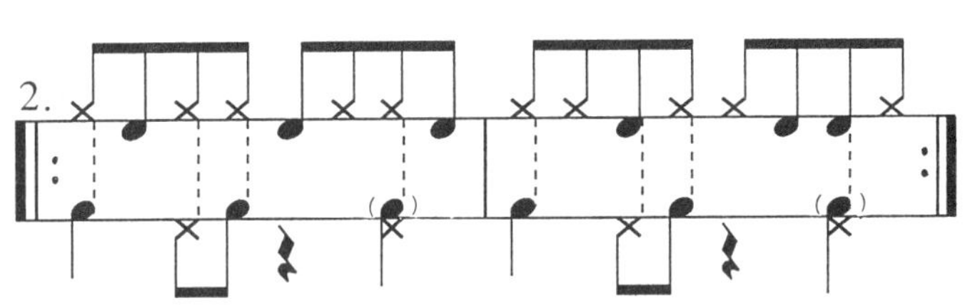

G. Guaguanco

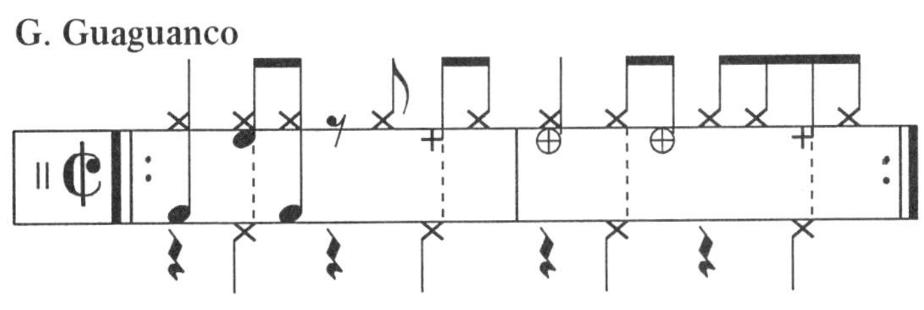

H. Merengue

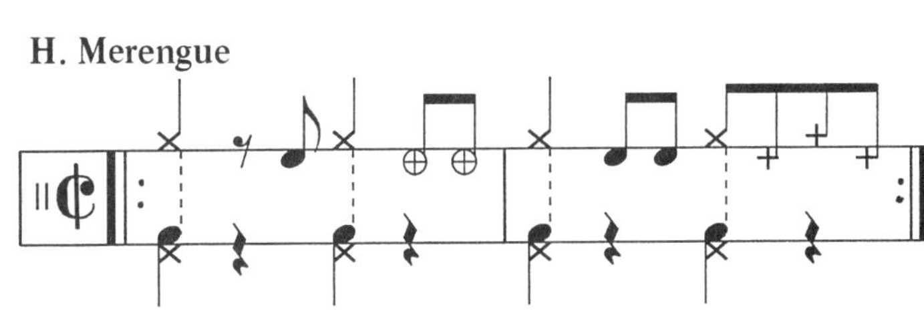

I. Samba

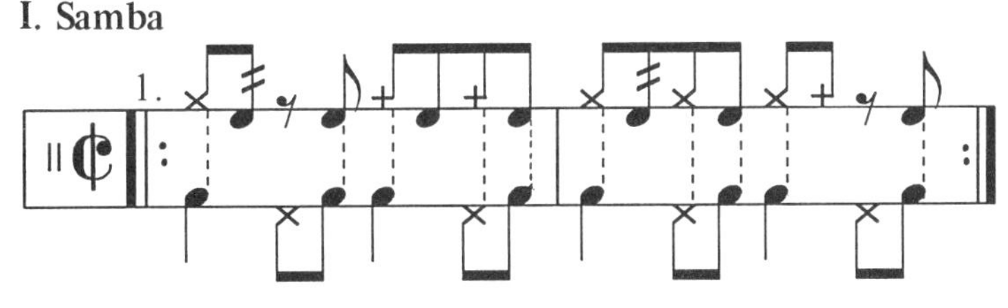

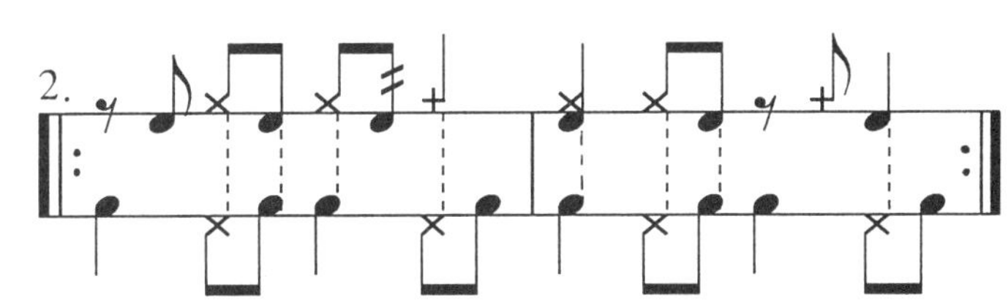

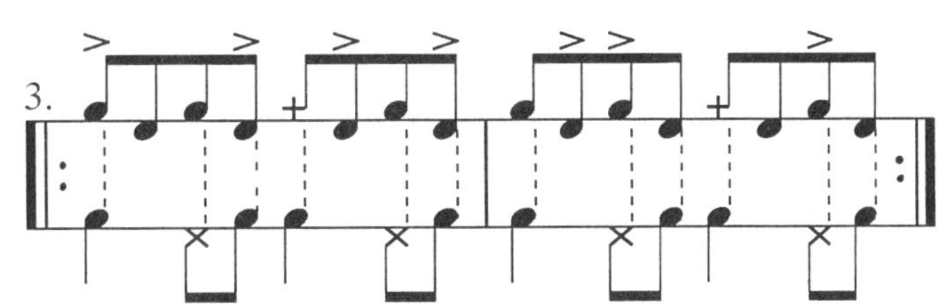

6 *Mozambique Grooves I*

Each groove incorporates the same left hand and feet pattern; only the ride changes from pattern to pattern.

Practice Options

- ☐ Play the ride part on a cymbal bell, cowbell, closed hi-hat (omit the left foot part), or shell of a tom.
- ☐ Play the snare part using a cross-stick effect, or alternate the snare drum part between the snare and toms.
- ☐ Combine the first half of any pattern ("a.") with the second half of any other pattern ("b.").
- ☐ Combine any two patterns.
- ☐ Substitute various appropriate hi-hat and feet patterns (see pp. 150–151).

7 *Mozambique Grooves II*

Each groove incorporates the same feet pattern.

Practice Options

- ☐ Play the ride part on a cymbal bell, cowbell, closed hi-hat (omit the left foot part), or shell of a tom.
- ☐ Combine the first half of any pattern ("a.") with the second half of any other pattern ("b.").
- ☐ Add the bass drum on beat 1 and/or delete the bass drum on the second half of beat 2.
- ☐ Substitute various appropriate hi-hat and feet patterns (see pp.150–151).

Variations

hands

- ☐ Play the snare drum on beat 2 only. Play the ride part as written.

Example (#5)

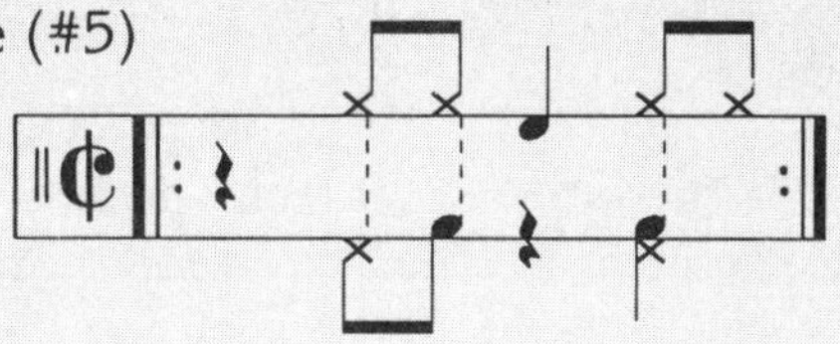

hands and feet

- ☐ Alternate each groove with one of the following patterns:

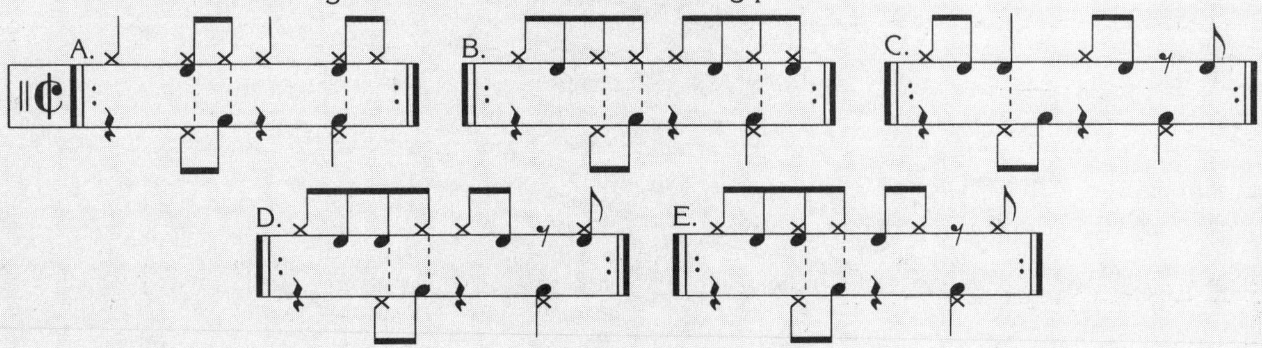

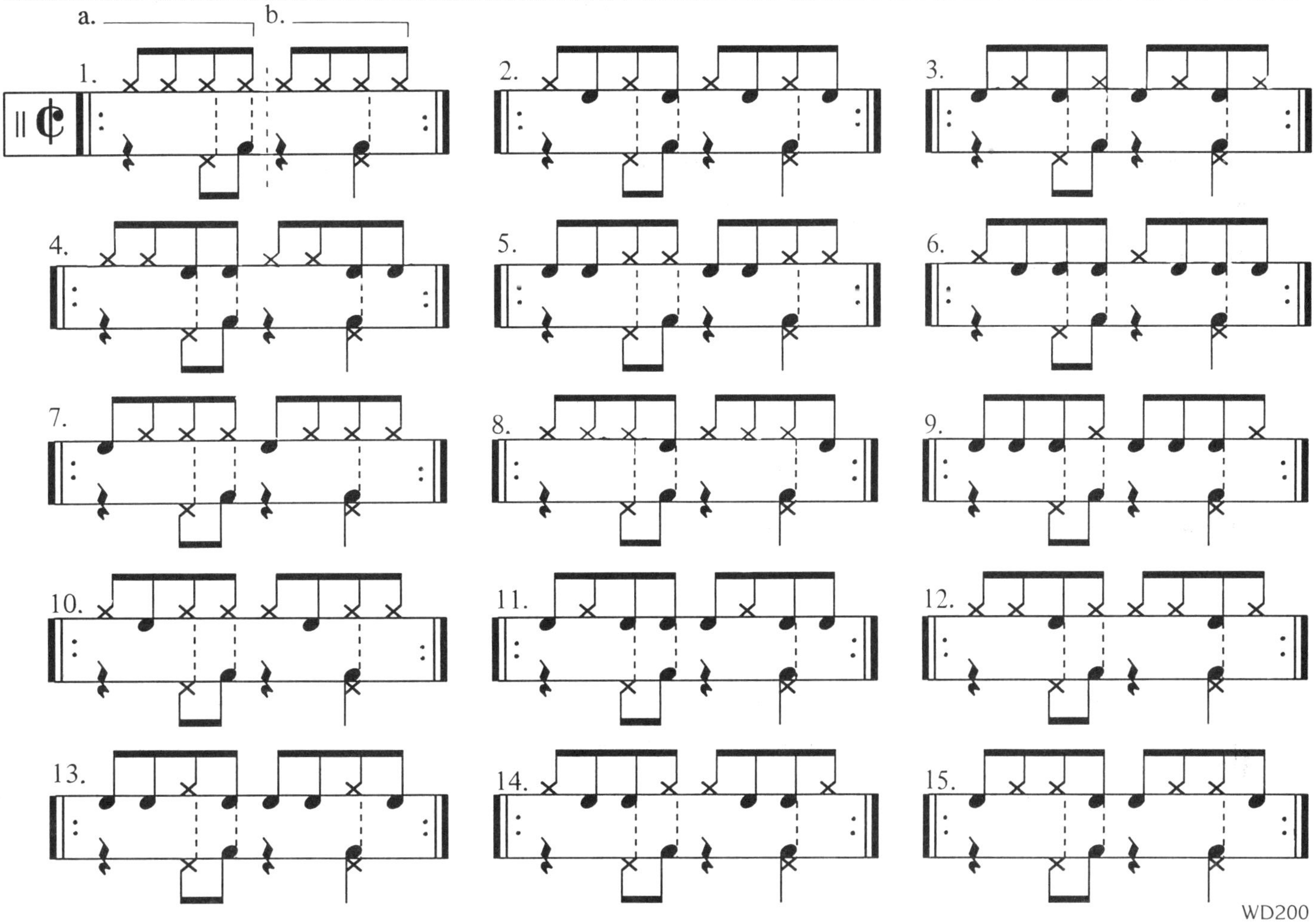

a. b.

1. 2. 3. 4. 5. 6. 7. 8. 9. 10. 11. 12. 13. 14. 15.

8 *Mambo Grooves*

The characteristic feet and left hand parts give these Mambo grooves a "Samba-like" feel.

Practice Options

- ☐ Play the ride part on a cymbal bell, cowbell, closed hi-hat (omit the left foot part), or shell of a tom.
- ☐ Substitute various appropriate hi-hat and feet patterns (see pp. 150–151).

9 *Samba Grooves I*

These Samba grooves are notated in cut-time, consistent with the traditional "two-feel" associated with this popular Afro-Brazilian dance style. Samba grooves are also frequently notated in $\frac{2}{4}$ or $\frac{4}{4}$ time, using sixteenth note subdivisions.

To achieve a more authentic sound, play with a lighter feel than you would when playing most rock styles, and accent the bass drum part on beat 2.

Practice Options

- ☐ Play the ride part on a cymbal bell or cowbell.
- ☐ Alternate the back-beats between the snare and a tom.
- ☐ Play the back-beats entirely on non-snare surfaces, or on the snare using a cross-stick effect.
- ☐ Repeatedly play only the first or second half of each pattern.
- ☐ Substitute various appropriate hi-hat and feet patterns (see pp. 150–151).

Variations

hands

- ☐ Substitute either of the following "back-beat" patterns.

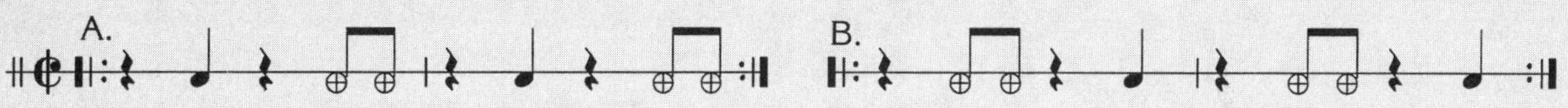

10 *Eighth Note Grooves IV*

These grooves combine a constant ride and feet pattern with various snare drum parts to create a three against two feel over two measures.

Practice Options

- ☐ Play the ride part on a cymbal bell or cowbell.
- ☐ Play the ride part on a closed hi-hat (omit the left foot part).
- ☐ Repeatedly play only the first half ("a.") or second half ("b.") of each pattern.
- ☐ Combine the first half of any pattern ("a.") with the second half of any other pattern ("b.").
- ☐ Repeatedly alternate pattern #1 with any other pattern.
- ☐ Omit snare drum notes *ad lib.*
- ☐ Swing the eighth notes (♫ = ♩³♪).
- ☐ Substitute various appropriate hi-hat and feet patterns (see pp. 150–151).

Variations

hands

☐ Substitute any of the following ride patterns.

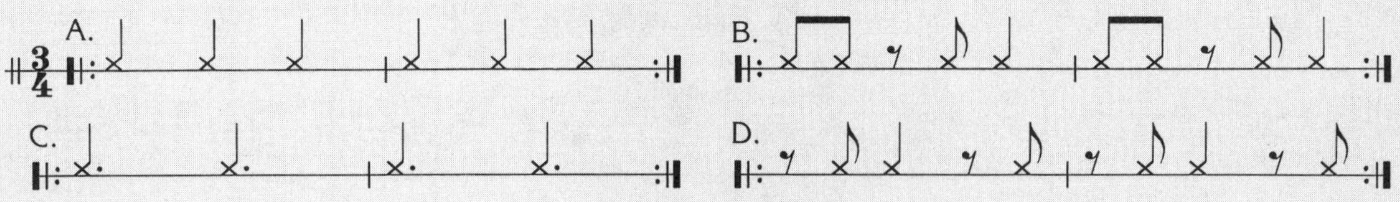

A. B. C. D.

hands and feet

☐ Play the written snare part on the bass drum. Play the snare drum on beat 2 and the hi-hat on all three beats.

Example (#10)

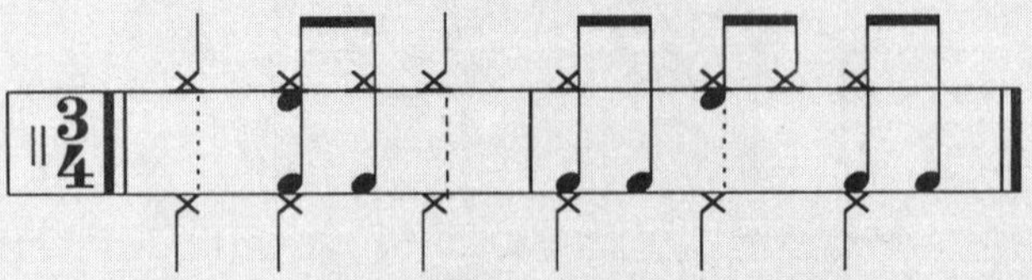

☐ While riding on a cowbell or cymbal bell, play each groove "double time" (one measure of $\frac{3}{4}$). Use any of the following feet patterns.

A. B. C.

Example (#4)

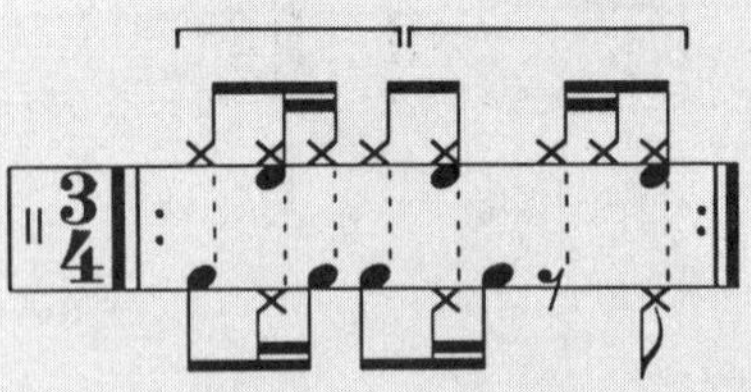

☐ At the end of each pattern, repeat the first two beats of the "a." or "b." part of the pattern to create a two measure $\frac{4}{4}$ groove. Either play the feet "as written" or substitute one of the following feet patterns.

A. B.

Example (#11)

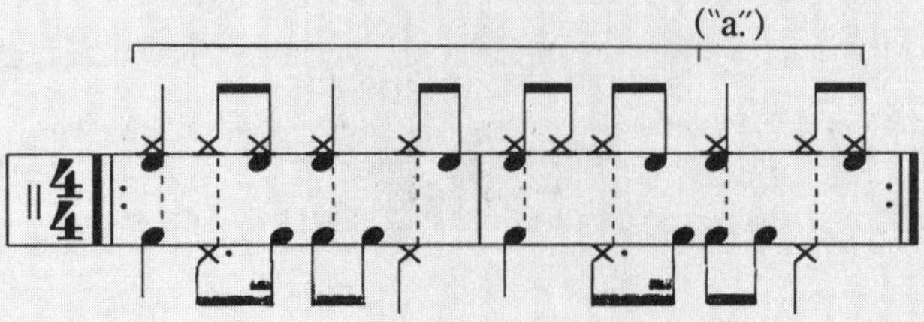

("a.")

a.
b.
1.
2.
3.
4.
5.
6.
7.
8.
9.
10.
11.
12.
13.
14.
15.
16.

11 *Eighth Note Fill Patterns II*

These fills (beginning on p. 26) are based on various sticking patterns in three.

Practice Options

- ☐ Play each fill in the context of time (see p. 6)
- ☐ Combine any two patterns.
- ☐ Swing the eighth notes (♫ = ♩♪).
- ☐ Substitute various appropriate hi-hat and feet patterns (see pp. 150–151).

Variations

hands

☐ Following the indicated sticking, play each fill using various surface combinations:
- — both right and left hand on snare drum.
- — right hand on tom, left hand on snare.
- — right hand moving from surface to surface, *ad lib.*; left hand stationary on snare.
- — left hand moving from surface to surface *ad lib.*; right hand stationary on snare or cymbal.
- — both hands moving from surface to surface, *ad lib.*

☐ Keeping the feet constant, play each hand pattern using 16th notes rather than eighth notes so that the hand patterns will be executed twice during each measure.

Example (#B4)

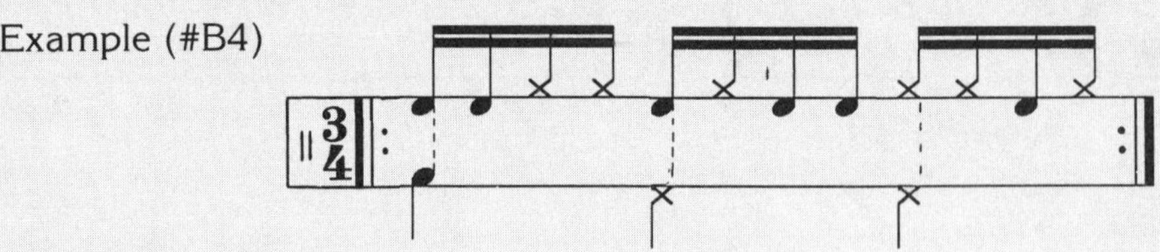

hands and feet

☐ Play the cymbal part on a cymbal bell. Double the cymbal part with the bass drum and play the hi-hat with your left foot on beats 2 and 3.

Example (#A8)

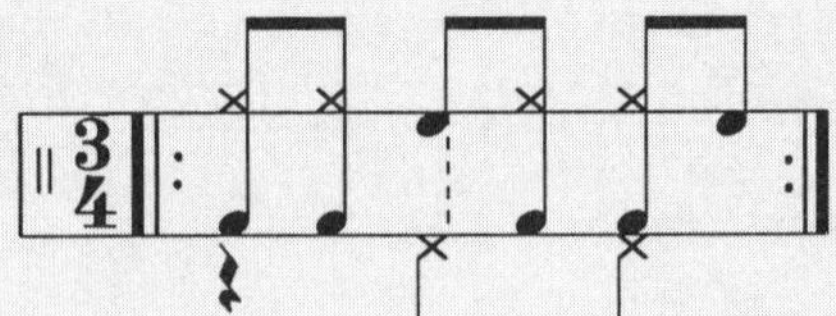

Play the cymbal part on the snare drum and the snare part on the hi-hat (loosely closed). With the bass drum, double the hi-hat part played by your hand.

Example (#A8)

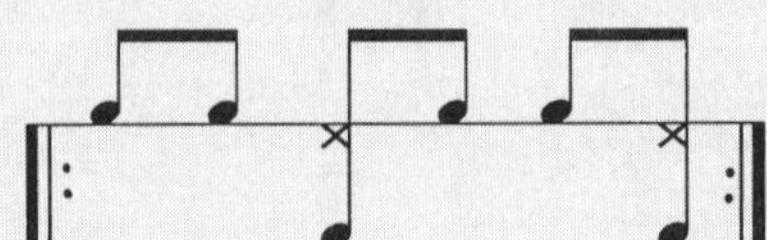

☐ Interpret each pattern as a two measure $\frac{4}{4}$ fill by playing each pattern twice and then repeating the first two beats of the pattern to complete the second measure. Use the following feet pattern.

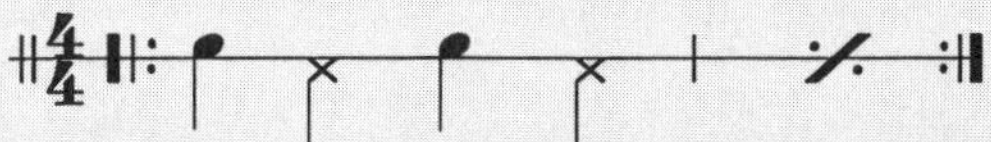

Example (#B12)

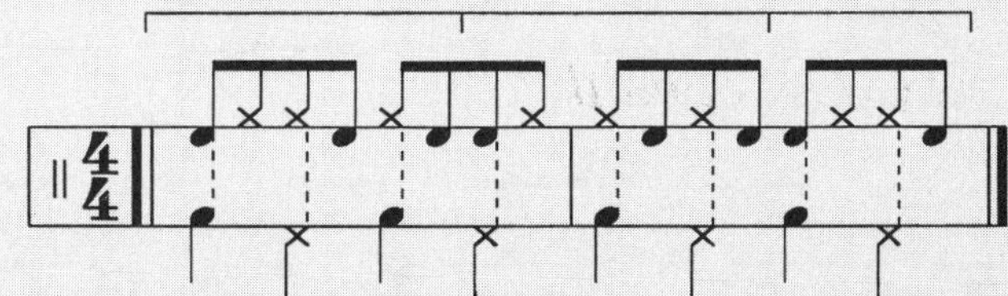

☐ Interpret each pattern as a two measure cut time samba groove by playing each pattern twice and then repeating the first two beats of the pattern to complete the second measure. Use either of the following feet patterns.

A.

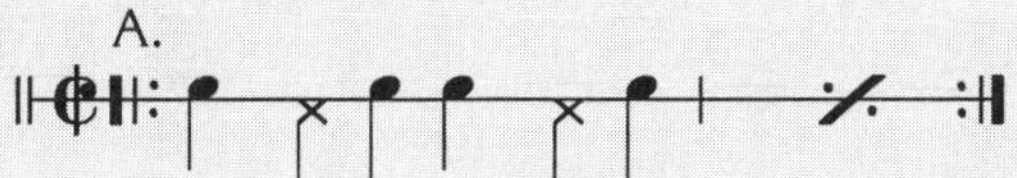

B.

Example (#B15)

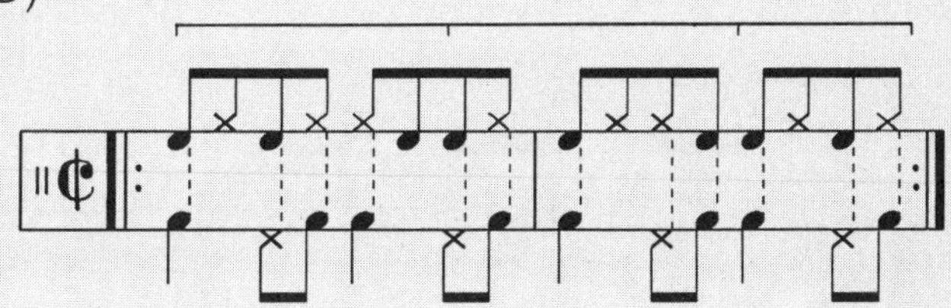

☐ Play each pattern three times, interpreting each group of three eighth notes as a triplet in two measures of $\frac{3}{4}$ time. Use any appropriate feet pattern (see p. 151).

Example (#B9)

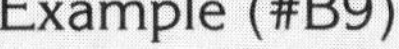

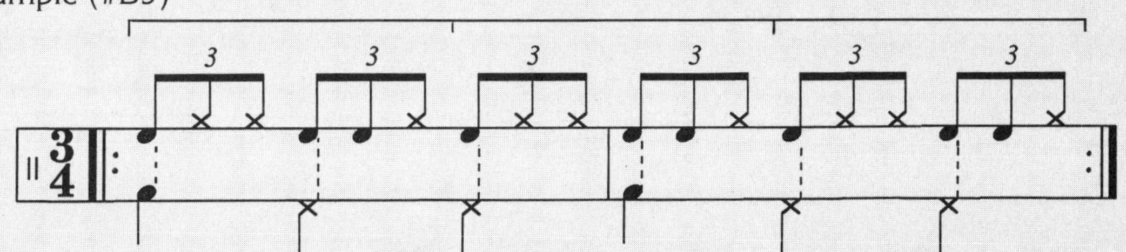

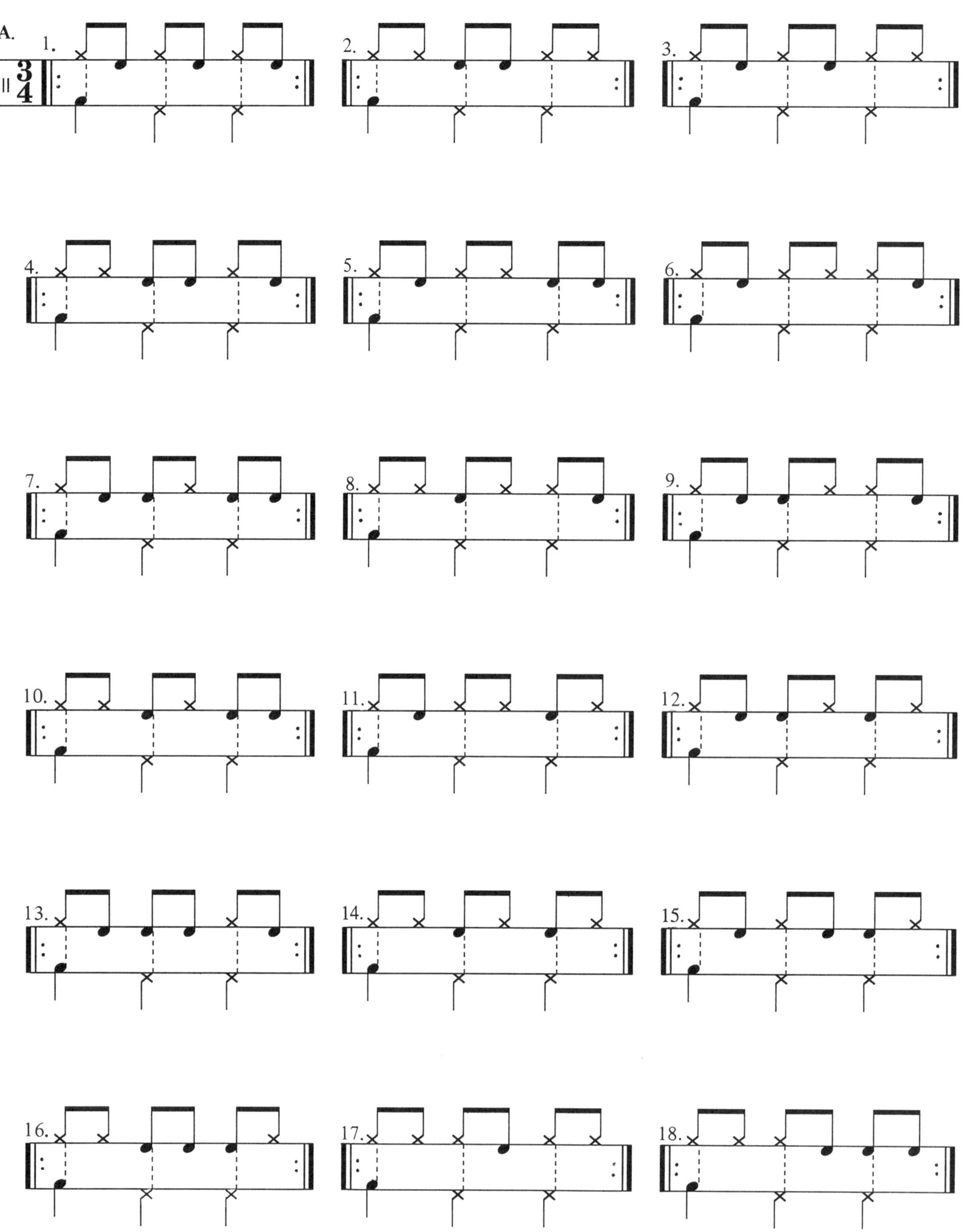
A.
1.
2.
3.
4.
5.
6.
7.
8.
9.
10.
11.
12.
13.
14.
15.
16.
17.
18.

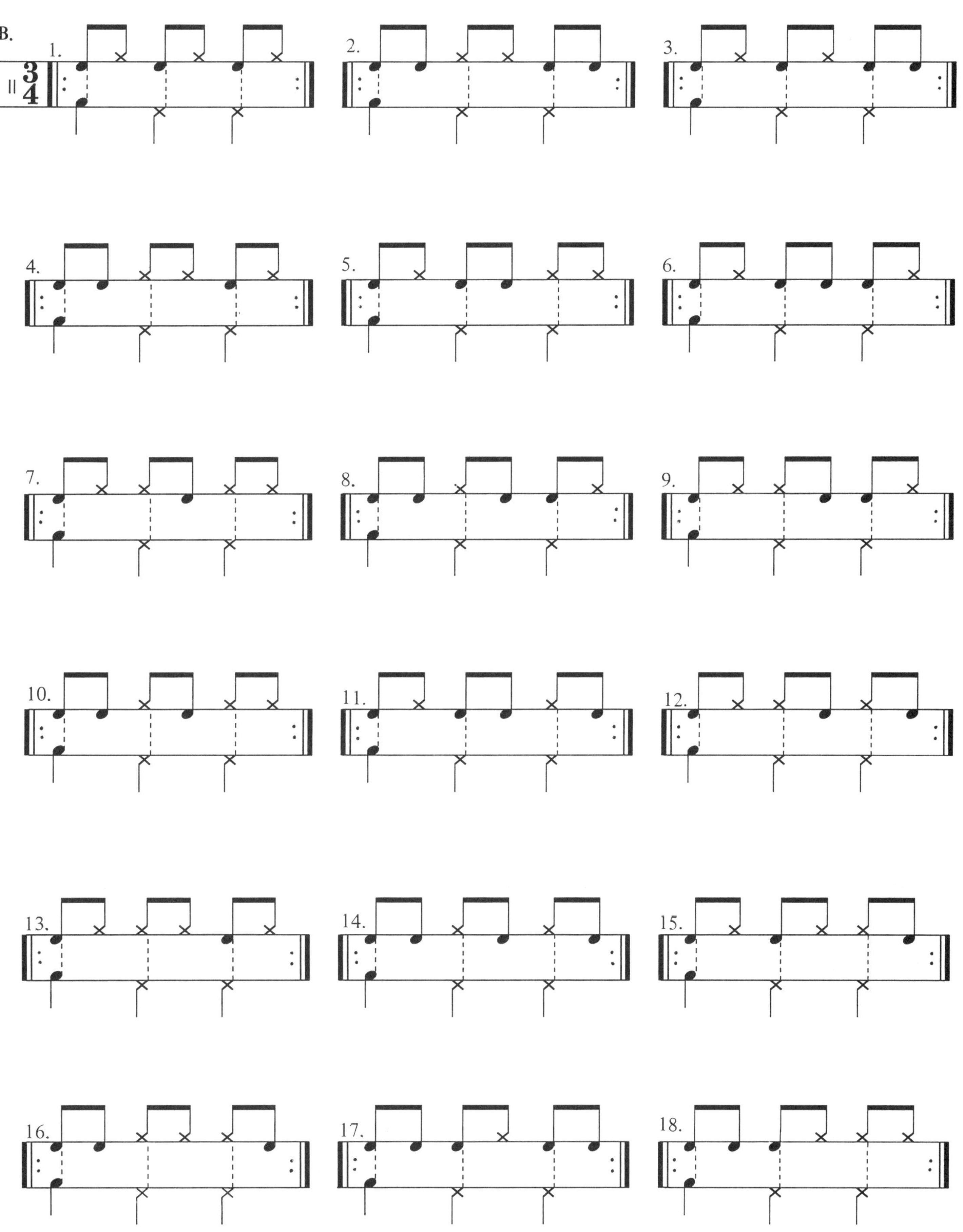
B.
1.
2.
3.
4.
5.
6.
7.
8.
9.
10.
11.
12.
13.
14.
15.
16.
17.
18.

12 *Eighth Note Fill Patterns III*

These fills involve movement between the hands and bass drum. Play the doublestops as written or as open flams.

Practice Options

- ☐ Play each fill in the context of time (see p. 6).
- ☐ Combine the first half of any pattern ("a") with the second half of any other pattern ("b").
- ☐ Combine any two patterns.
- ☐ Swing the eighth notes (♫ = ♩♪ triplet).
- ☐ Substitute various appropriate hi-hat patterns (see pp. 150–151).

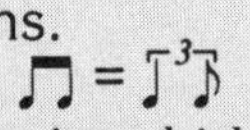

Variations

hands

- ☐ Play the right and left hand parts on various surface combinations.
- ☐ Play each doublestop as two sixteenth note double stops.

Example (#3)

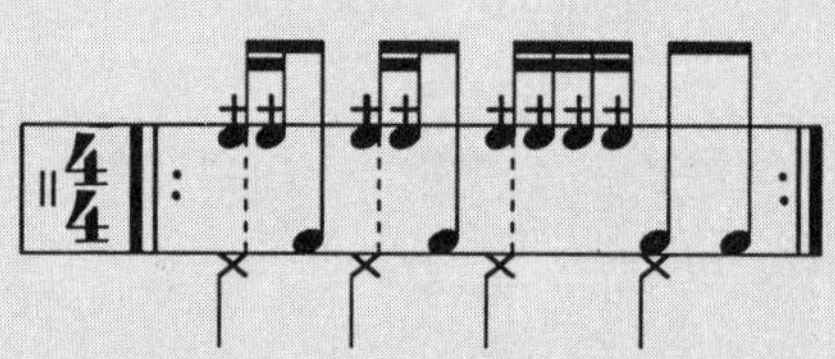

- ☐ Play each doublestop as two independent sixteenth notes, beginning with either hand.

Example (#12)

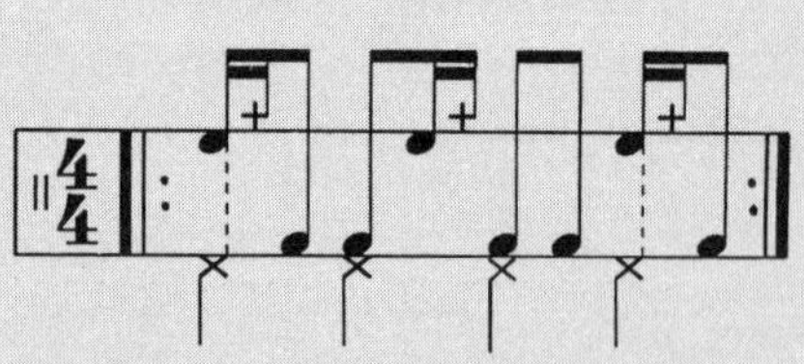

- ☐ Play each doublestop as two independent sixteenth notes beginning with either hand; play each independent sixteenth note as an open double stroke.

Example (#4)

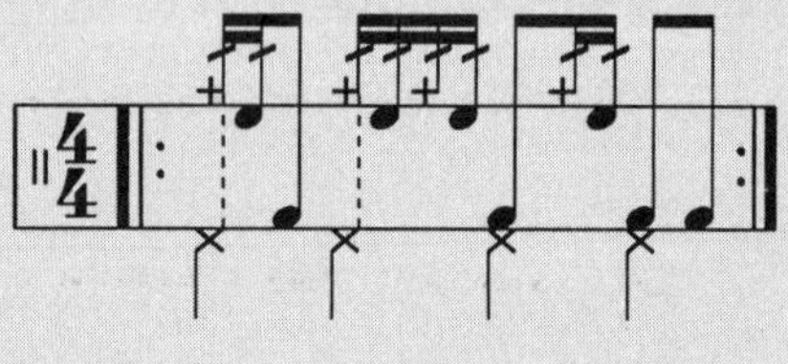

feet

- ☐ Reverse the roles of the feet, playing the bass drum part on the hi-hat, and the hi-hat part on the bass drum.

Example (#8)

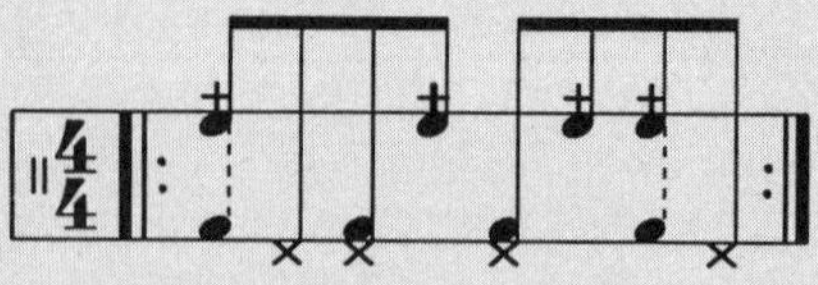

- ☐ Using double bass drums or a double bass pedal, play each bass drum note as two independent sixteenth notes, beginning with either foot.

hands and feet

- ☐ Reverse the roles of the hands and bass drum.

Example (#15)

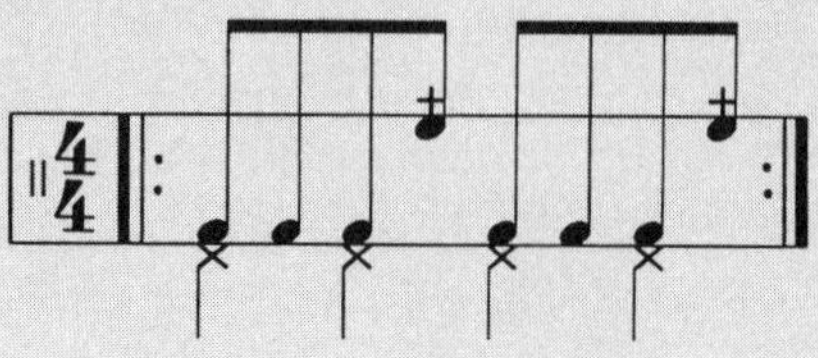

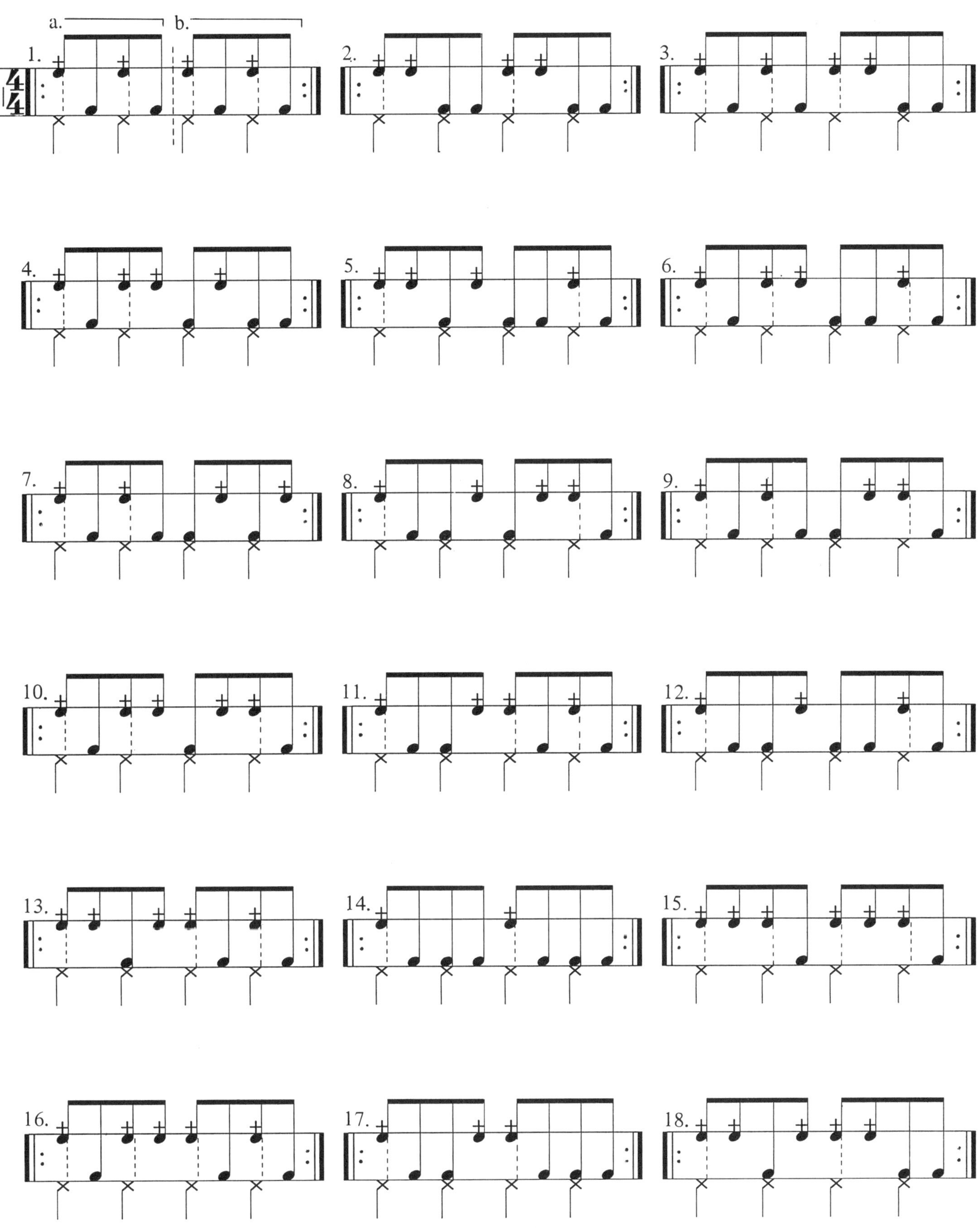
a.
b.
1.
2.
3.
4.
5.
6.
7.
8.
9.
10.
11.
12.
13.
14.
15.
16.
17.
18.

13 *Eighth Note Groove/Fill Patterns I*

These linear patterns involve movement between the hands and feet. The feet part is written to allow several interpretations.

— Play the feet part on the bass drum and hi-hat in unison.

Example (#B5)

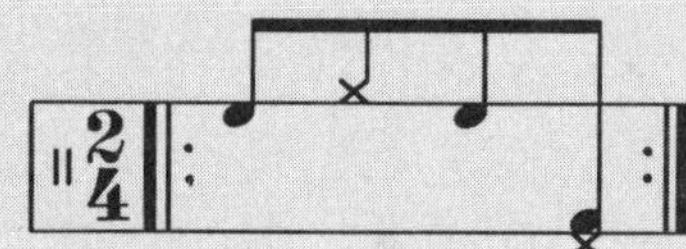

— Play the feet part on the bass drum and keep time with the hi-hat.

Examples (#B5)

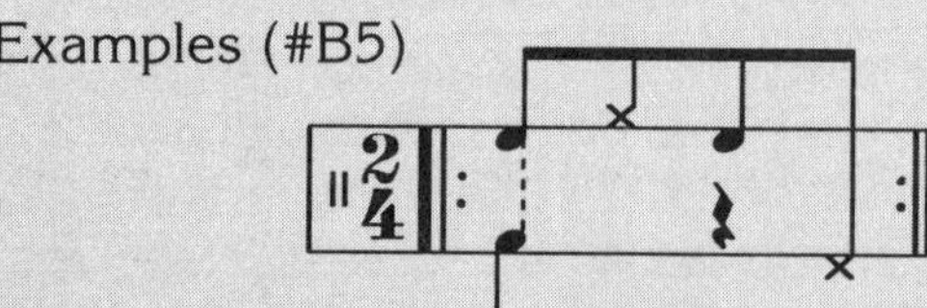

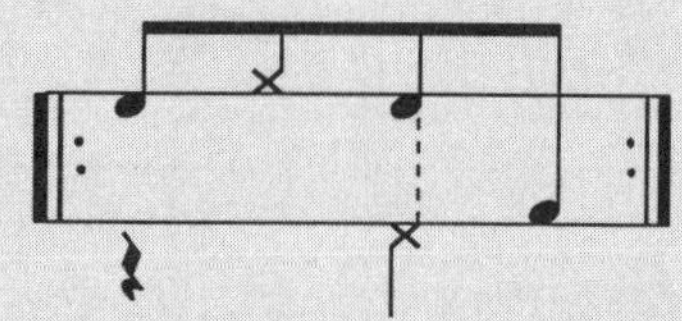

— Play the feet part on the hi-hat and keep time with the bass drum.

Examples (#B5)

Practice Options

- ☐ Play each pattern in the context of time (see p. 6).
- ☐ Swing the eighth notes (♫ = ♩³♪).
- ☐ Combine any two, three, or four patterns, interpreting each pattern as four sixteenth notes.

Variations

hands

- ☐ Following the indicated sticking, play each pattern using various surface combinations:
  - — both right and left hand on snare drum.
  - — right hand on tom, left hand on snare.
  - — right hand moving from surface to surface, *ad lib.*; left hand stationary on snare.
  - — left hand moving from surface to surface, *ad lib.*; right hand stationary on cymbal, snare, or tom.
  - — both hands moving from surface to surface, *ad lib.*

hands and feet

- ☐ Play each pattern three times, interpreting the combination as four triplets in 4/4 time. Play the feet part on the bass drum and close the hi-hat on beats 2 and 4 or all four beats.

Example (#A3)

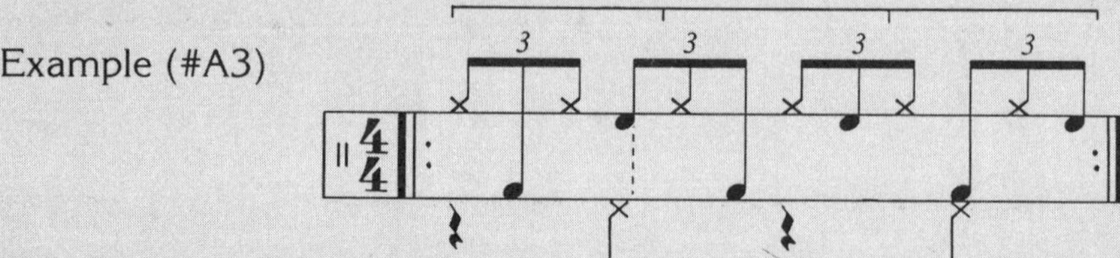

Also try combining three <u>different</u> patterns.

A.
1.
2.
3.
4.
5.
6.
7.
8.
9.
10.
11.
12.
13.
14.
15.
16.
B.
1.
2.
3.
4.
5.
6.
7.
8.
9.
10.
11.
12.
13.
14.
15.
16.

14 *Eighth Note Fill Patterns IV*

These extended linear fills involve movement between the hands and bass drum. Notice the asymmetrical placement of the three beat motive in each pattern to create a three against four feel.

Practice Options

- ☐ Insert four measures of jazz time between each fill (as if "trading fours").
- ☐ Repeatedly play only the first or second half of any of the fills (measures 1 and 2 or 3 and 4).
- ☐ Combine various measures from any of the fills in any order.

Example (#1d.-#5a.–#4c.- #3d.)

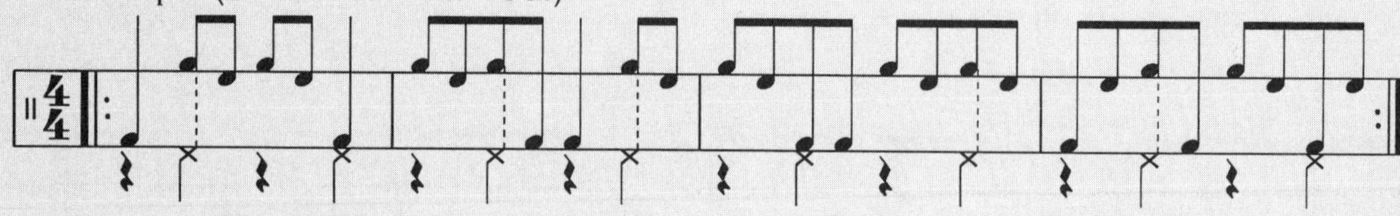

- ☐ Play the eight fills consecutively to create a thirty-two measure solo.
- ☐ Swing the eighth notes (♫ = ♩♪).
- ☐ Play each fill in cut time.
- ☐ Substitute various appropriate hi-hat patterns (see p. 151).

Variations

hands

- ☐ Following the indicated sticking, play each fill using various surface combinations:
  - — right hand on cymbal bell or special effects cymbal, left hand on snare.
  - — right hand moving from surface to surface, *ad lib.*; left hand stationary on snare.
  - — left hand moving from surface to surface, *ad lib.*; right hand stationary on cymbal, snare, or tom.
  - — both hands moving from surface to surface, *ad lib.*
- ☐ Play any hand stroke as a flam or double stroke.
- ☐ Play the snare drum part using various sticking patterns.

Example (#1) — using paradiddle-based sticking

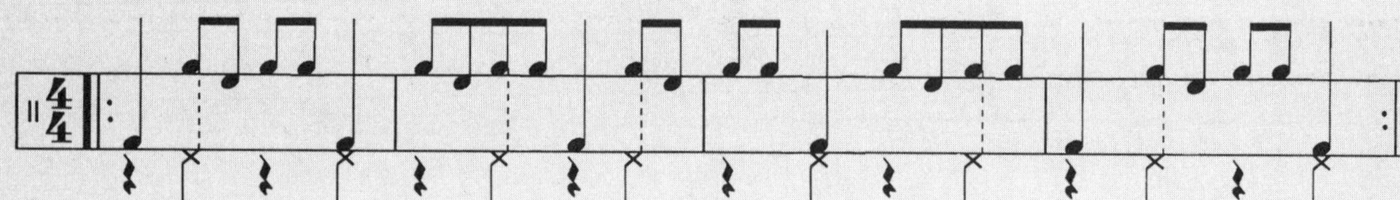

hands and feet

- ☐ Reverse the roles of the feet, playing the bass drum part on the hi-hat (left foot), and the hi-hat part on the bass drum. Play the right and left hand parts on the hi-hat, opening the hi-hat ½ beat before you close it.

Example (#6)

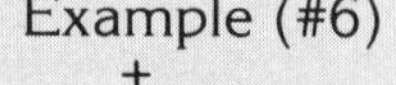

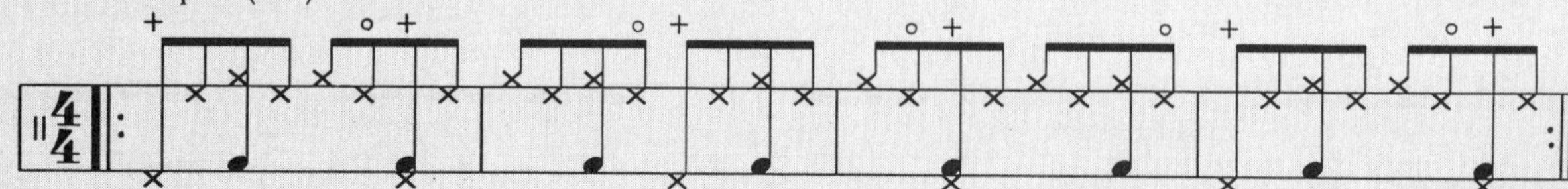

Also play the bass drum when the hi-hat is open only (rather than on the back-beats as shown in the example above).

a.
b.
c.
d.
1.
2.
3.
4.
5.
6.
7.
8.

15 *Eighth Note Groove/Fill Patterns II*

These patterns involve movement between the hands and feet. Note that in sections "A." and "B." the feet and snare are constant, while in sections "C." and "D." the feet and cymbal are constant. The feet part is written to allow several interpretations.

— Play feet part on the bass drum and hi-hat in unison.

Example (#A10)

— Play the feet part on the bass drum and keep time with the hi-hat.

Examples (#A10)

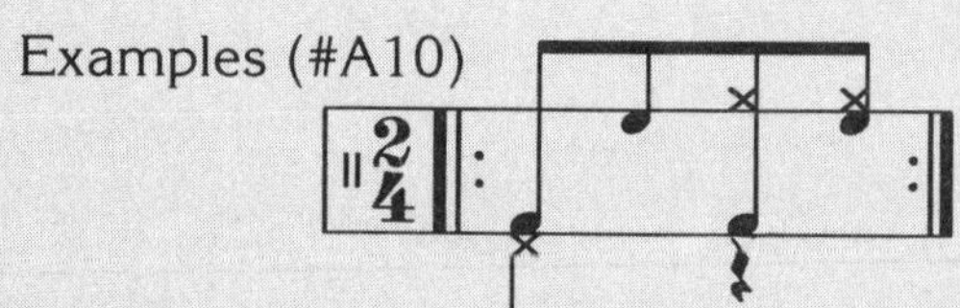

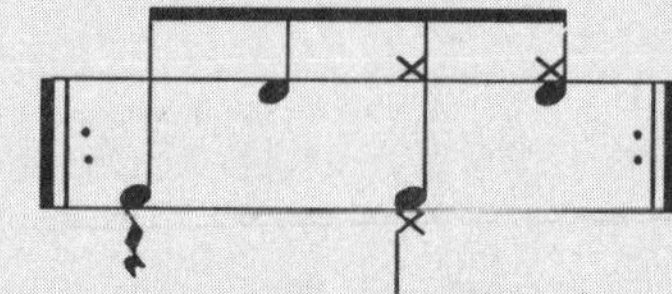

— Play the feet part on the hi-hat and keep time with the bass drum.

Examples (#A10)

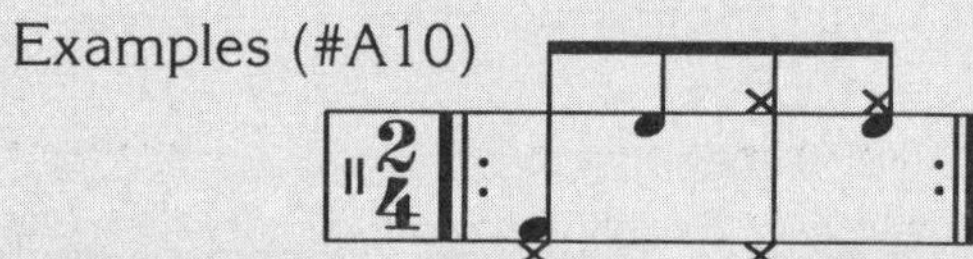

Practice Options

- ☐ Play each pattern in the context of time (see p. 6).
- ☐ Swing the eighth notes (♫ = ♩³♪).
- ☐ Combine any two, three, or four patterns, interpreting each pattern as four sixteenth notes.
- ☐ Repeatedly alternate pattern #1 in each lettered section with any other pattern in the section.

Variations

hands

- ☐ Following the indicated sticking, play each pattern using various surface combinations:
  - — both right and left hand on snare drum.
  - — right hand moving from surface to surface, *ad lib.*; left hand stationary on snare.
  - — left hand moving from surface to surface, *ad lib.*; right hand stationary on cymbal, snare, or tom.
  - — both hands moving from surface to surface, *ad lib.*

hands and feet

- ☐ Play each pattern three times, interpreting the combination as four triplets in $\frac{4}{4}$ time. Play the feet part on the bass drum and close the hi-hat on beats 2 and 4 or all four beats.

Example (#B15)

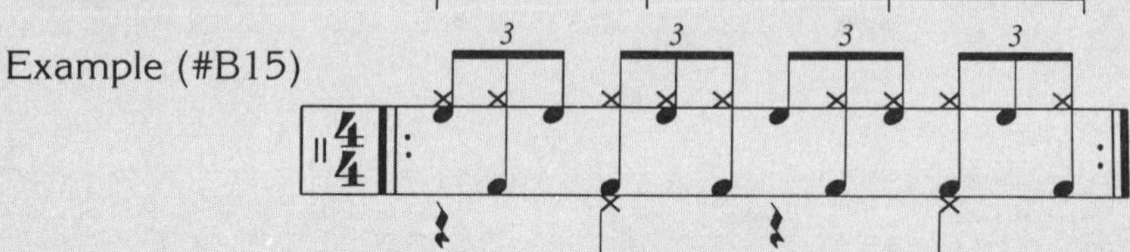

- ☐ Play each pattern three times, interpreting the combination as two measures in $\frac{3}{4}$ time. Play the hi-hat using one of the $\frac{3}{4}$ hi-hat patterns on page 151.

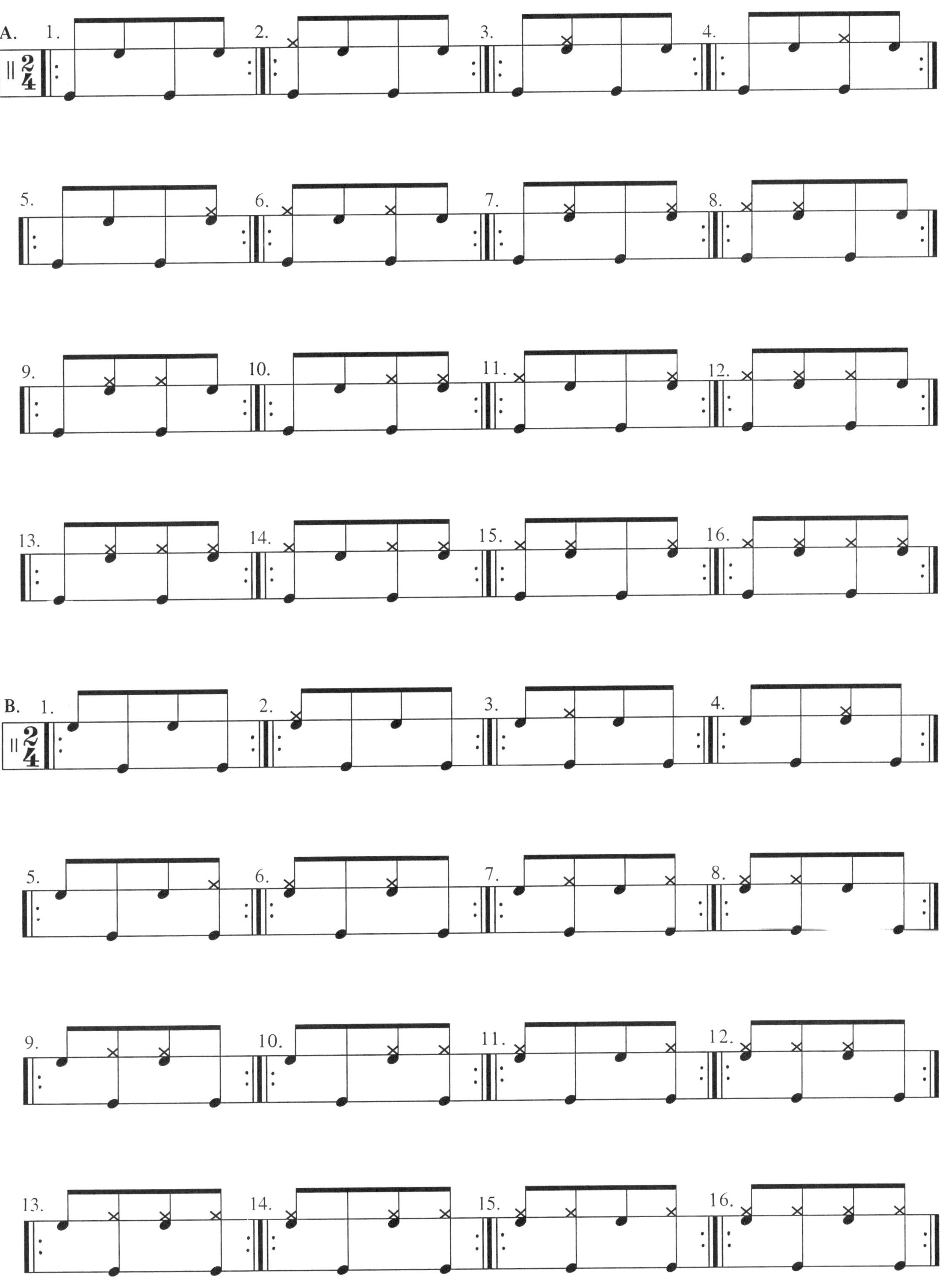
A.
1.
2.
3.
4.
5.
6.
7.
8.
9.
10.
11.
12.
13.
14.
15.
16.
B.
1.
2.
3.
4.
5.
6.
7.
8.
9.
10.
11.
12.
13.
14.
15.
16.

C.
1.
2.
3.
4.
5.
6.
7.
8.
9.
10.
11.
12.
13.
14.
15.
16.
D.
1.
2.
3.
4.
5.
6.
7.
8.
9.
10.
11.
12.
13.
14.
15.
16.

16 *Eighth Note Grooves V*

These grooves in three combine constant ride and hi-hat parts with various snare and bass drum parts to create unbroken eighth note patterns.

Practice Options

- ☐ Play the ride part on a cymbal bell or cowbell.
- ☐ Play the ride part on a closed hi-hat (omit the left foot part).
- ☐ Repeatedly play combinations of "a.," "b.," and complete patterns to create new grooves in various meters. For example:
  - — "a." or "b." alone ($\frac{2}{4}$).
  - — "a." followed by "b." or "b." followed by "a." ($\frac{4}{4}$).
  - — entire pattern followed by "a." or "b." ($\frac{5}{4}$).
  - — entire pattern followed by "a." and "b." ($\frac{7}{4}$).
  - — entire pattern twice followed by "a." and "b." ($\frac{10}{4}$).
- ☐ Omit snare drum notes *ad lib.*
- ☐ Swing the eighth notes (♫ = ♩♪ with triplet 3).
- ☐ Substitute various appropriate hi-hat patterns (see p. 151).

Variations

hands

- ☐ Play the snare part on various surfaces, *ad lib.*
- ☐ Substitute any of the following ride patterns.

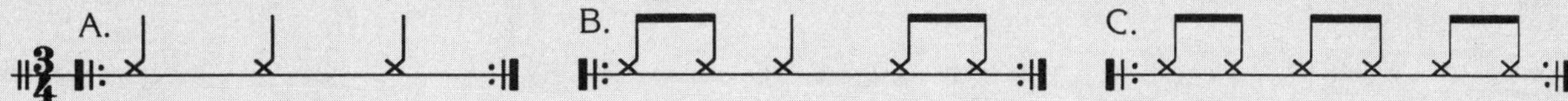

hands and feet

- ☐ Play only the hand parts as written, and keep time with the feet.
- ☐ Play only the feet parts as written, and keep time with the hands.

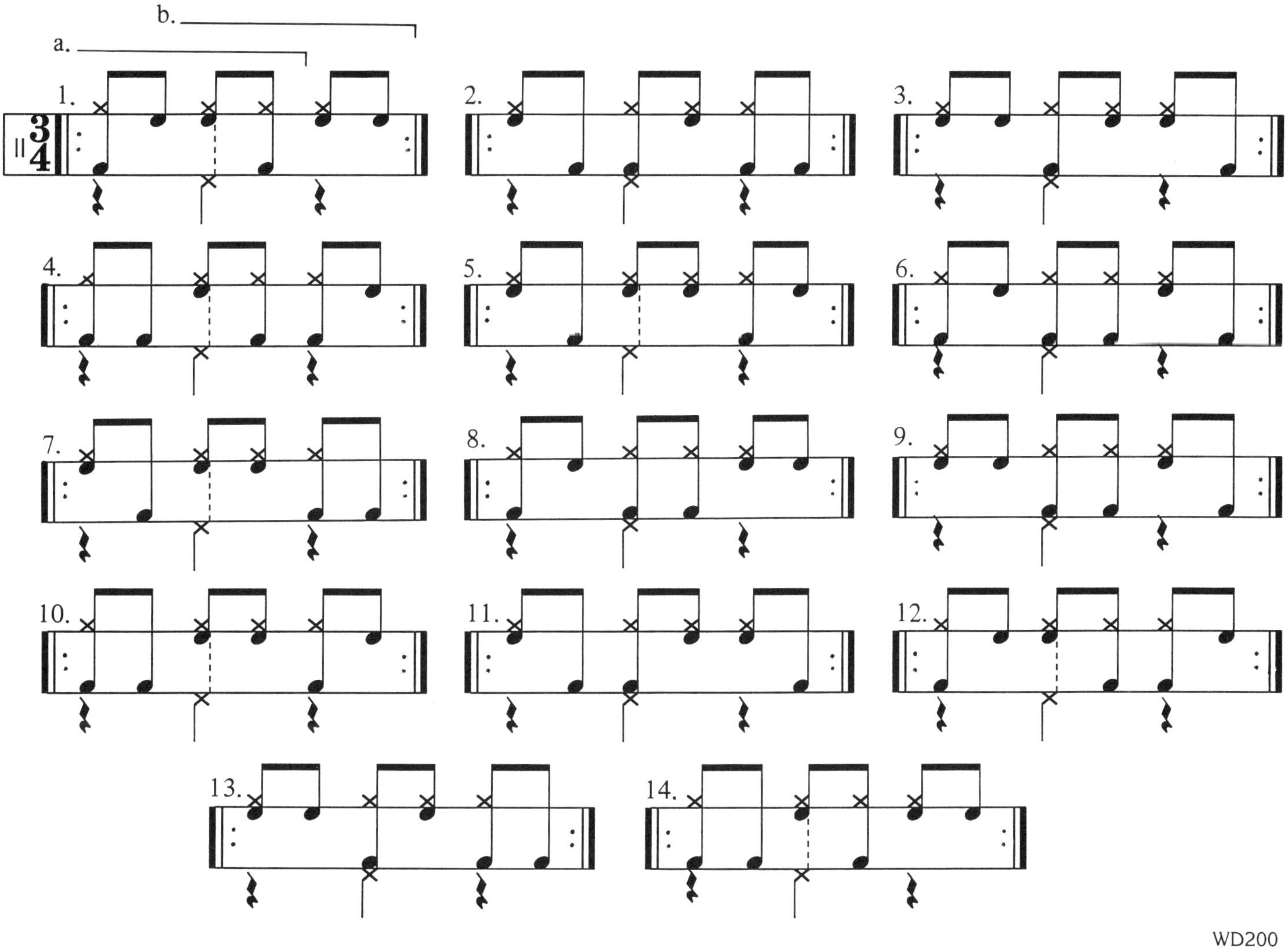

b.
a.

1. 2. 3. 4. 5. 6. 7. 8. 9. 10. 11. 12. 13. 14.

17 *Sixteenth Note Grooves I*

These grooves combine a constant ride and snare/hi-hat back-beat with various bass drum parts.

Practice Options

- ☐ Play the ride part on a cymbal bell or cowbell.
- ☐ Play the ride part on a closed hi-hat (omit the left foot part).
- ☐ Play the ride part on the hi-hat, opening it $1/2$ or $1/4$ beat before you close it on the back-beats. Omit the ride when the hi-hat closes. (In other words, do not strike the hi-hat with your stick when you are closing it with your foot.)
- ☐ Combine the first half of any pattern ("a.") with the second half of any other pattern ("b.").
- ☐ Repeatedly alternate pattern #1 with any other pattern.
- ☐ Combine any two patterns.
- ☐ Swing the sixteenth notes (=).
- ☐ Substitute various appropriate hi-hat patterns (see p. 151).

Variations

hands

- ☐ While playing the ride on a cymbal or closed hi-hat, add any of the following accent patterns to the ride. Play the accented notes with the shoulder of the stick on the cymbal bell or hi-hat edge.

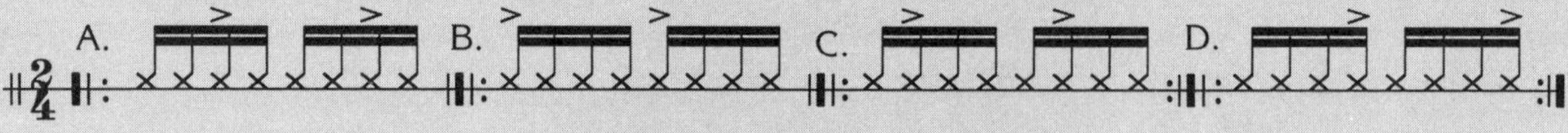

- ☐ Substitute any of the following ride patterns.

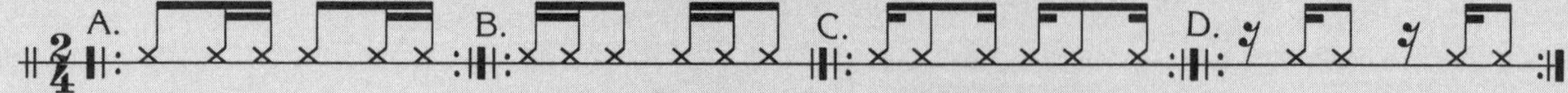

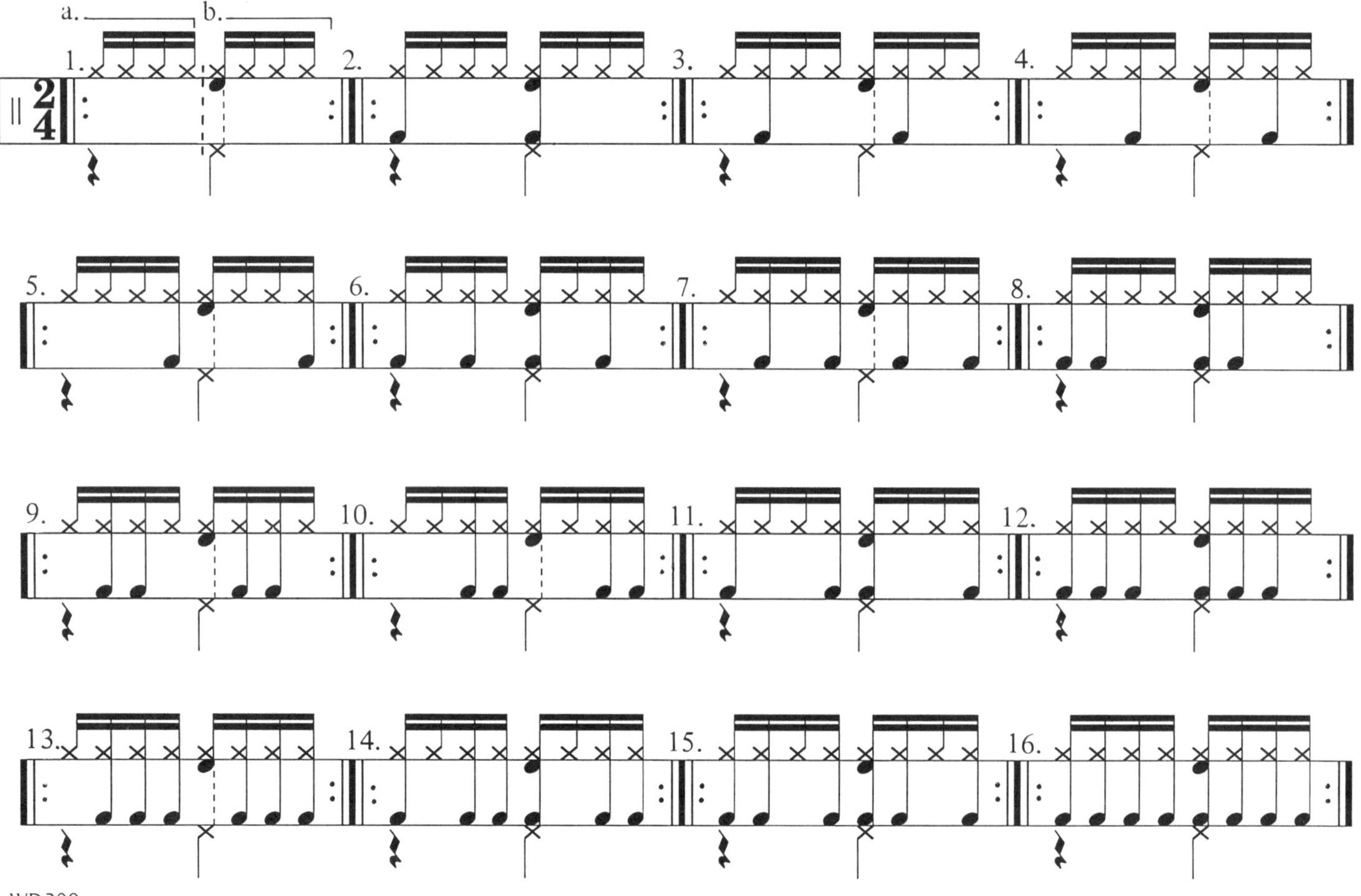

18 *Eighth/Sixteenth Note Grooves I*

These grooves combine a constant ride and snare/hi-hat back-beat with various bass drum parts.

Practice Options

- ☐ Play the ride part on a cymbal bell or cowbell.
- ☐ Play the ride part on a closed hi-hat (omit the left foot part).
- ☐ Play the ride part on the hi-hat, opening it 1/2 or 1/4 beat before you close it on the back-beats. Omit the ride when the hi-hat closes. (In other words, do not strike the hi-hat with your stick when you are closing it with your foot.)
- ☐ Combine the first half of any pattern ("a.") with the second half of any other pattern ("b.").
- ☐ Repeatedly alternate pattern #1 with any other pattern.
- ☐ Combine any two patterns.
- ☐ Swing the sixteenth notes (♬♬ = ♪𝄾♪♪𝄾♪). 
- ☐ Substitute various appropriate hi-hat patterns (see p. 151).

Variations

hands

- ☐ While playing the ride on a cymbal or closed hi-hat, add any of the following accent patterns to the ride. Play the accented notes with the shoulder of the stick on the cymbal bell or hi-hat edge.

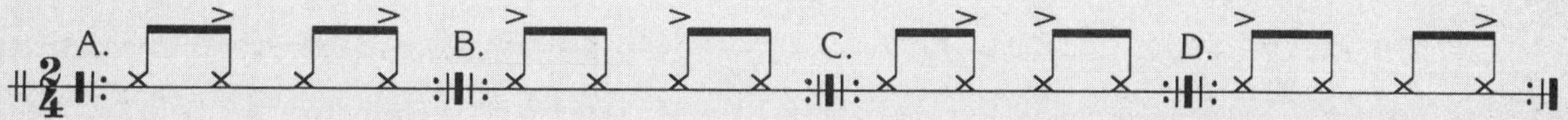

- ☐ Substitute either of the following ride patterns.

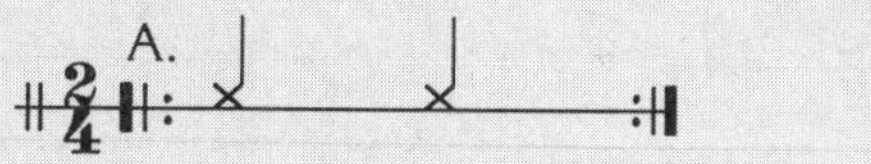

a. b.

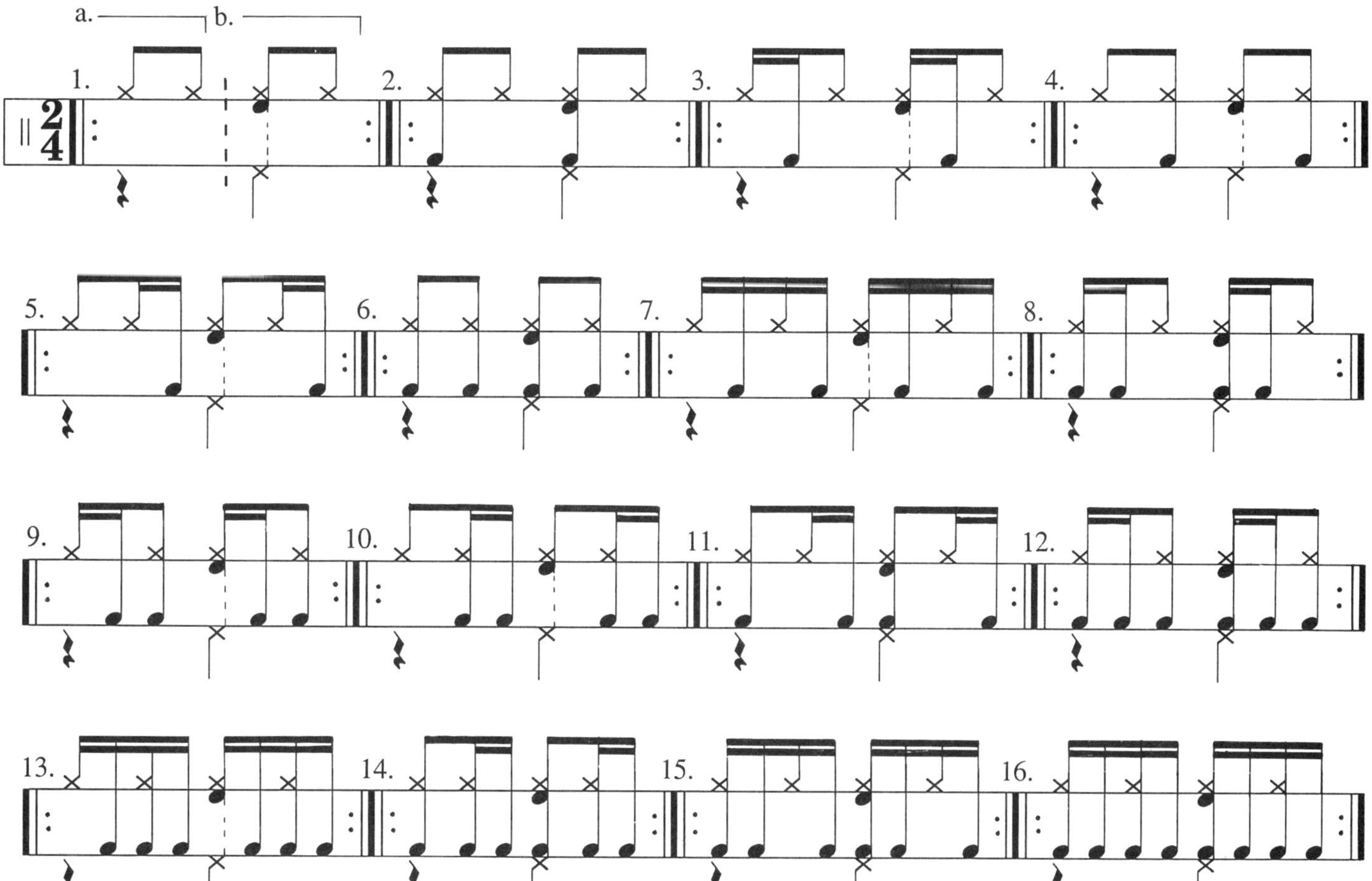

1. 2. 3. 4.

5. 6. 7. 8.

9. 10. 11. 12.

13. 14. 15. 16.

19 *Eighth/Sixteenth Note Grooves II*

These grooves combine a constant ride and snare/hi-hat back-beat with various bass drum parts.

Practice Options

- ☐ Play the ride part on a closed hi-hat (omit the left foot part).
- ☐ Play the ride part on the hi-hat, opening it $1/2$ or $1/4$ beat before you close it on the back-beats. Omit the ride when the hi-hat closes. (In other words, do not strike the hi-hat with your stick when you are closing it with your foot.)
- ☐ Repeatedly alternate pattern #1 with any other pattern.
- ☐ Combine any two patterns.
- ☐ Swing the sixteenth notes (=).
- ☐ Substitute various appropriate hi-hat patterns (see p. 151).

Variations

hands

- ☐ While playing the ride and feet as written, play a snare drum cross-stick effect on beat 1, and a tom on beat 2 (the back-beat).

Example (#14)

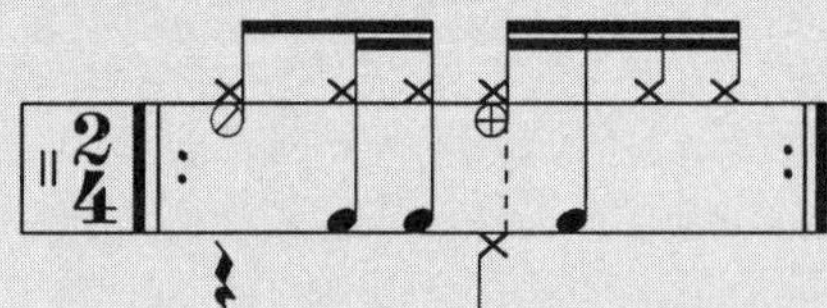

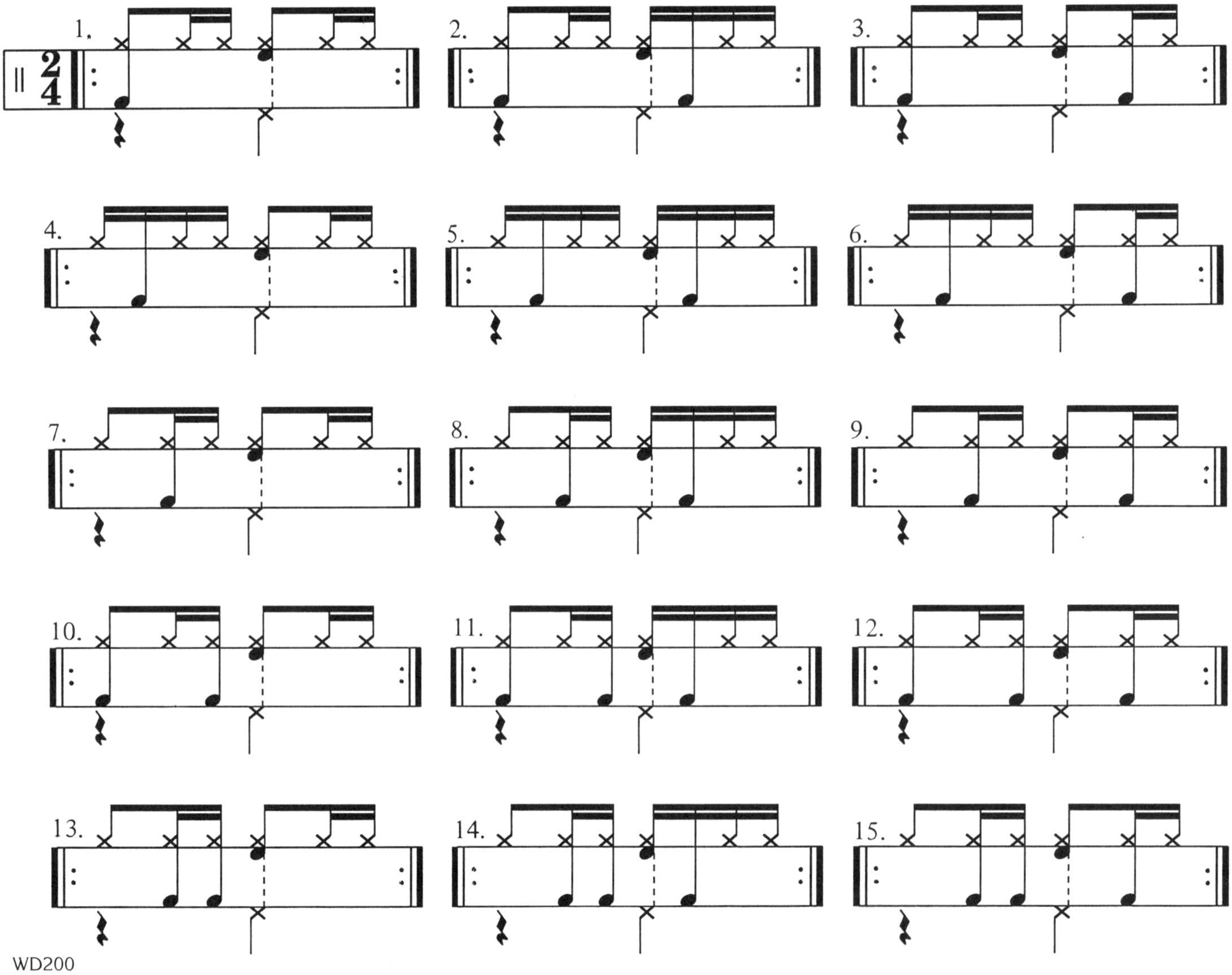

1. 2. 3.

4. 5. 6.

7. 8. 9.

10. 11. 12.

13. 14. 15.

20 *Sixteenth Note Grooves II*

In these grooves, the constant sixteenth note pulse is created by movement between the bass drum and ride. Only the snare drum back-beat and hi-hat remain constant.

Practice Options

- ☐ Play the cymbal part on a closed hi-hat (omit the left foot part).
- ☐ Play the cymbal part on the hi-hat, opening it 1/2 or 1/4 beat before you close it on the back-beats.
- ☐ Combine the first half of any pattern ("a.") with the second half of any other pattern ("b.").
- ☐ Repeatedly alternate pattern #1 with any other pattern.
- ☐ Combine any two patterns.
- ☐ Swing the sixteenth notes (♬♬ = ³♪𝄾♪ ³♪𝄾♪).
- ☐ Substitute various appropriate hi-hat patterns (see p. 151).

Variations

hands

- ☐ Replace the broken ride part in each pattern with a constant sixteenth note ride.

feet

- ☐ When two or more consecutive notes exist in the bass drum part, omit the hi-hat part and alternate the feet (RL or LR) to play the consecutive notes (use the bass drum and hi-hat, double bass drums, or a double bass pedal).

hands and feet

- ☐ Reverse the roles of the feet, playing the bass drum part on the hi-hat (left foot), and the hi-hat part on the bass drum. Play the ride part on the hi-hat, opening the hi-hat 1/4 beat before you close it.

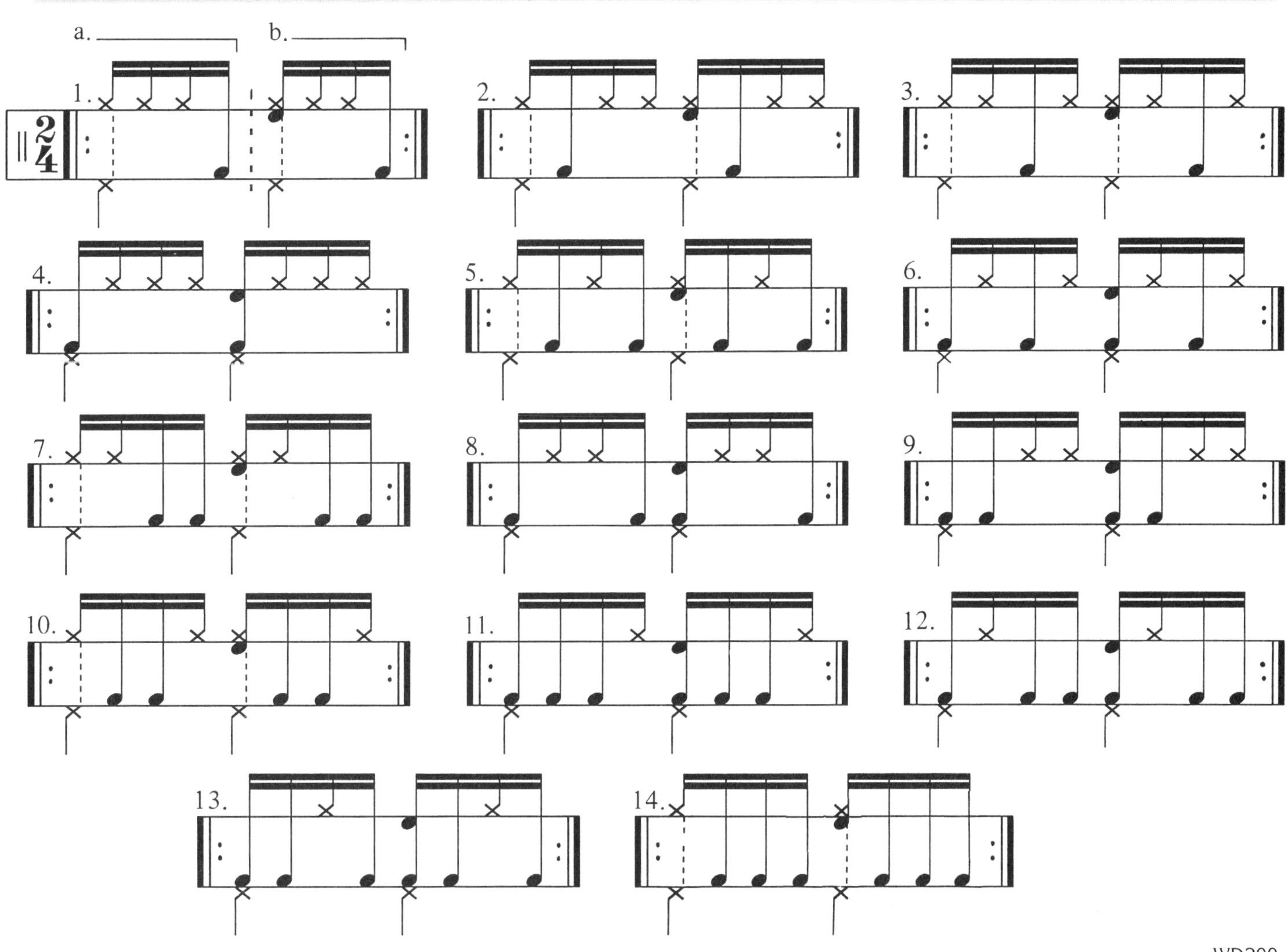

21 *Sixteenth Note Grooves III*

Each groove incorporates a constant ride on an opening and closing hi-hat to create a slightly syncopated feel. Ride on the edge of the hi-hat cymbals with the shoulder of your stick to increase the opening and closing effect.

Practice Options

- ☐ Omit the ride when the hi-hat closes. (In other words, do not strike the hi-hat with your stick when you are closing it with your foot.)
- ☐ Combine the first half of any pattern ("a.") with the second half of any other pattern ("b.").
- ☐ Combine any two patterns.
- ☐ Play the ride part on a cymbal, and play the feet part using double bass drums or a double bass pedal; or play both the bass drum and hi-hat parts with your right foot on a single bass drum.
- ☐ Swing the sixteenth notes (♬♬ = ♪𝄾♪ ♪𝄾♪).

Variations

hands

- ☐ Except for the back-beats, play a tom any time the hi-hat is open. On the back-beats, play the snare drum as written.

Example (#22)

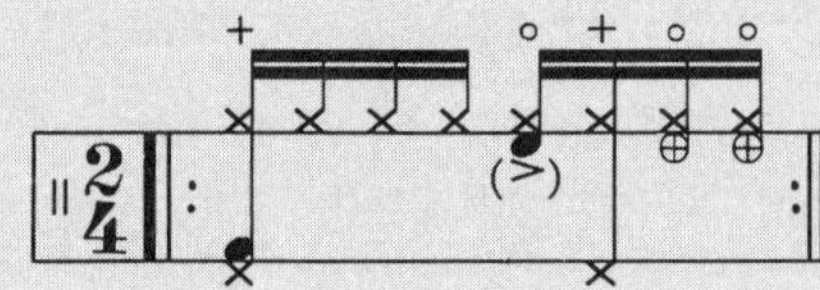

feet

- ☐ In addition to playing the bass drum as written, play it any other time the hi-hat is open.

Example (#23)

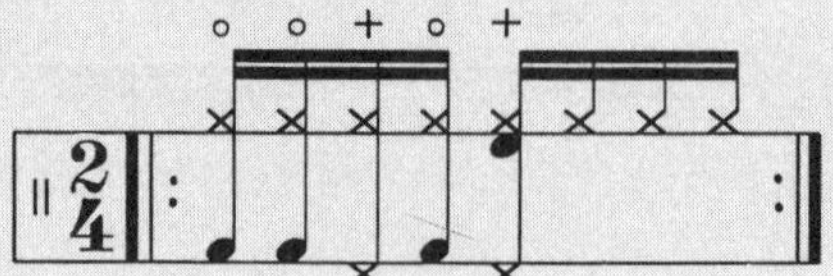

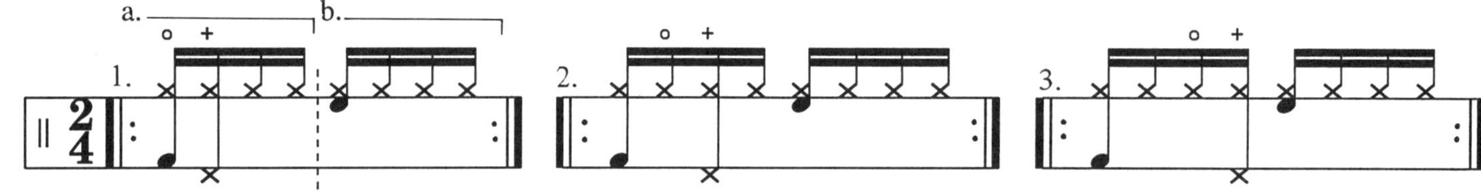

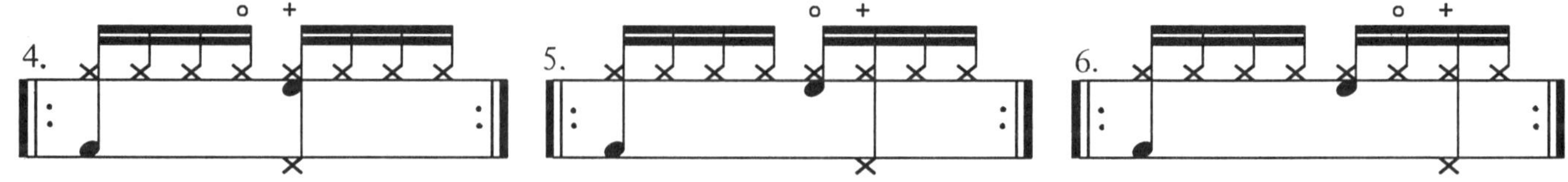

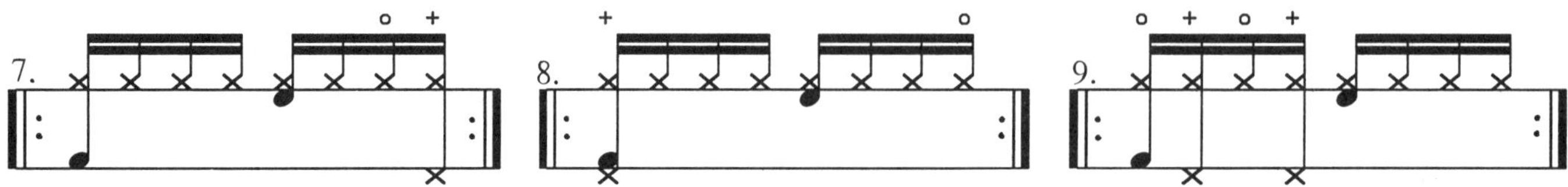

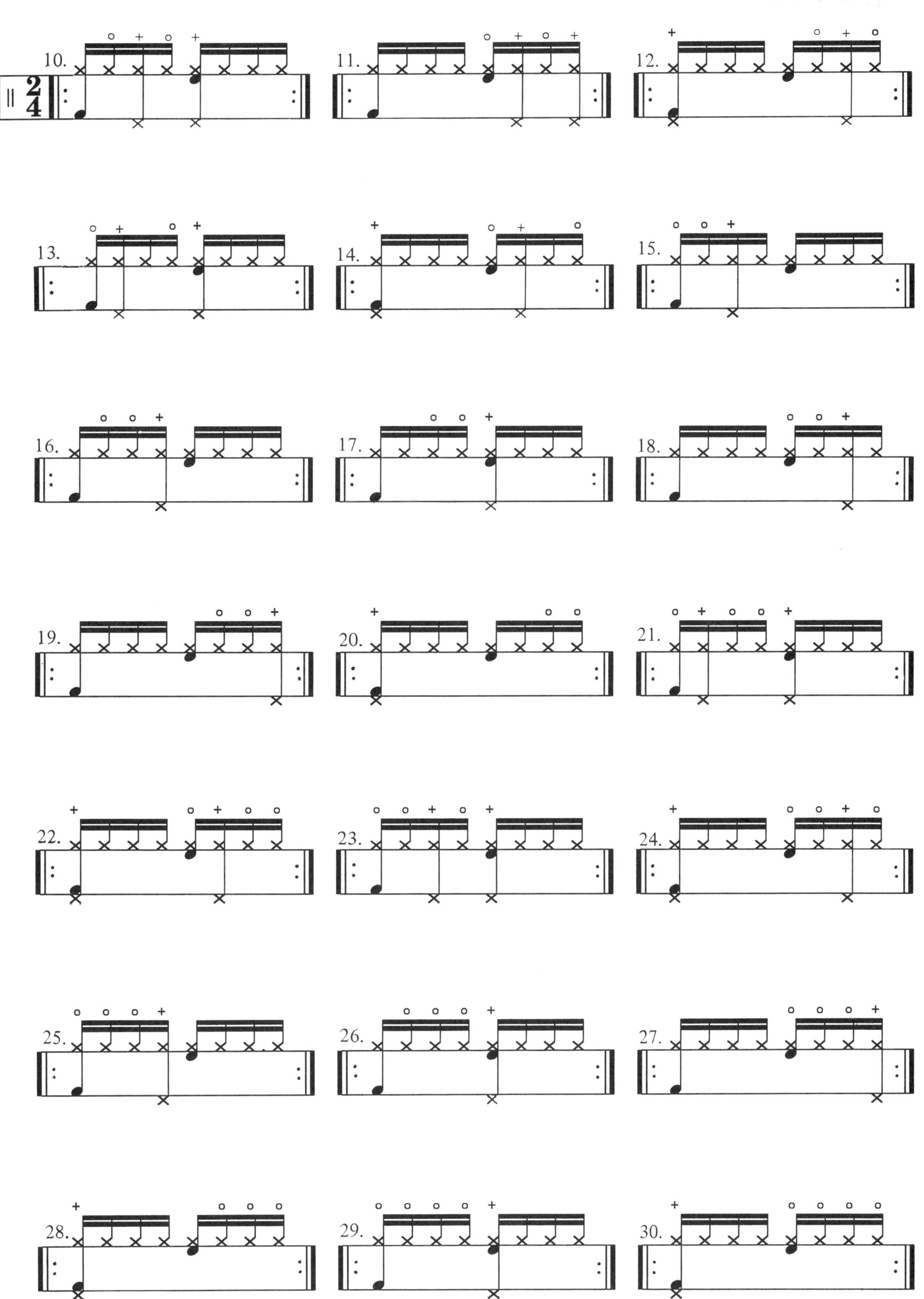
10.
11.
12.
13.
14.
15.
16.
17.
18.
19.
20.
21.
22.
23.
24.
25.
26.
27.
28.
29.
30.

22 *Sixteenth Note Fill Patterns I*

These fills contain a simple alternating sticking pattern moving around the drums.

Practice Options

- ☐ Play each fill in the context of time (see p. 6).
- ☐ Play portions of each fill <u>within</u> the time.

Example (#5)

- ☐ Combine any "a." with any "b." with any "c." with any "d."

Example (#2a.-#3b.-#4c.-#1d.)

- ☐ Combine any two fills.
- ☐ Play the sixteen fills consecutively.
- ☐ Substitute various appropriate hi-hat and feet patterns (see pp. 150–151).

Variations

hands

- ☐ Play any snare note as an open double stroke.

hand and feet

- ☐ Delete any snare drum note and replace it with a bass drum note. (Omit the written bass drum part when using this variation.)

Example (#10)

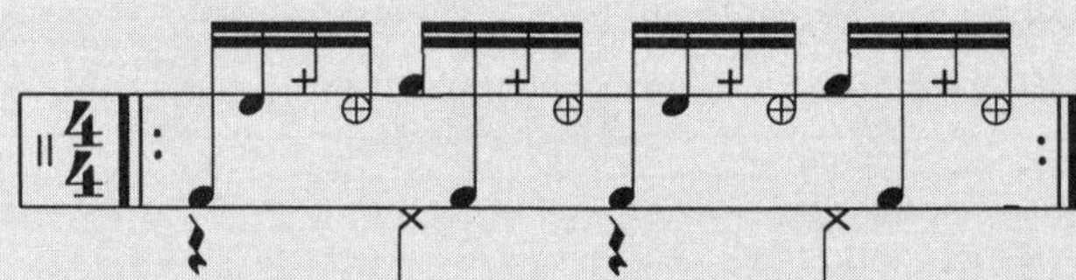

- ☐ Play each pattern (or portions of each pattern) in various rhythmic and metric contexts:

Example (#11) — portion of pattern in $\frac{3}{4}$

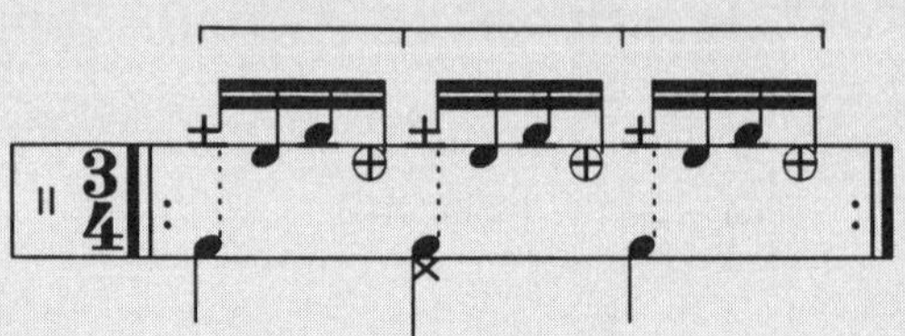

Example (#11) — complete pattern in $\frac{5}{4}$

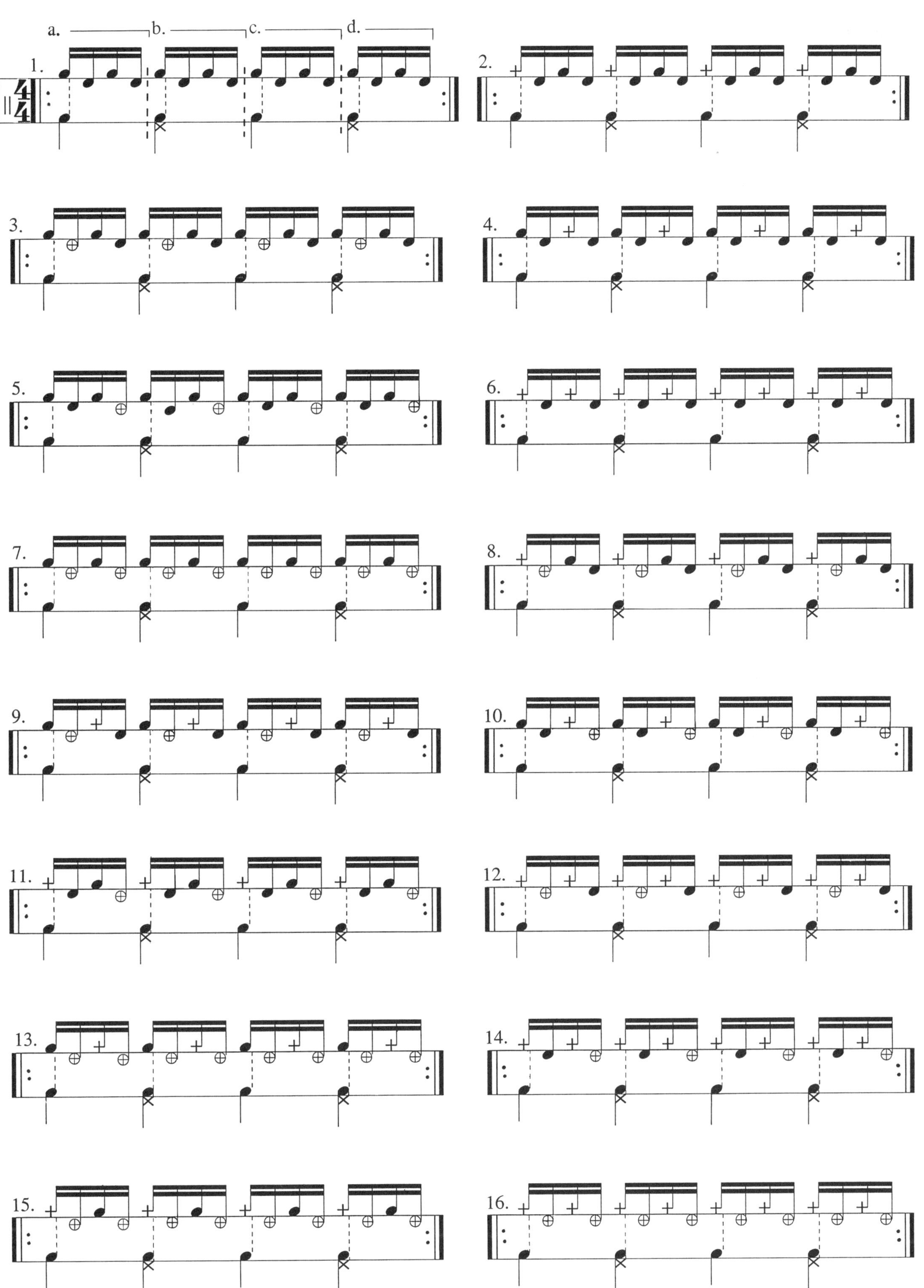
a.
b.
c.
d.
1.
2.
3.
4.
5.
6.
7.
8.
9.
10.
11.
12.
13.
14.
15.
16.

23 *Eighth/Sixteenth Note Fill Patterns I*

While these fills incorporate a wide variety of eighth/sixteenth note combinations, placement of the toms on each beat remains the same within each pattern. Only the use of the snare drum changes.

Practice Options

- ☐ Play each fill in the context of time (see p. 6).
- ☐ Combine any "a." with any "b." with any "c." with any "d."

Example (#5a.-#7b.-#8b.-#16a.)

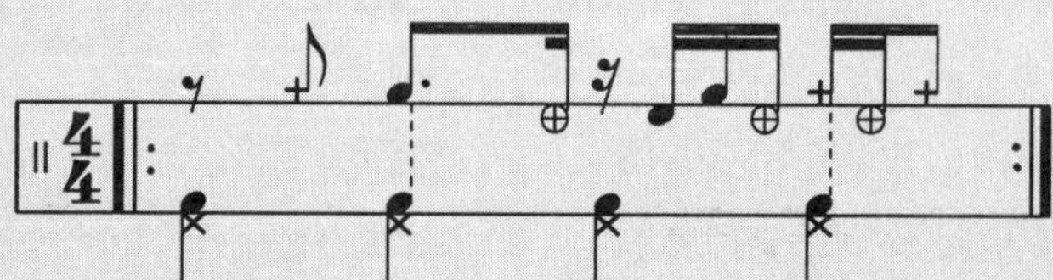

Also combine two, three, and five beats to create $\frac{2}{4}$, $\frac{3}{4}$, and $\frac{5}{4}$ fills.

- ☐ Play the sixteen fills consecutively.
- ☐ Substitute various appropriate hi-hat and feet patterns (see pp. 150–151).

Variations

hands

- ☐ Play notes as flams or open double strokes, *ad lib.*

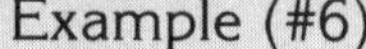

Example (#6) Example (#13)

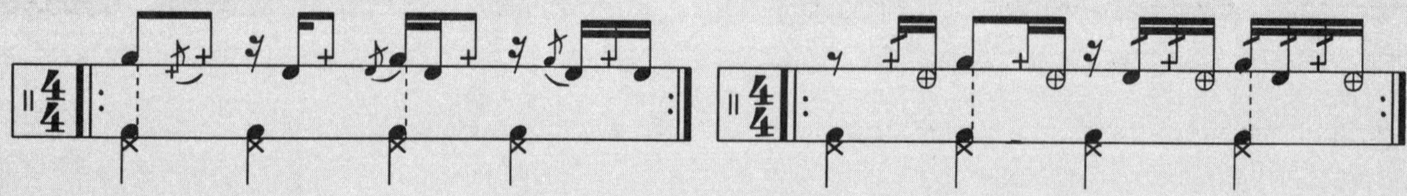

feet

- ☐ Play the bass drum on any sixteenth note subdivision on which the hands do not play (omit the written bass drum part). Play the hi-hat on all four beats.

Example (#2)

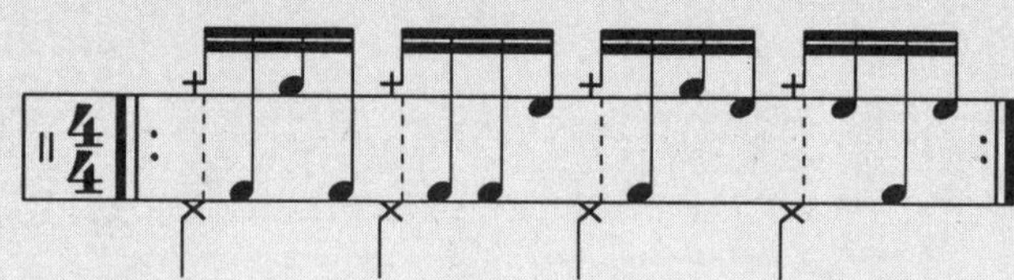

a.
b.
c.
d.
1.
2.
3.
4.
5.
6.
7.
8.
9.
10.
11.
12.
13.
14.
15.
16.

24 *Sixteenth Note Fill Patterns II*

These fills are based on the triplet patterns on page 89. By interpreting those six-note fills in a duple setting, an asymmetrical feel is created. (Depending on your playing background, you may find it helpful to master the p. 89 patterns before working through this study.)

Practice Options

- ☐ Play each fill in the context of time (see p. 6).
- ☐ Combine any "a." with any "b." with any "c."
- ☐ Combine any two fills.
- ☐ Play the eighteen fills consecutively.
- ☐ Substitute various appropriate hi-hat and feet patterns (see pp. 150–151).

Variations

hands

- ☐ Play any snare note as an open double stroke.
- ☐ Play the last two sixteenth notes of each pattern as double strokes.
- ☐ Omit sixteenth notes *ad lib.*, creating syncopated rhythmic figures.

hands and feet

- ☐ Delete the hand part whenever the bass drum is playing. (Try this variation with feet patterns shown on pp. 150–151.)

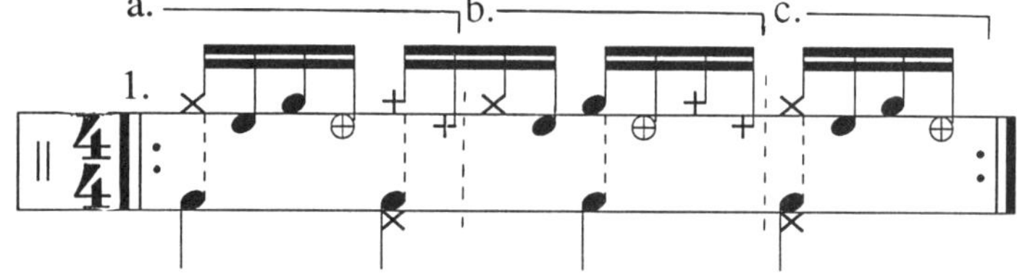

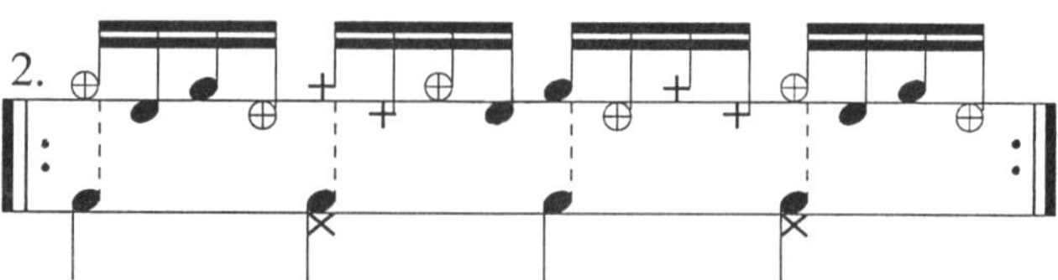

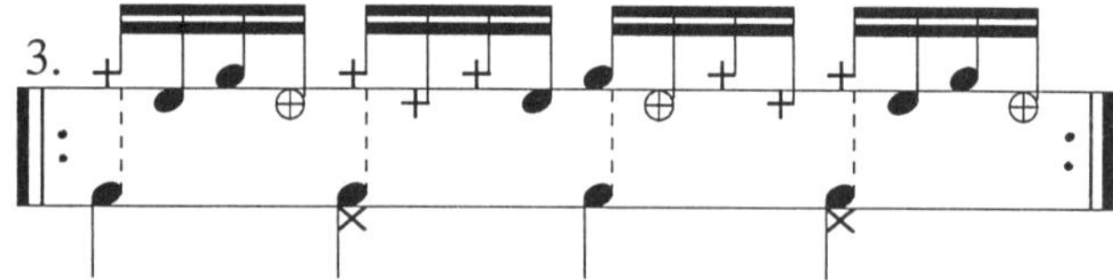

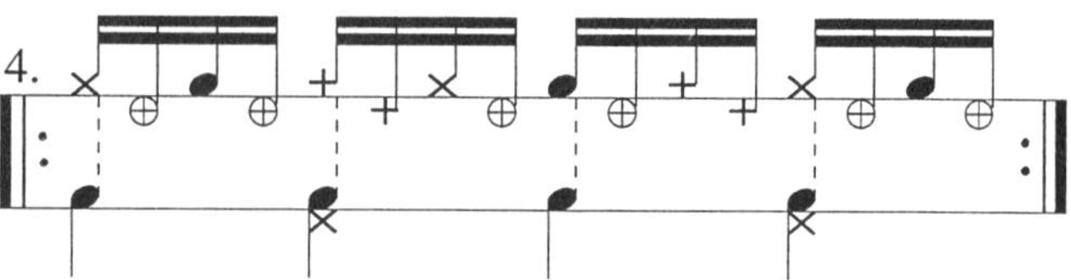

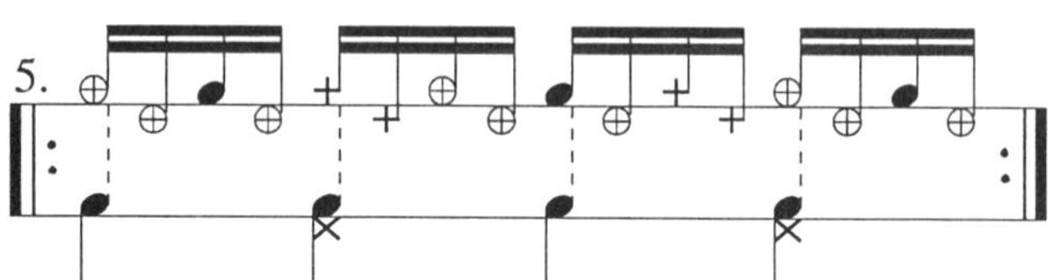

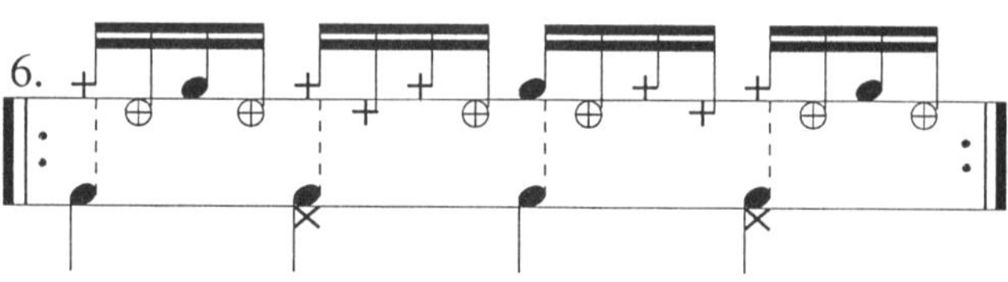

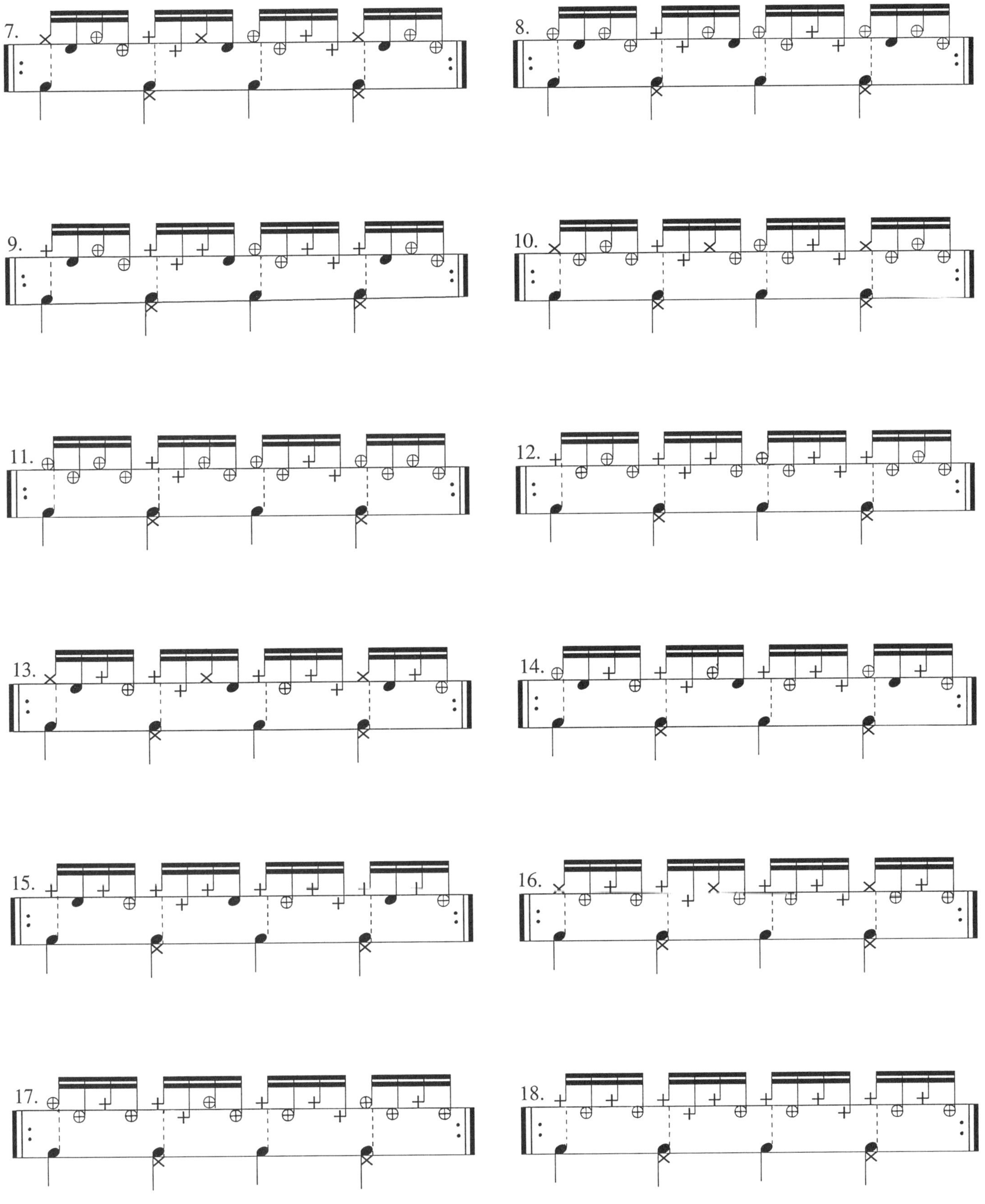
7.
8.
9.
10.
11.
12.
13.
14.
15.
16.
17.
18.

25 *Sixteenth Note Fill Patterns III*

In these fills, the bass drum and cymbal break up simple patterns around the drums on beats 3 and 4.

Practice Options

- ☐ Play each fill in the context of time (see p. 6).
- ☐ Omit beat 1 or beats 1 and 2 to create $\frac{3}{4}$ or $\frac{2}{4}$ fills.
- ☐ Play beat 1 twice to create $\frac{5}{4}$ fills.

Variations

hands

- ☐ Play all tom notes on the snare drum.
- ☐ On the second half of each fill, delete the right hand part whenever you play the bass drum. (In other words, delete all cymbal notes.)

Example (#12)

feet

- ☐ On beats 1 and 2, play the same bass drum rhythms as written for beats 3 and 4 (play the hands as written throughout).
- ☐ On beats 1 and 2, substitute any of the following feet patterns, or any other appropriate two beat feet pattern (see pp. 150–151).

A.

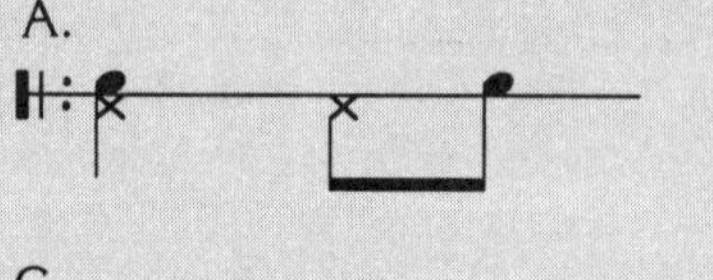

B.

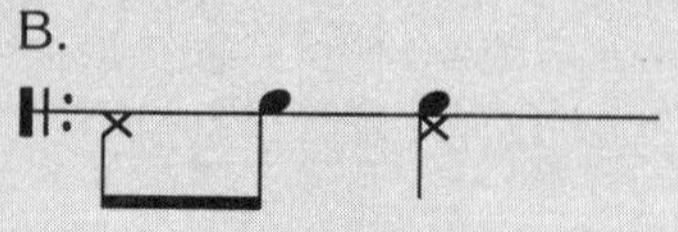

C.

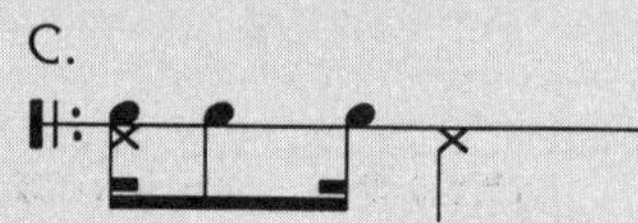

D.

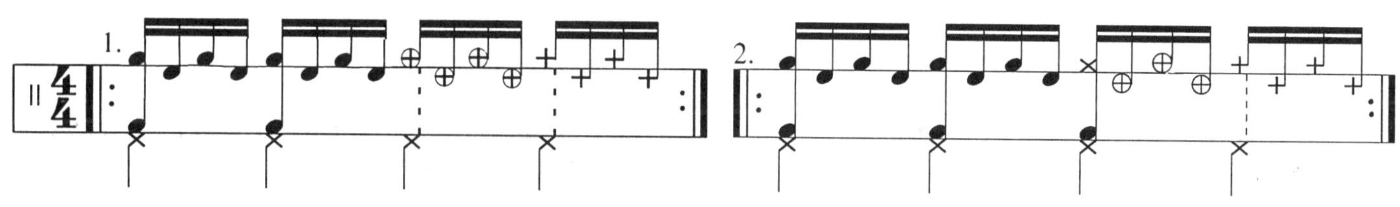

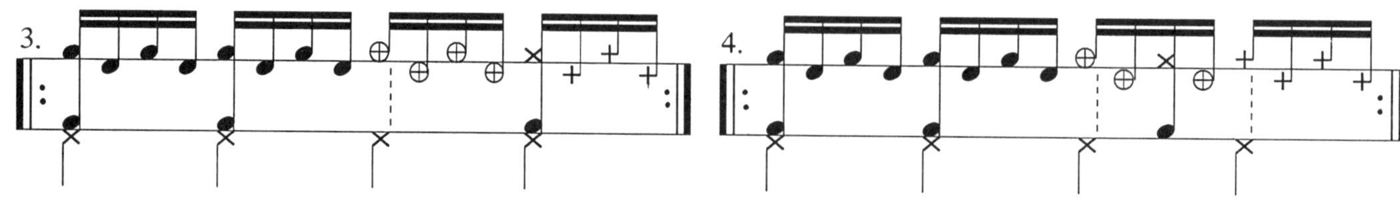

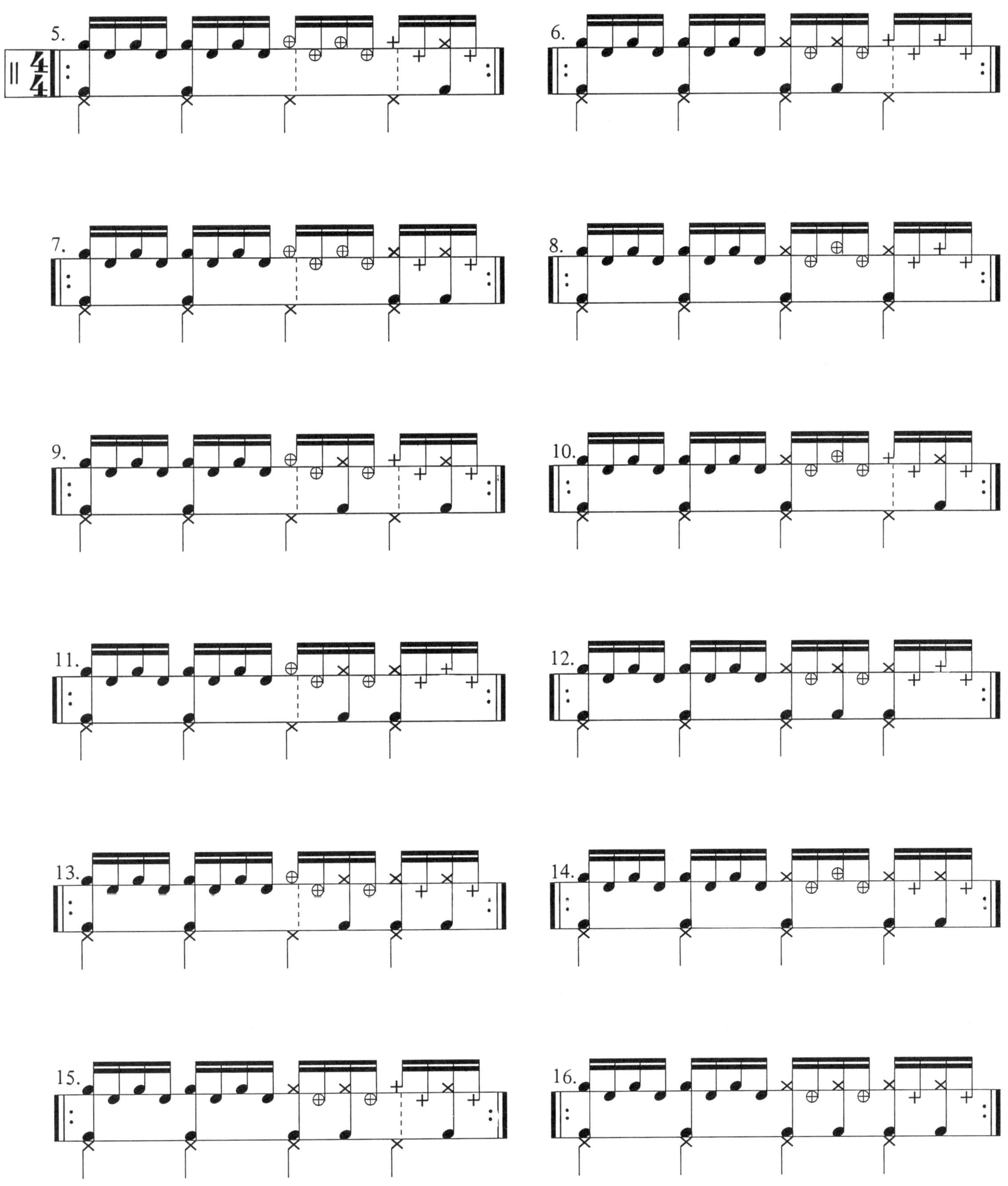
5.
6.
7.
8.
9.
10.
11.
12.
13.
14.
15.
16.

26 *Sixteenth Note Fill Patterns IV*

These fills (beginning on p. 54) are based on various sticking patterns.

Practice Options

- ☐ Play each fill in the context of time (see p. 6).
- ☐ Combine the first half of any pattern ("a.") with the second half of any other pattern ("b.").
- ☐ Combine any complete pattern with any part of any other pattern to create odd meter fills (for example, one complete pattern combined with the first six notes of another to create a $\frac{7}{8}$ fill).
- ☐ Combine any two patterns.
- ☐ Substitute various appropriate hi-hat and feet patterns (see pp. 150–151).

Variations

hands

- ☐ Following the indicated sticking, play each fill using various surface combinations:
  - — both right and left hand on snare drum.
  - — right hand on tom, left hand on snare.
  - — right hand moving from surface to surface, *ad lib.*; left hand stationary on snare.
  - — left hand moving from surface to surface, *ad lib.*; right hand stationary on snare.
  - — both hands moving from surface to surface, *ad lib.*

- ☐ Play each pattern twice, first with your right hand on a cymbal or closed hi-hat and left hand on the snare, then with your left hand on a cymbal or closed hi-hat and right hand on the snare.

Example (#A3, with hi-hat closed)

hands and feet

☐ Play the cymbal part on a cymbal bell or cowbell. Double the cymbal part with the bass drum, and close the hi-hat on all four beats.

Example (#B12)

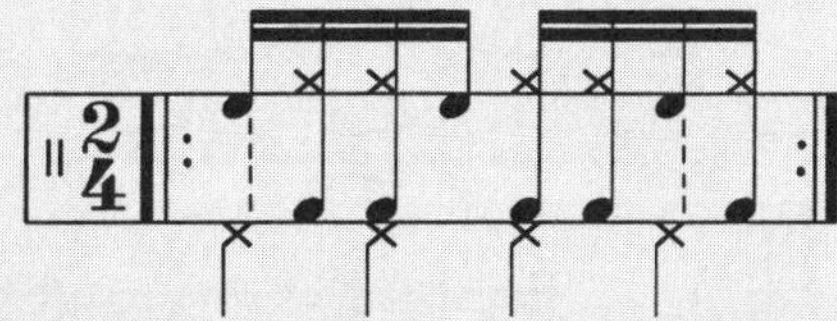

☐ Play each pattern twice, first with your right hand on a cymbal or closed hi-hat and left hand on the snare, then with your left hand on a cymbal or closed hi-hat and right hand on the snare. Double the cymbal/hi-hat part with the bass drum both times.

Example (#A3, with hi-hat closed)

☐ Play each sticking pattern with your feet while you play any of the following with your hands:

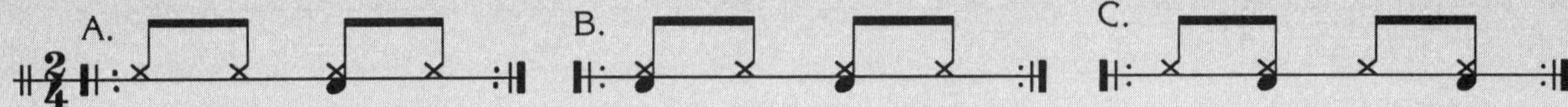

Example (#B10 with hand pattern "A.")

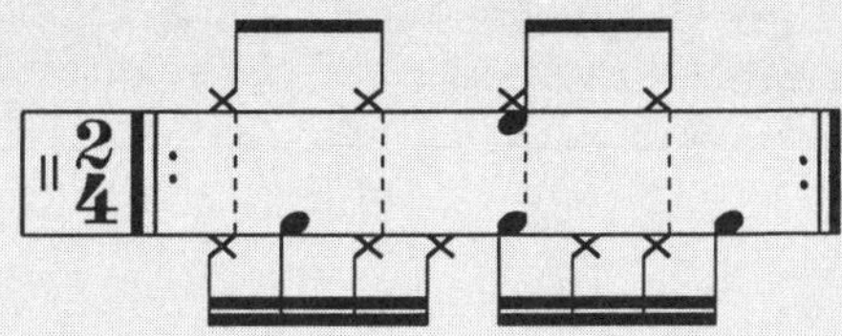

☐ Interpret each pattern as two groups of four thirty-second notes and play in the context of time. Use any appropriate feet pattern (see p. 150).

Example (#A9)

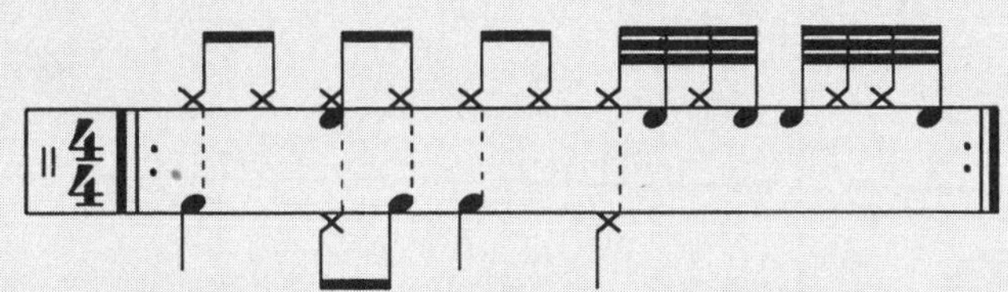

a.
b.
A.
1.
2.
3.
4.
5.
6.
7.
8.
9.
10.
11.
12.
13.
14.
15.
16.
17.
18.

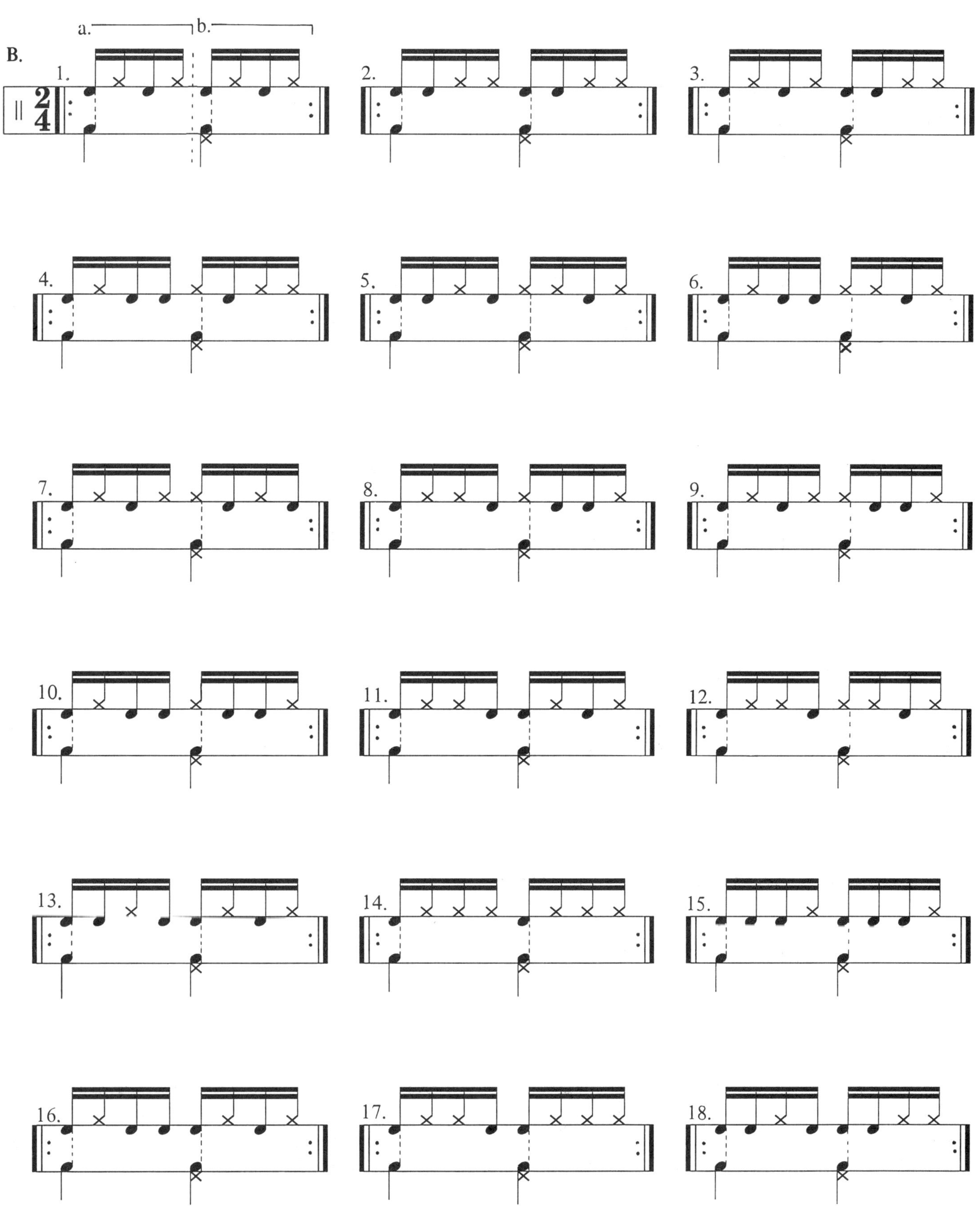

a.
b.
B.
1.
2.
3.
4.
5.
6.
7.
8.
9.
10.
11.
12.
13.
14.
15.
16.
17.
18.

27 *Sixteenth Note Fill Patterns V*

These fills combine three and six note sticking patterns in duple settings.

Practice Options

- ☐ Play each fill in the context of time (see p. 6)
- ☐ Combine any "a." with any "b." with any "c." Any order of "a.," "b.," and "c." is possible.
- ☐ Combine any two patterns.
- ☐ Substitute various appropriate hi-hat and feet patterns (see pp. 150–151).

Variations

hands

☐ Following the indicated sticking, play each fill using various surface combinations:
- — right hand on tom, cymbal bell, or special effects cymbal; left hand on snare.
- — right hand moving from surface to surface, *ad lib.*; left hand stationary on snare.
- — left hand moving from surface to surface, *ad lib.*; right hand stationary on snare.
- — both hands moving from surface to surface, *ad lib.*

☐ Replace any "a." in Section "A." with any of the following:

Replace any "a." in Section "B." with any of the following:

i. ii. iii. iv. v. vi.

Example (#B3)

iv b. c.

hands and feet

☐ Play each pattern with your right hand on a closed hi-hat. Double the right hand part with the bass drum.

Example (#B6)

☐ Play the right hand part using snare/tom doublestops, and play the left hand part on the bass drum. Close the hi-hat on all four beats.

Example (#A5)

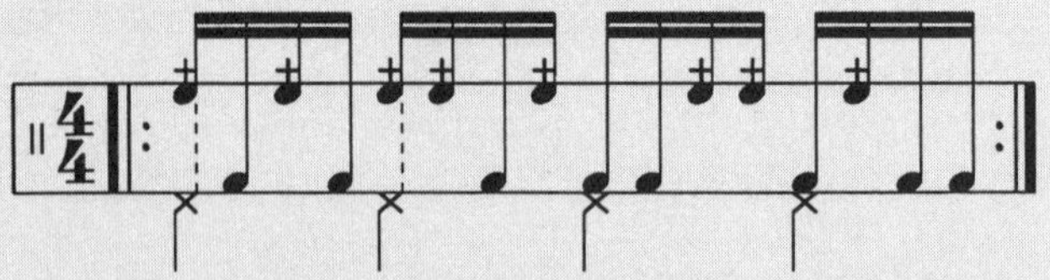

☐ Play each sticking pattern with your feet while your hands play the following:

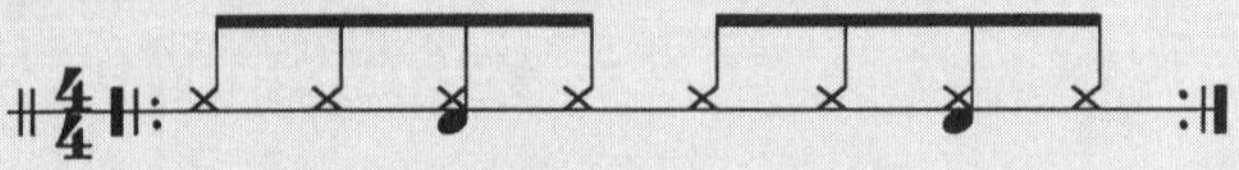

Example (#B7)

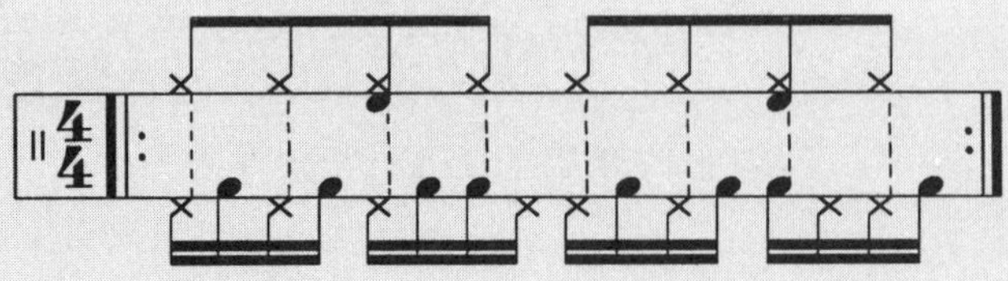

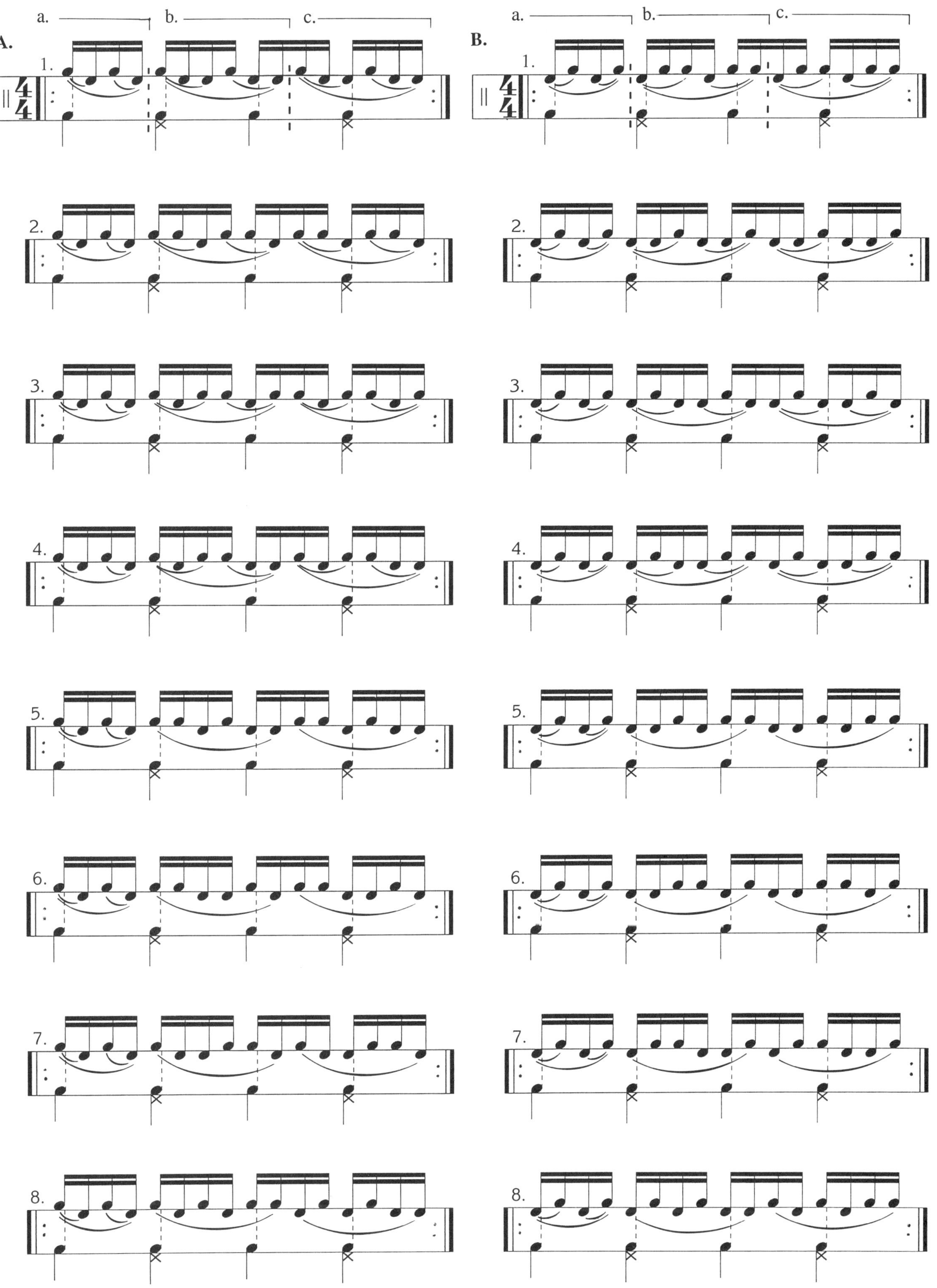
a.
b.
c.
A.
B.
1.
2.
3.
4.
5.
6.
7.
8.

28 *Sixteenth Note Grooves IV*

Each groove combines constant feet with a constant inverted paradiddle pattern in the hands. The only variable is the placement of the accents. The accent falling on the back-beat should be stronger than the other accents in the measure.

Practice Options

- ☐ Play the cymbal part on a closed hi-hat (omit the left foot part).
- ☐ Play the accented cymbal notes with the shoulder of the stick on the cymbal bell or hi-hat edge.
- ☐ Play some or all of the accented notes on alternate surfaces.
- ☐ Repeatedly alternate pattern #1 with any other pattern.
- ☐ Combine any two patterns.
- ☐ Substitute various appropriate hi-hat and feet patterns (see pp. 150–151).
- ☐ Play each pattern as a fill in the context of time (see p. 6).

Variations

hands

- ☐ Substitute any of the following accent patterns on beat 2.

a. b. c.

d. e. f. g.

Example (#10)

f.

- ☐ Play each accent pattern using other sticking patterns. Be sure the snare drum always falls on the back-beat.

Examples (#7)

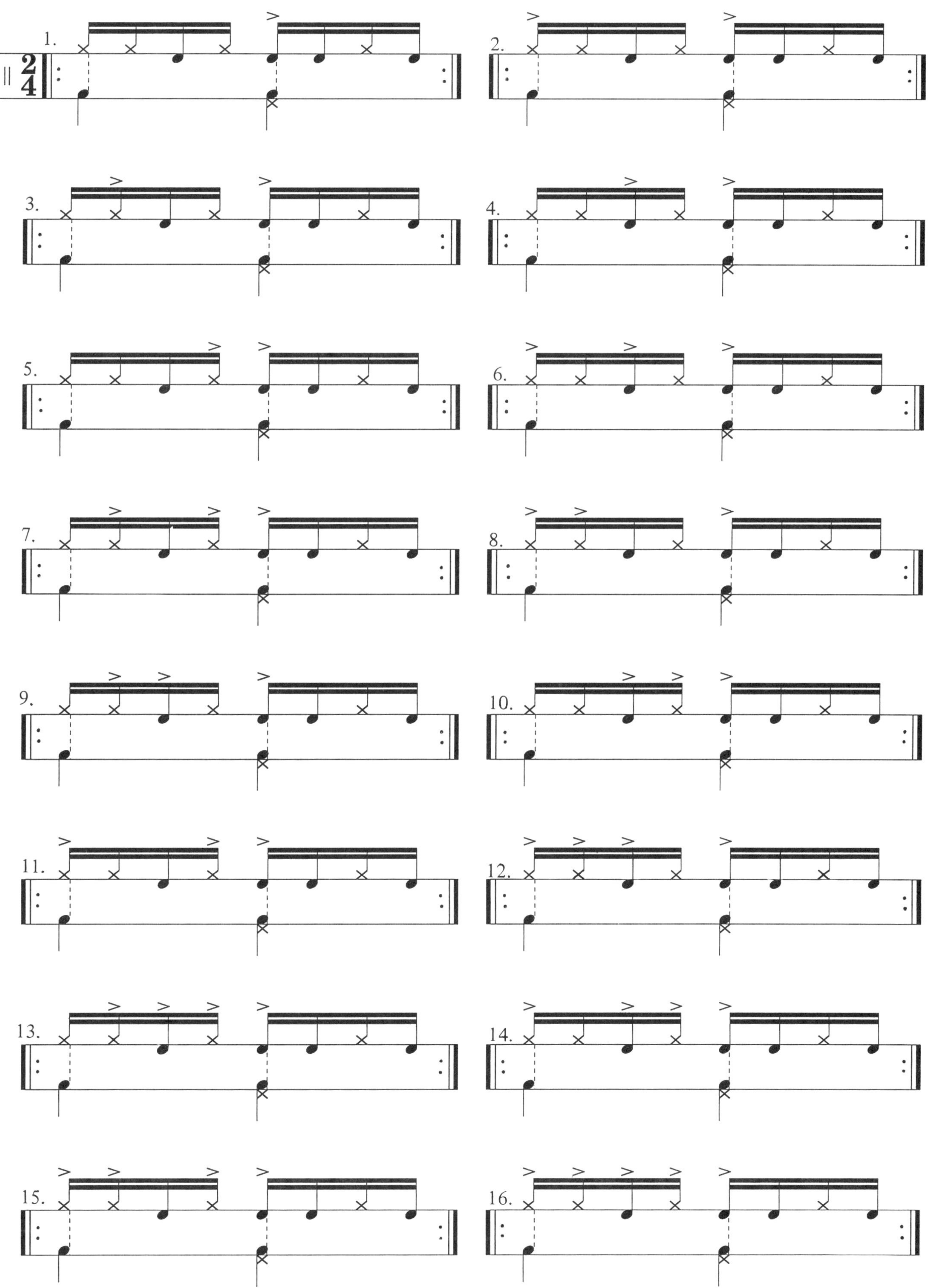
1.
2.
3.
4.
5.
6.
7.
8.
9.
10.
11.
12.
13.
14.
15.
16.

29 *Eighth/Sixteenth Note Fill Patterns II*

In this study, you create fills by combining any lettered one beat pattern with any numbered three beat pattern.

Practice Options

- ☐ Play each fill in the context of time (see p. 6).
- ☐ Play the cymbal part on a closed hi-hat (omit the left foot part).
- ☐ Play the accented cymbal notes with the shoulder of the stick on the cymbal bell or hi-hat edge.
- ☐ Play the numbered patterns alone to create $\frac{3}{4}$ fills.
- ☐ Play lettered patterns before and after any numbered pattern to create $\frac{5}{4}$ fills.
- ☐ Substitute various appropriate hi-hat and feet patterns (see pp. 150–151).

Variations

hands

- ☐ Play the accented notes on toms.

Example (#B5)

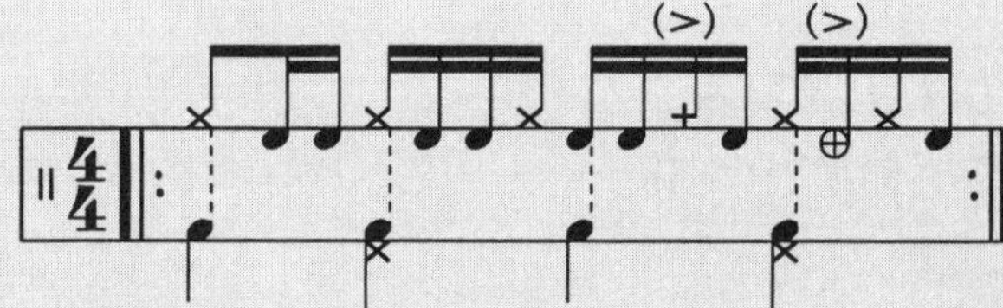

feet

- ☐ Double the cymbal part with the bass drum. Close the hi-hat on all four beats.

Example (#G10)

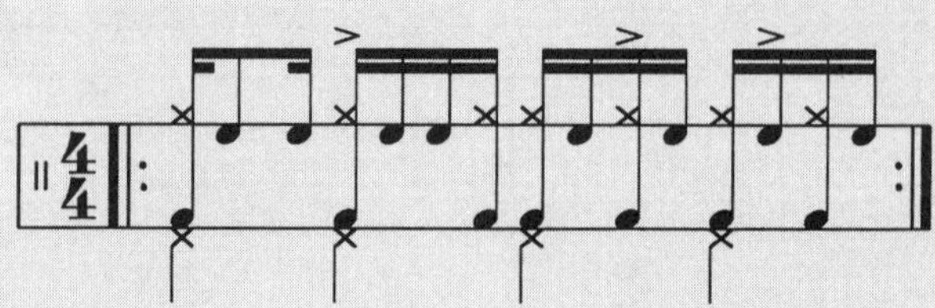

hands and feet

- ☐ Play the bass drum on all accented cymbal notes. Play a rim shot on all accented snare drum notes.
- ☐ Play the cymbal part on a closed hi-hat. On all accented cymbal notes, delete the cymbal part and play the bass drum instead.

Example (#H10)

- ☐ Play the cymbal part on a closed hi-hat. On <u>all</u> accented notes, delete the hand part and play the bass drum instead.

Example (#H10)

A.
B.
C.
D.
E.
F.
G.
H.
I.
J.
1.
2.
3.
4.
5.
6.
7.
8.
9.
10.
11.
12.
13.
14.
15.
16.
17.
18.
19.
20.

30 *Samba Grooves II*

While these Samba grooves are notated in $\frac{4}{4}$, they should maintain the traditional cut-time "two-feel." Notice that the snare drum part and characteristic feet pattern remain constant within each lettered section; only the syncopated ride changes.

To achieve a more authentic sound, play with a lighter feel than you would when playing most rock styles, and accent the bass drum part on beats 2 and 4.

Practice Options

- ☐ Play the ride part on a cymbal bell or cowbell.
- ☐ Alternate the snare drum part between the snare and a tom, or play it entirely on other surfaces, *ad lib.*
- ☐ Repeatedly play only the first or second half of each pattern.
- ☐ Substitute various appropriate hi-hat and feet patterns (see pp. 150–151).

Variations

hands

- ☐ Replace the written snare drum part in section "A." with a simple off-beat eighth note pattern.

Example (#A1, hands only)

A.

1.

2.

3.

4.

5.

6.

7.

8.

9.

10.

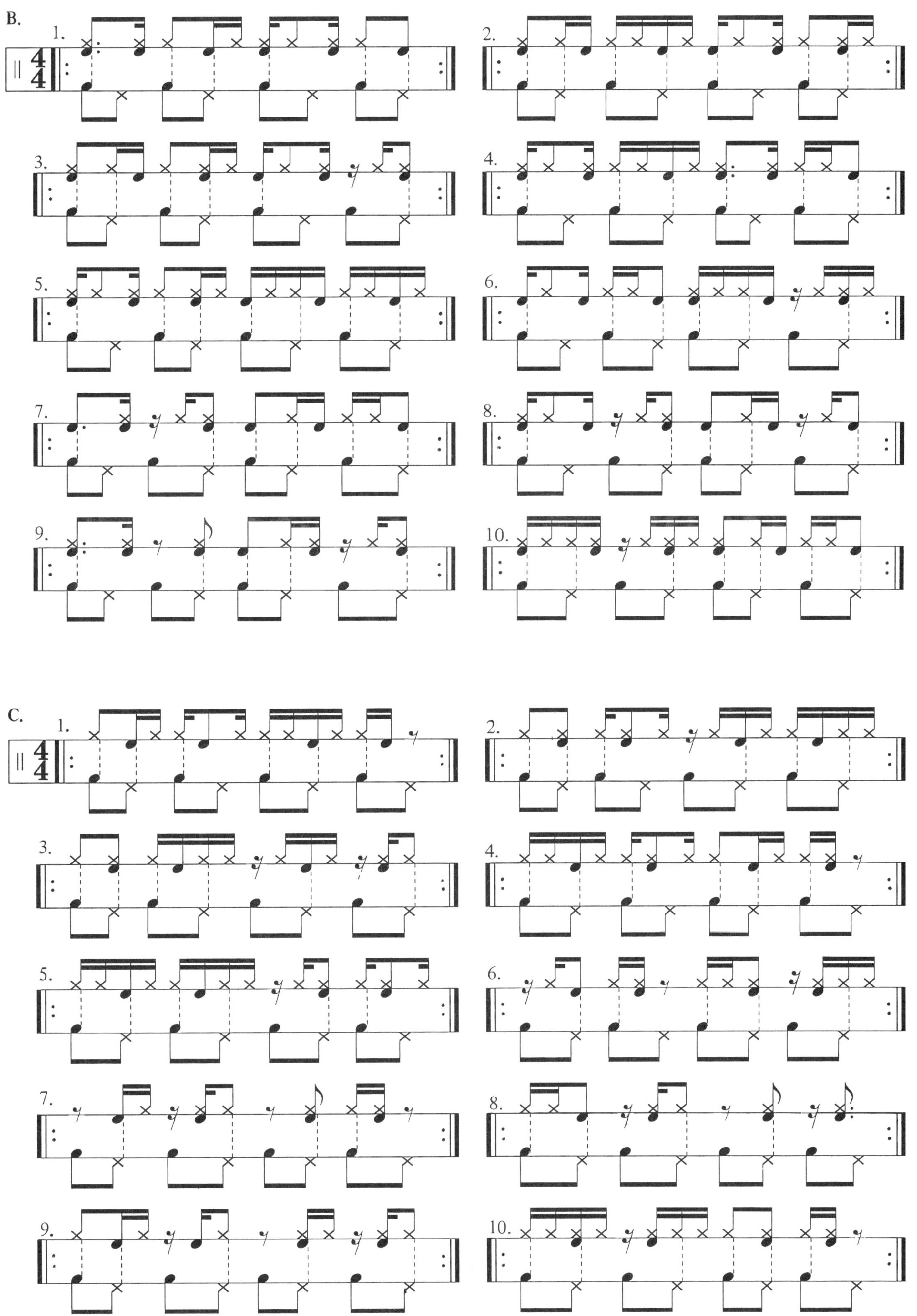
B.
1.
2.
3.
4.
5.
6.
7.
8.
9.
10.
C.
1.
2.
3.
4.
5.
6.
7.
8.
9.
10.

31 *Samba Grooves III*

While these Samba grooves are notated in $\frac{4}{4}$, they should maintain the traditional cut-time "two-feel." Notice that the ride and characteristic feet pattern remain constant within each lettered section; only the syncopated snare drum part changes.

To achieve a more authentic sound, play with a lighter feel than you would when playing most rock styles, and accent the bass drum part on beats 2 and 4.

Practice Options

- ☐ Play the ride part on a cymbal bell or cowbell.
- ☐ Play the snare part on other surfaces, *ad lib.*
- ☐ Combine the first half of any pattern ("a.") with the second half of any other pattern ("b.").
- ☐ Repeatedly play only the first or second half of each pattern.
- ☐ Substitute various appropriate hi-hat and feet patterns (see pp. 150–151).

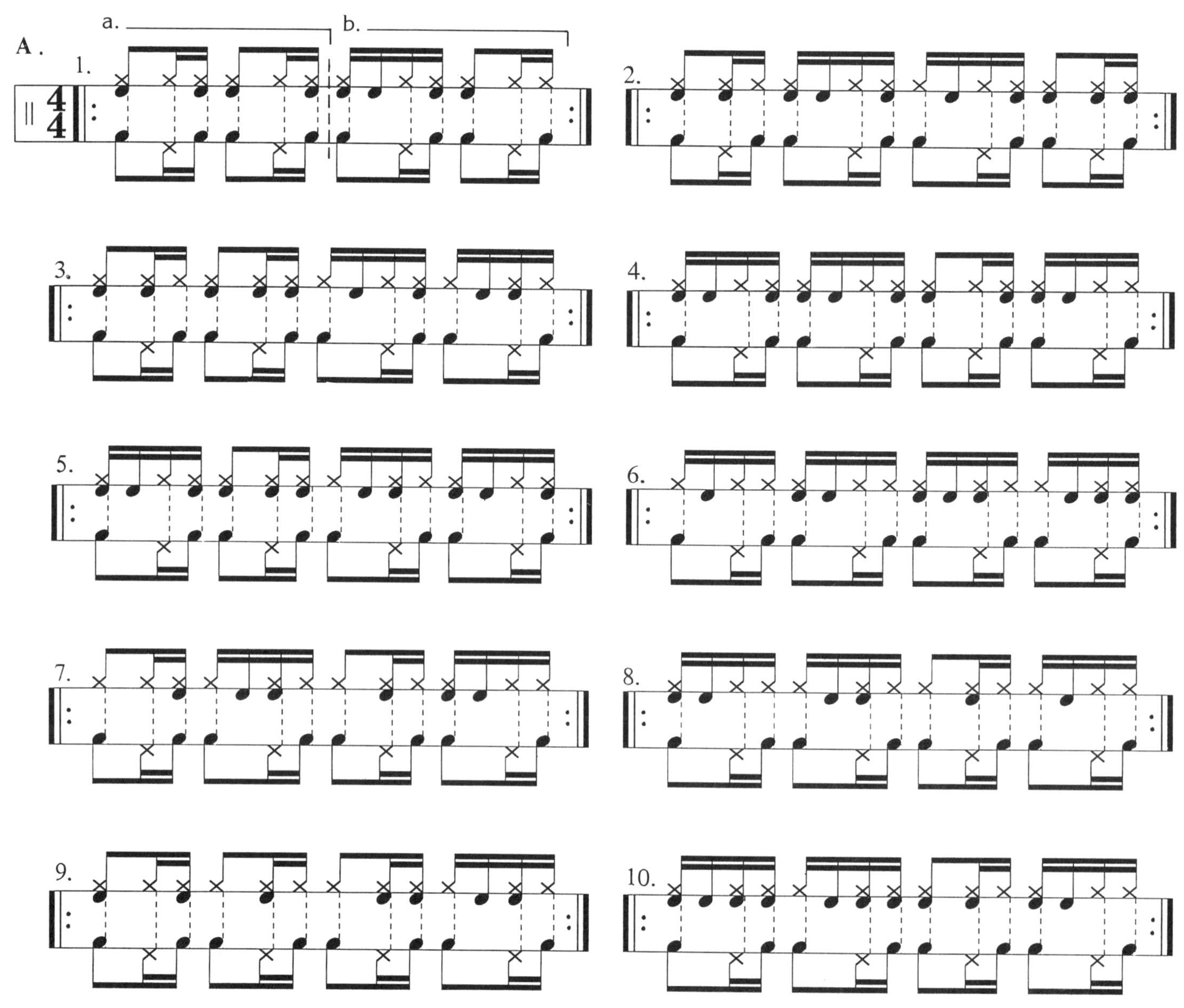

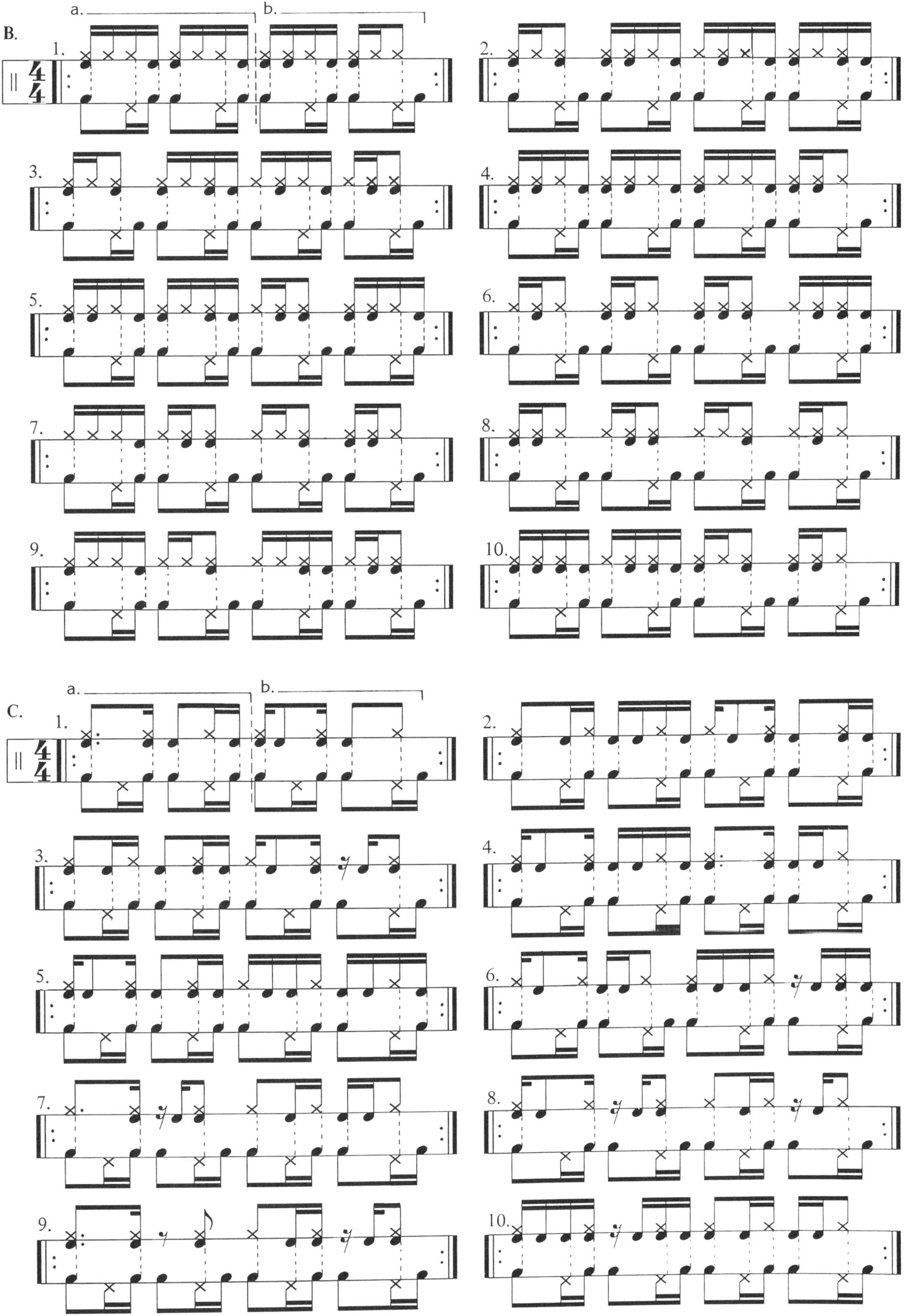
a.
b.
B.
1.
2.
3.
4.
5.
6.
7.
8.
9.
10.
a.
b.
C.
1.
2.
3.
4.
5.
6.
7.
8.
9.
10.

32 *Sixteenth Note Fill Patterns VI*

These patterns combine syncopated patterns in each hand to create constant sixteenth note patterns.

Practice Options

- ☐ Play each fill in the context of time (see p. 6).
- ☐ Play the cymbal part on a cymbal bell or cowbell.
- ☐ Play the cymbal part on a closed hi-hat (omit the left foot part).
- ☐ Play snare drum notes on non-snare surfaces, *ad lib.*
- ☐ Play the snare part on a cymbal bell or closed hi-hat (omit the left foot part); play the cymbal part on the snare, toms, and special effect cymbals, *ad lib.*
- ☐ Omit the first or last beat of each pattern to create $\frac{3}{4}$ fills.
- ☐ Repeat the first beat of each pattern at the end of the patterns to create $\frac{5}{4}$ fills.
- ☐ Substitute various appropriate hi-hat and feet patterns (see pp. 150–151).

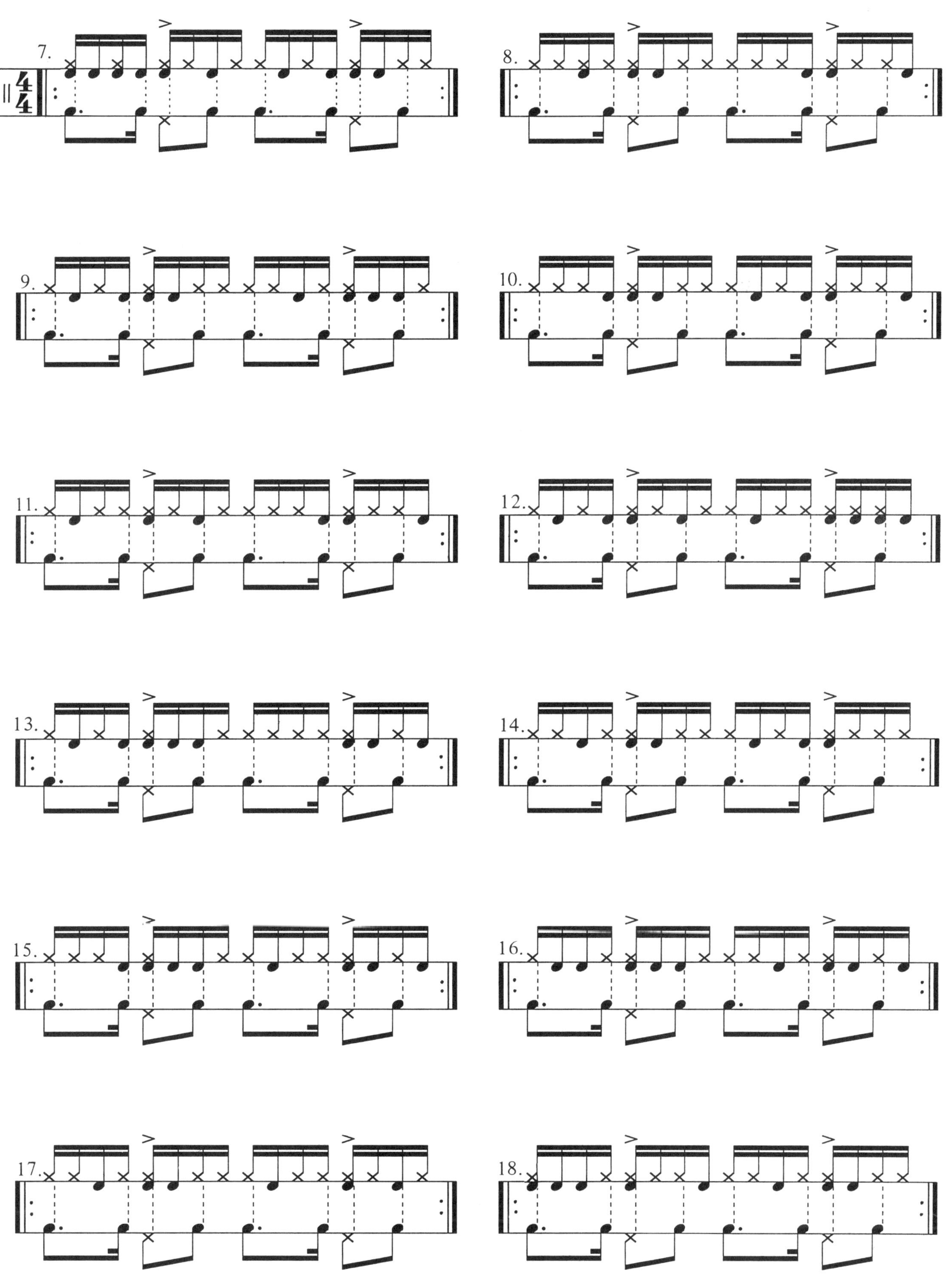
7.
8.
9.
10.
11.
12.
13.
14.
15.
16.
17.
18.

33 *Eighth/Sixteenth Note Grooves III*

These grooves combine a constant eighth note ride/back-beat pattern and constant feet with various snare drum parts.

Practice Options

- ☐ Play the cymbal off-beats (the "&'s") on the cymbal bell. Play beat 1 on the cymbal bow.
- ☐ Play the cymbal part on a closed hi-hat (omit the left foot part).
- ☐ Play the cymbal part on the hi-hat, opening it ½ beat before you close it. Omit the ride when the hi-hat closes. (In other words, do not strike the hi-hat with your stick when you are closing it with your foot.)
- ☐ With the exception of the back-beat, play one hand part on a cymbal and the other hand part on a closed hi-hat (omit the left foot part). Play the back-beat on the snare drum or any other surface.
- ☐ With the exception of the back-beat, play both hand parts entirely on the hi-hat. Play the back-beat on the snare drum or any other surface. Open the hi-hat ½ beat before you close it.
- ☐ Repeatedly alternate pattern #1 with any other pattern.
- ☐ Combine any two patterns.
- ☐ Play the sixteen patterns consecutively, starting ***pp*** and gradually crescendoing to ***ff***, or vice versa.
- ☐ Substitute various appropriate hi-hat and feet patterns (see pp. 150–151).

34 *Sixteenth Note Grooves V*

These grooves combine a constant feet pattern with a constant alternating pattern in the hands; the only variable is the placement of the accents. Accents falling on the back-beat should be stronger than any other accents appearing in the measure. (Note that all accents are played on the snare drum.)

Practice Options

- ☐ Play the cymbal part on a cymbal bell.
- ☐ Play the cymbal part on a closed hi-hat (omit the left foot part).
- ☐ Play the cymbal part on the hi-hat, opening it $\frac{1}{2}$ beat before you close it. Omit the ride when the hi-hat closes. (In other words, do not strike the hi-hat with your stick when you are closing it with your foot.)
- ☐ Play some or all of the accented notes on other surfaces.
- ☐ With the exception of the back-beat, play both hand parts entirely on the hi-hat. Keep the hi-hat closed and play the accented cymbal notes on the hi-hat edge with the shoulder of the stick.
- ☐ Repeatedly alternate pattern #1 with any other pattern.
- ☐ Combine any two patterns.
- ☐ Play the sixteen patterns consecutively, starting ***pp*** and gradually crescendoing to ***ff***, or vice versa.
- ☐ Substitute various appropriate hi-hat and feet patterns (see pp. 150–151).

Variations

hands and feet

- ☐ With the exception of the back-beat, play both hand parts entirely on the hi-hat. Open the hi-hat on accented notes, and close it on the subsequent non-accented notes.

Example (#7)

35 *Eighth/Sixteenth Note Grooves IV*

These grooves combine a constant eighth note cymbal/tom back-beat pattern and constant feet with various snare parts.

Practice Options

- ☐ Play the cymbal part on a cymbal bell or special effects cymbal.
- ☐ Play the cymbal part on the hi-hat, opening it $1/2$ beat before you close it.
- ☐ Play the cymbal part on a cymbal bell and the snare drum part on the hi-hat with your hand. Open the hi-hat $1/4$ or $1/2$ beat before you close it (or keep it closed throughout the groove).
- ☐ Play the tom note on other surfaces.
- ☐ Play the snare drum notes on other surfaces.
- ☐ Add various accent patterns to the hand parts.
- ☐ Combine the first half of any pattern ("a.") with the second half of any other pattern ("b.").
- ☐ Combine any two patterns.
- ☐ Play the sixteen patterns consecutively, starting ***pp*** and gradually crescendoing to ***ff***, or vice versa.
- ☐ Substitute various appropriate hi-hat and feet patterns (see pp. 150–151).

36 *Eighth/Sixteenth Note Grooves V*

These grooves combine a constant eighth note cymbal/snare back-beat pattern and constant feet with various cymbal parts.

Practice Options

- ☐ Play the constant cymbal part on the hi-hat. Play the variable cymbal part on the hi-hat, a cymbal bell, or a special effects cymbal. Open the hi-hat 1/4 or 1/2 beat before you close it (or keep it closed throughout the groove).
- ☐ Play the cymbal notes in either or both hands on other surfaces.
- ☐ Combine the first half of any pattern ("a.") with the second half of any other pattern ("b.").
- ☐ Combine any two patterns.
- ☐ Play the sixteen patterns consecutively, starting ***pp*** and gradually crescendoing to ***ff***, or vice versa.
- ☐ Substitute various appropriate hi-hat and feet patterns (see pp. 150–151).

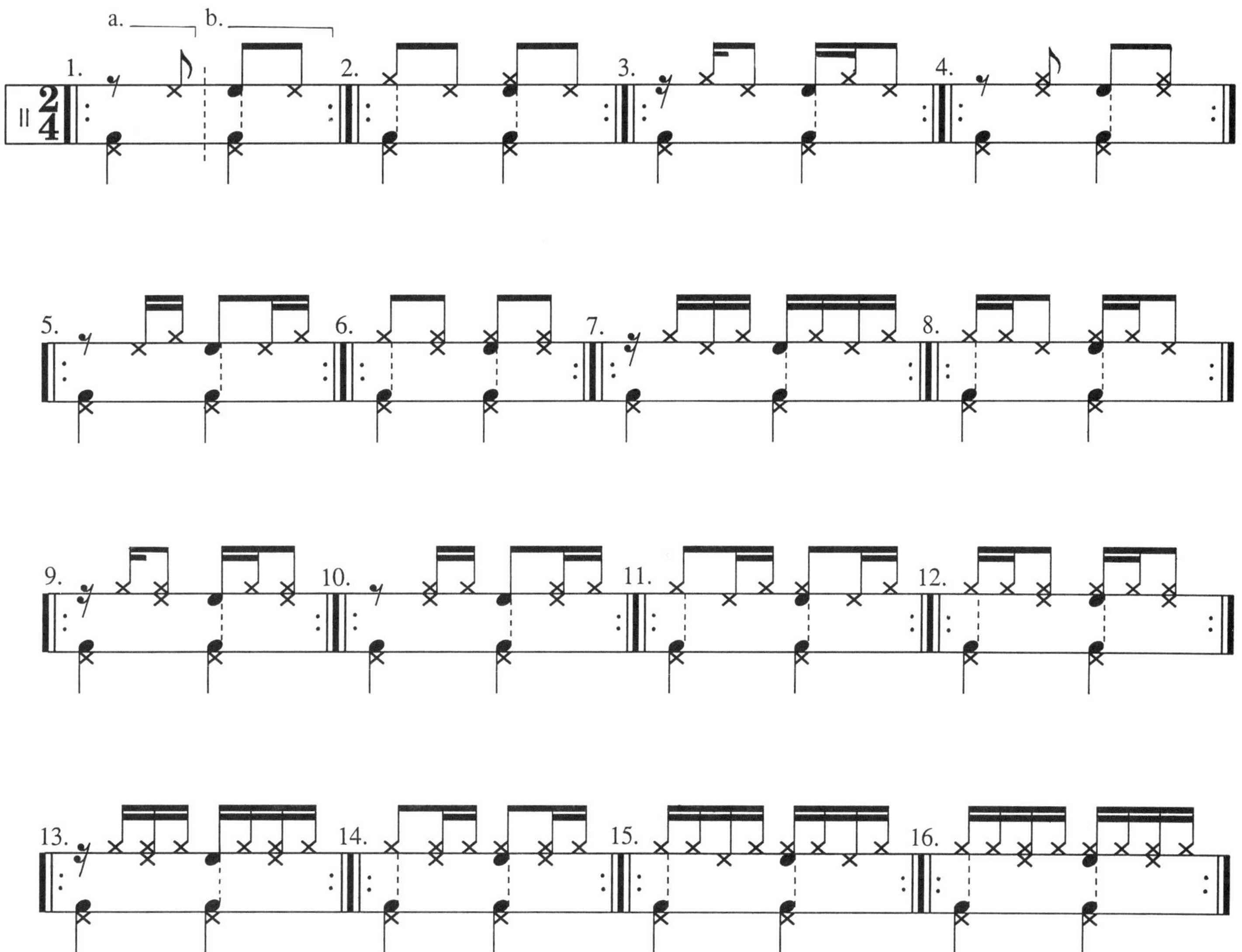

37 *Sixteenth Note Grooves VI*

These grooves combine a constant cymbal/snare drum hand pattern and constant left foot hi-hat part with various bass drum parts.

Practice Options

- ☐ Play the cymbal part with both hands on the hi-hat, both hands on cymbal bells, or one hand on the hi-hat and the other on a cymbal bell.
- ☐ Combine the first half of any pattern ("a.") with the second half of any other pattern ("b.").
- ☐ Combine any two patterns.
- ☐ Play the sixteen patterns consecutively, starting ***pp*** and gradually crescendoing to ***ff***, or vice versa.
- ☐ Substitute various appropriate hi-hat patterns (see p. 151).

Variations

hands

- ☐ Substitute hand patterns which involve other surfaces. For example:

hands and feet

- ☐ Substitute the following hand pattern. Play the cymbal part on the hi-hat, closing it on beat 2 or beats 1 and 2.

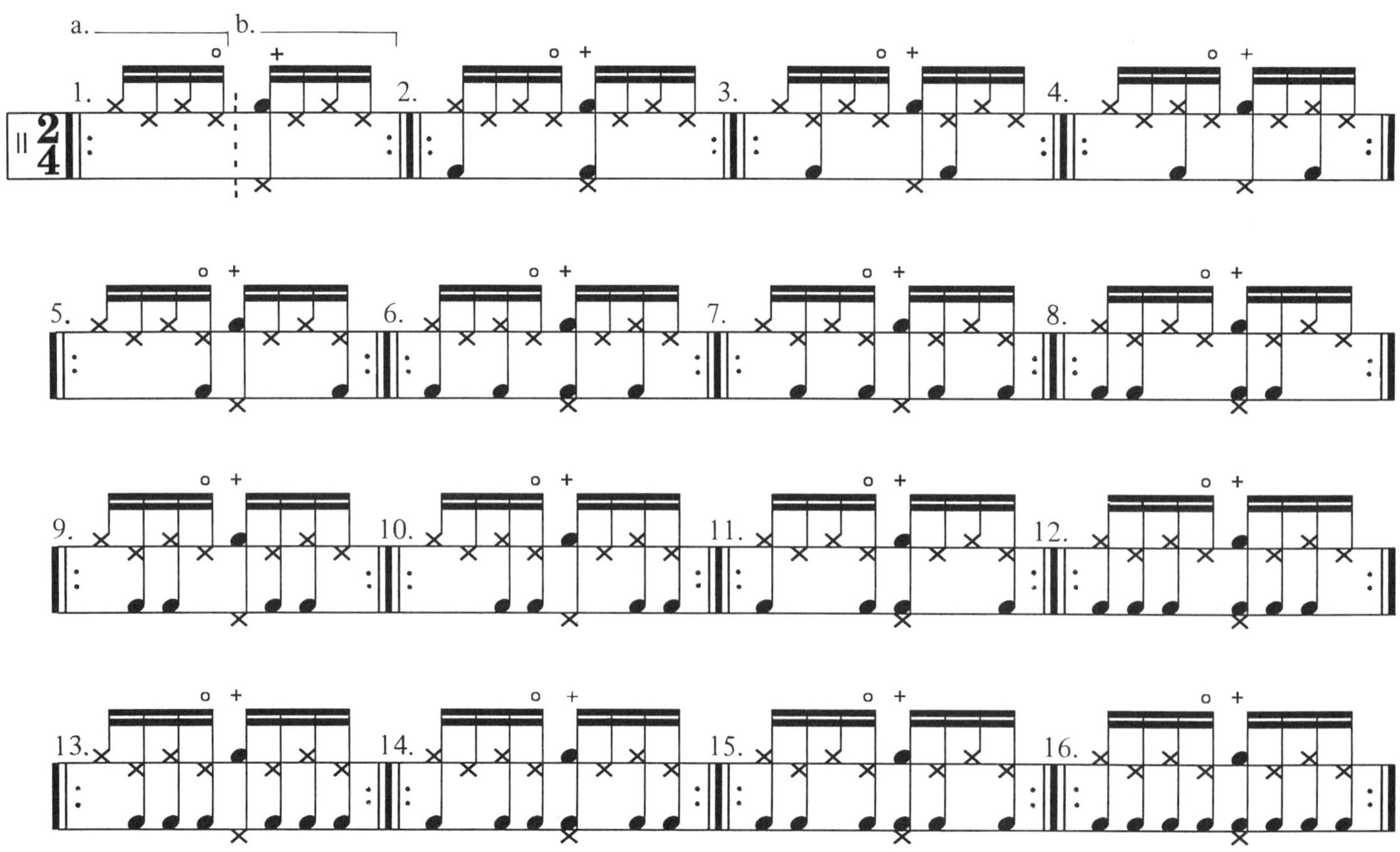

38 *Sixteenth Note Grooves VII*

These grooves combine a constant cymbal/snare drum hand pattern and constant bass drum pattern with various hi-hat parts.

Practice Options

- ☐ Play the cymbal part with one hand on a cymbal bell or cowbell and the other hand on the hi-hat.
- ☐ Play the snare drum back-beat on other surfaces.
- ☐ Play the entire cymbal part on the hi-hat (both hands).
- ☐ With the exception of the back-beat, omit the hand part when you are closing the hi-hat with your foot.
- ☐ Combine the first half of any pattern ("a.") with the second half of any other pattern ("b.").
- ☐ Repeatedly alternate pattern #1 with any other pattern.
- ☐ Combine any two patterns.

Variations

feet

- ☐ Play the bass drum when the hi-hat is open only.

Example (#21)

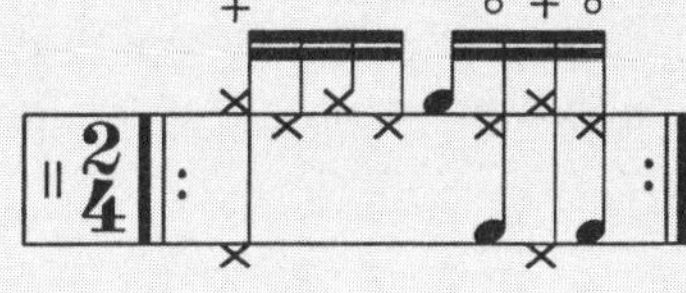

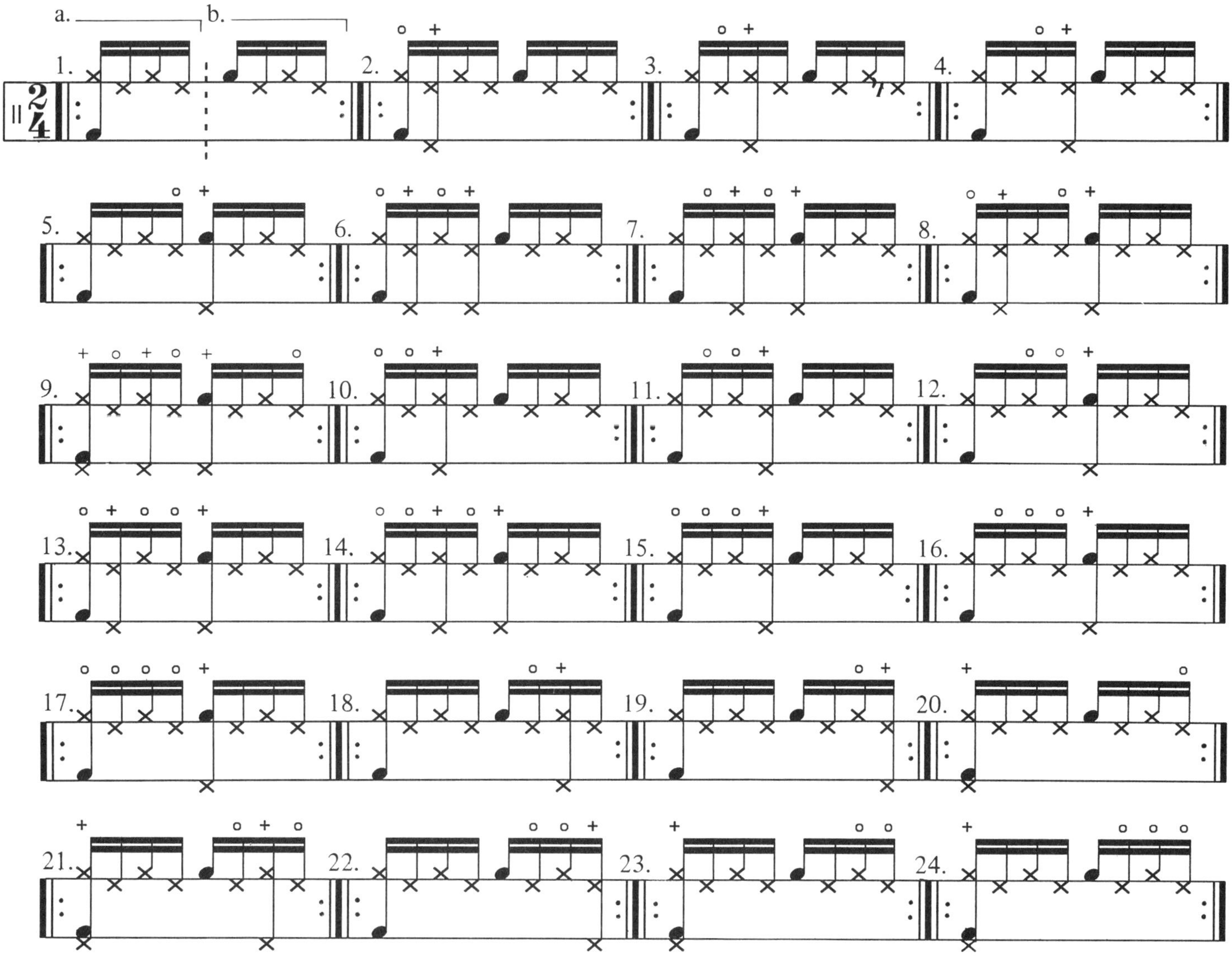

a. b.

1. 2. 3. 4. 5. 6. 7. 8. 9. 10. 11. 12. 13. 14. 15. 16. 17. 18. 19. 20. 21. 22. 23. 24.

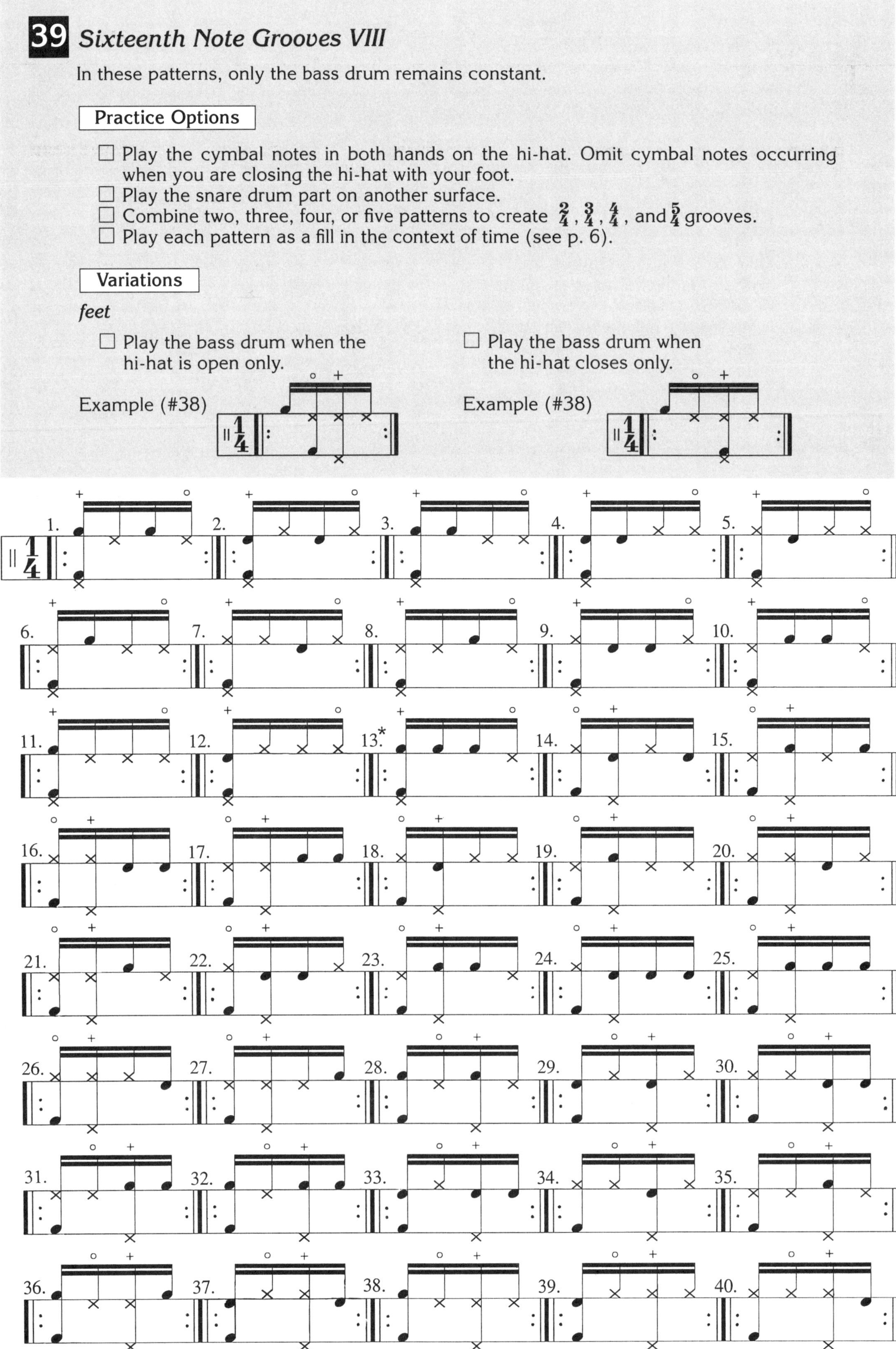
39 Sixteenth Note Grooves VIII
In these patterns, only the bass drum remains constant.
Practice Options
☐ Play the cymbal notes in both hands on the hi-hat. Omit cymbal notes occurring when you are closing the hi-hat with your foot.
☐ Play the snare drum part on another surface.
☐ Combine two, three, four, or five patterns to create 2/4, 3/4, 4/4, and 5/4 grooves.
☐ Play each pattern as a fill in the context of time (see p. 6).
Variations
feet
☐ Play the bass drum when the hi-hat is open only.
Example (#38)
☐ Play the bass drum when the hi-hat closes only.
Example (#38)
1. 2. 3. 4. 5. 6. 7. 8. 9. 10. 11. 12. 13.* 14. 15. 16. 17. 18. 19. 20. 21. 22. 23. 24. 25. 26. 27. 28. 29. 30. 31. 32. 33. 34. 35. 36. 37. 38. 39. 40.

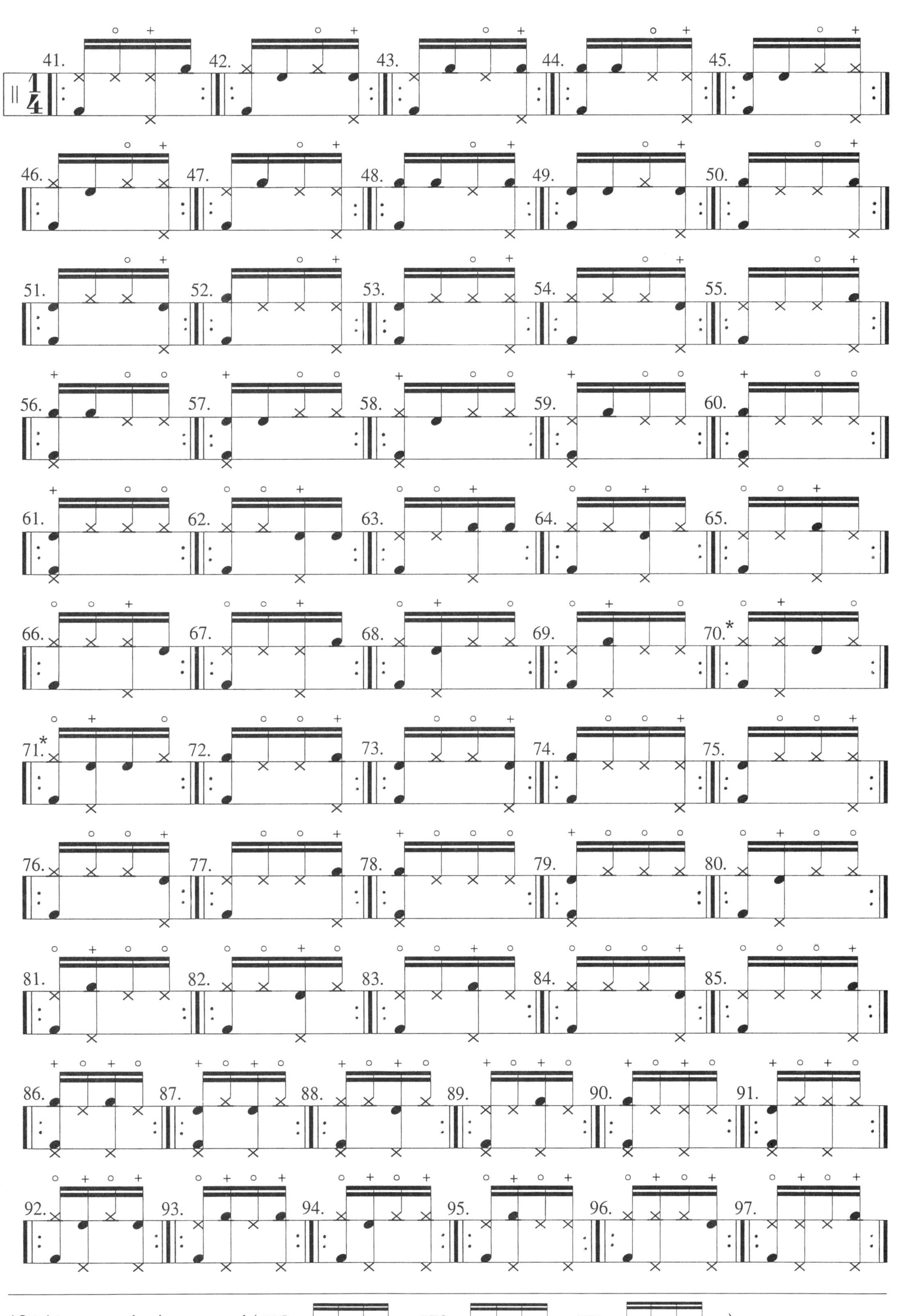

*Sticking may also be reversed (#13 ; #70 ; #71).

40 *Sixteenth Note Latin Grooves*

These grooves combine constant feet with various hand and accent patterns. They take on a more samba-like feel when combined with Brazilian-type feet patterns (see pp. 150–151).

Practice Options

- ☐ Play the cymbal part on a cymbal bell or cowbell.
- ☐ Play the cymbal part on a closed hi-hat (omit the left foot part).
- ☐ Play the accented cymbal notes with the shoulder of the stick on the cymbal bell or hi-hat edge. Play the unaccented cymbal notes on the cymbal or hi-hat bow.
- ☐ Play some or all of the accented notes on other surfaces.
- ☐ Combine any two patterns.
- ☐ Substitute various appropriate hi-hat and feet patterns (see pp.150–151).

Variations

hands and feet

- ☐ Play the cymbal part on the hi-hat. Play the snare drum part on the hi-hat with your hand, except for the back-beat, which you should play on the snare. Open the hi-hat on accented notes, and close it on the subsequent non-accented note. Play the bass drum on beat 1 only.

Example (#5)

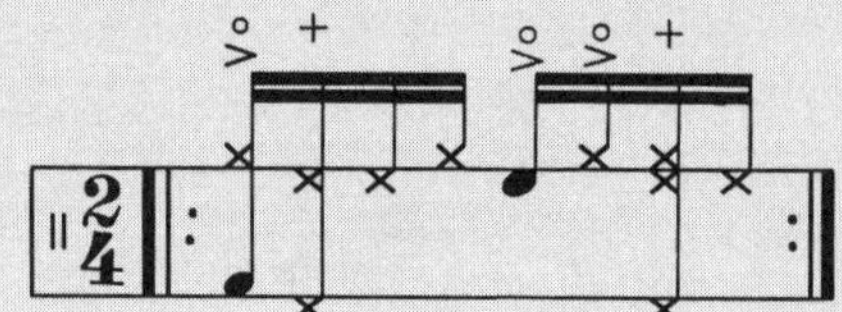

41 *Sixteenth Note Grooves IX*

These patterns combine a constant eighth note ride and quarter note hi-hat pattern with sixteenth note patterns moving between the snare drum and bass drum.

Practice Options

- ☐ Play the ride part on a cymbal bell or cowbell.
- ☐ Play the ride part on a closed hi-hat (omit the left foot part).
- ☐ Play the ride part on the hi-hat, opening it ½ beat before you close it. As an option, omit the ride when the hi-hat closes. (In other words, do not strike the hi-hat with your stick when you are closing it with your foot.)
- ☐ Swing the sixteenth notes (=).
- ☐ Combine two, three, four, or five patterns to create $\frac{2}{4}$, $\frac{3}{4}$, $\frac{4}{4}$, and $\frac{5}{4}$ grooves.
- ☐ Substitute various appropriate hi-hat patterns (see p. 151).
- ☐ Play each pattern as a fill in the context of time (see p. 6).

Variations

hands

- ☐ Substitute any of the following ride patterns. Play the accented notes with the shoulder of the stick on the cymbal bell or hi-hat edge.

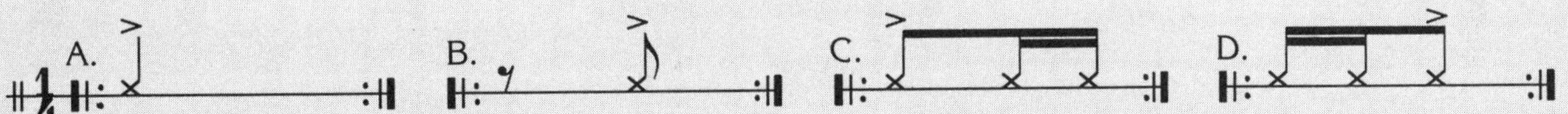

1. 2. 3. 4.

5. 6. 7. 8.

9. 10. 11. 12.

13. 14. 15. 16.

42 *Eighth/Sixteenth Note Grooves VI*

These grooves combine a constant eighth note ride and back-beat hi-hat pattern with eighth/sixteenth note patterns moving between the snare drum and bass drum. (Note that section "A." mirrors section "B.")

Practice Options

- ☐ Play the ride part on a closed hi-hat (omit the left foot part).
- ☐ Play the ride part on the hi-hat, opening it ½ beat before you close it. As an option, omit the ride when the hi-hat closes. (In other words, do not strike the hi-hat with your stick when you are closing it with your foot.)
- ☐ Repeatedly alternate pattern #A1 or #B1 with any other pattern within the same section ("A." or "B.").
- ☐ Combine any two patterns within the same section ("A." or "B.").
- ☐ Repeatedly alternate patterns with the same number from Sections "A." and "B." (alternate #A3 with #B3, #A7 with #B7, etc.).
- ☐ Swing the sixteenth notes ().
- ☐ Substitute various appropriate hi-hat patterns (see p. 151).

Variations

hands

- ☐ While playing the ride on a cymbal or closed hi-hat, add any of the following accent patterns to the ride. Play the accented notes with the shoulder of the stick on the cymbal bell or hi-hat edge.

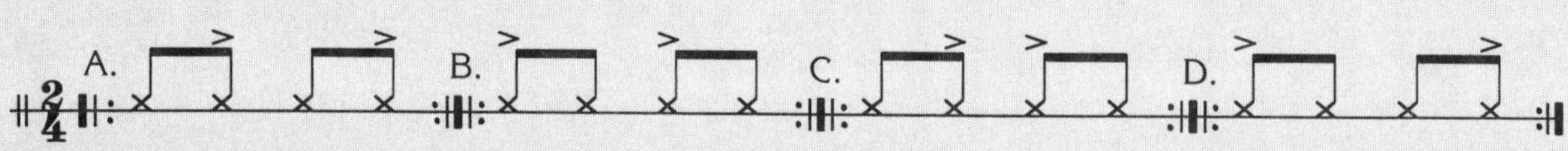

A. B. C. D.

- ☐ Substitute any of the following ride patterns.

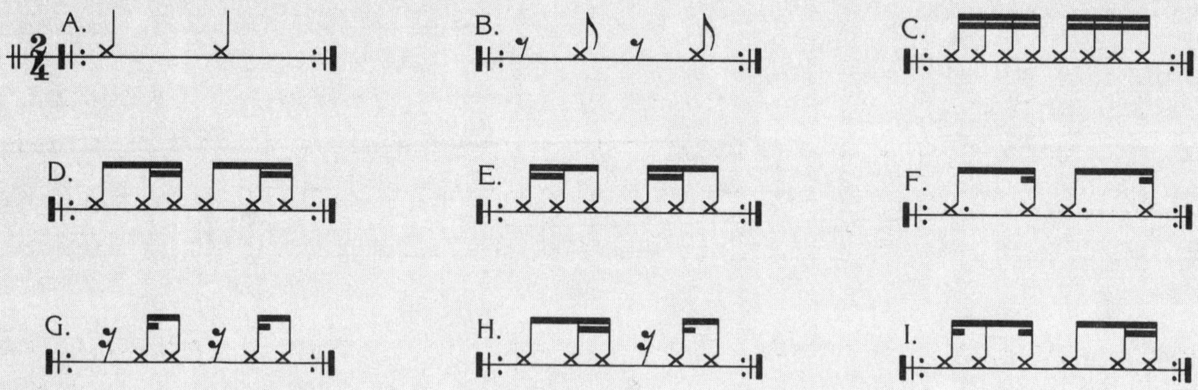

A. B. C.

D. E. F.

G. H. I.

A.
1.
2.
3.
4.
5.
6.
7.
8.
9.
10.
11.
12.
13.
14.
15.
16.
B.
1.
2.
3.
4.
5.
6.
7.
8.
9.
10.
11.
12.
13.
14.
15.
16.

43 Sixteenth Note Grooves X

In these linear grooves, the hands and bass drum combine to create continuous sixteenth notes.

Practice Options

- ☐ Play the cymbal part on a cymbal bell or cowbell.
- ☐ Play the cymbal part on a closed hi-hat (omit the left foot part).
- ☐ Play accents on both beats 1 and 2.
- ☐ Play some or all of the cymbal notes on other surfaces.
- ☐ Combine any two patterns.
- ☐ Substitute various appropriate hi-hat patterns (see p. 151).
- ☐ Play each pattern as a fill in the context of time (see p. 6).

Variations

feet

☐ Play the hands as written. Substitute any of the following constant feet patterns.

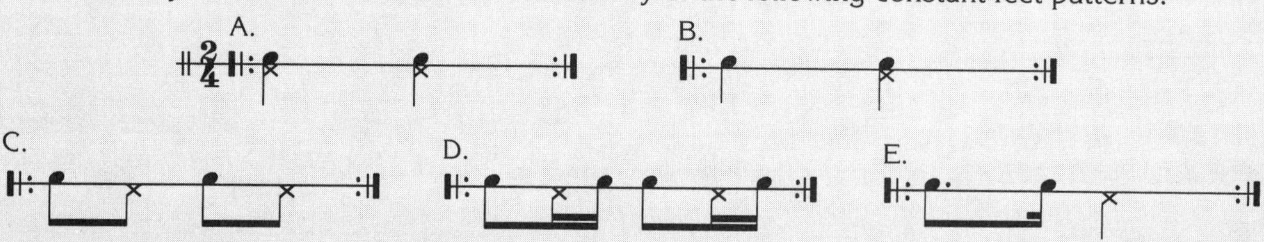

☐ Play the bass drum part with both the bass drum and hi-hat in unison (omit the written hi-hat part).

hands and feet

☐ Replace the first half of any groove with the following pattern.

Example (#18)

☐ Replace the second half of any groove with the following pattern.

Example (#21)

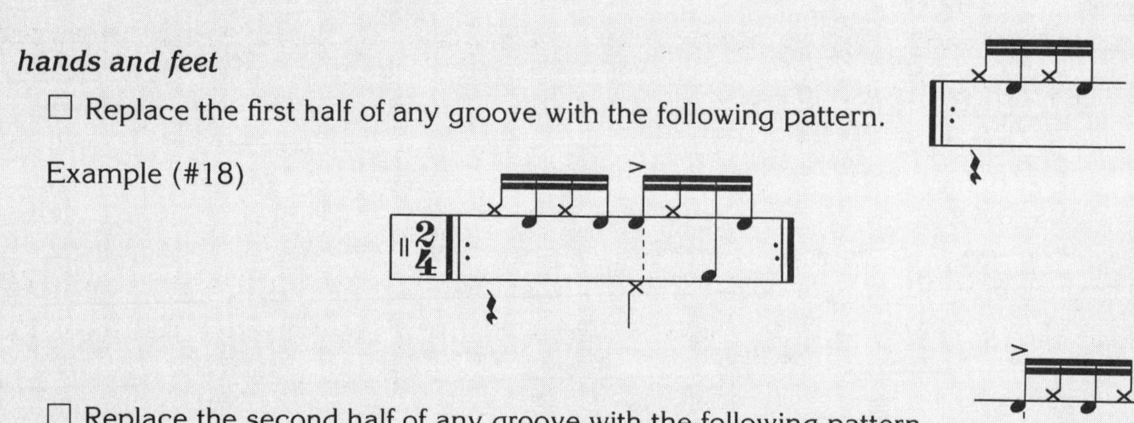

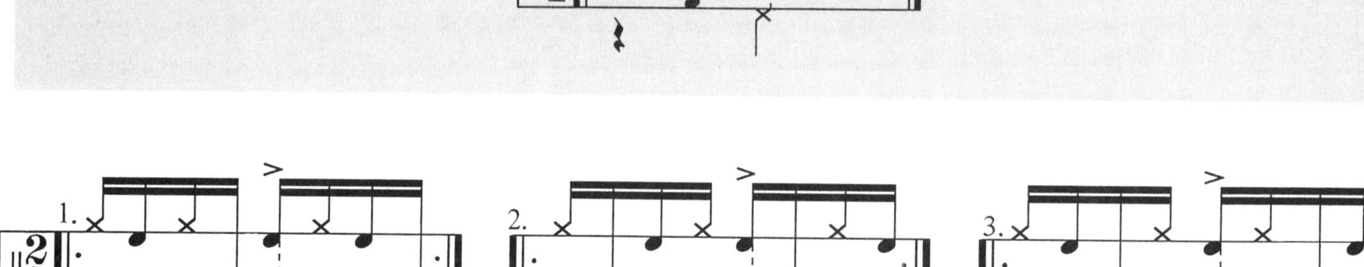

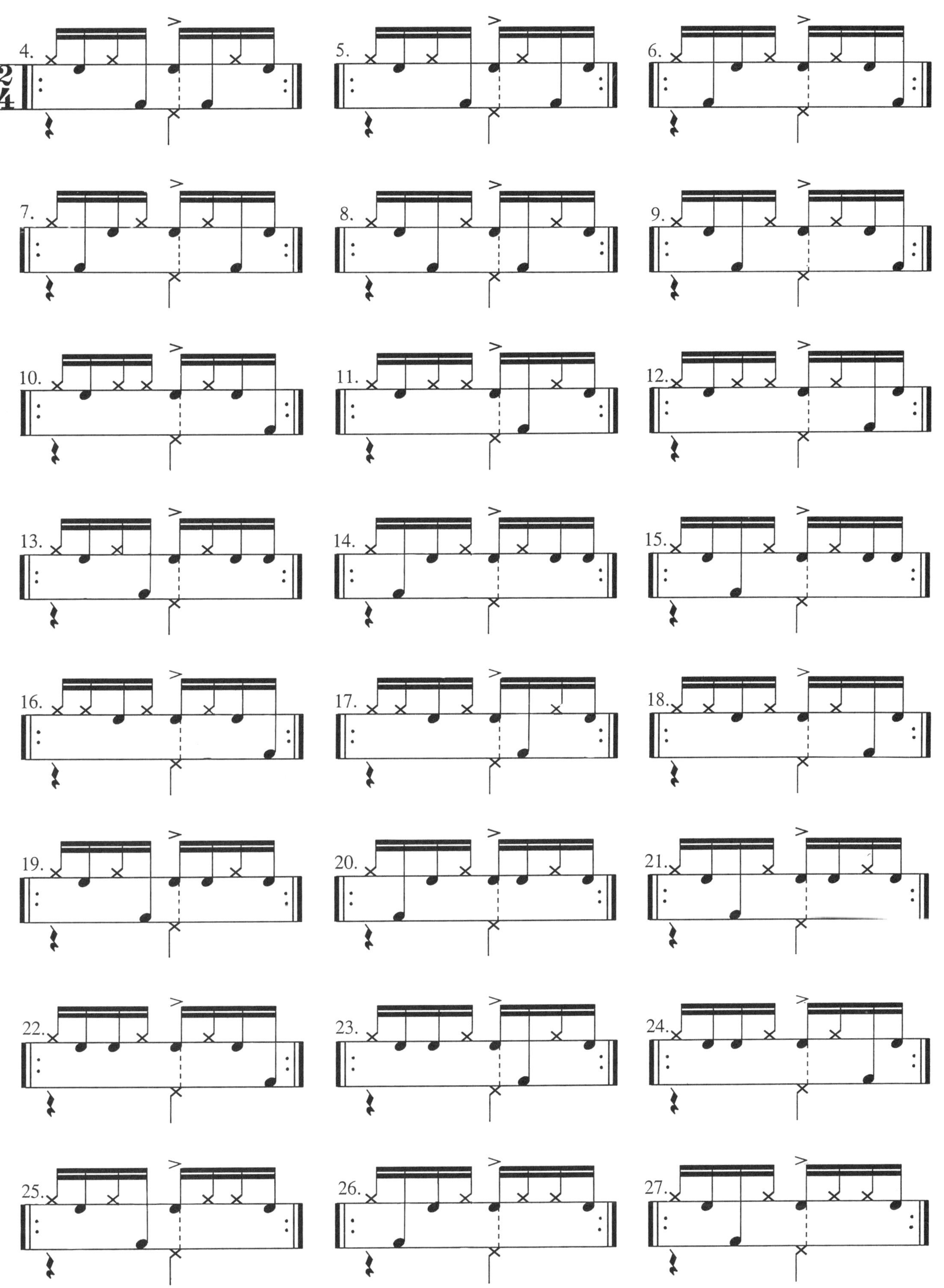
4.
5.
6.
7.
8.
9.
10.
11.
12.
13.
14.
15.
16.
17.
18.
19.
20.
21.
22.
23.
24.
25.
26.
27.

44 *Eighth Note Triplet Grooves I*

These grooves combine a constant jazz ride and constant feet with various snare parts. Play the snare drum and bass drum with a lighter feel than you would when playing most pop or rock grooves.

Practice Options

- ☐ Omit the bass drum part.
- ☐ Combine the first half of any pattern ("a.") with the second half of any other pattern ("b.").
- ☐ Combine any two patterns.
- ☐ Substitute various appropriate hi-hat and feet patterns (see pp. 150–151).

Variations

hands

- ☐ Substitute any of the following ride patterns.

A. B. C. D.

hands and feet

- ☐ Play the snare drum part on the bass drum (omit the written bass drum part). Omit the snare drum completely, or play it on beat 2.

Example (#B6)

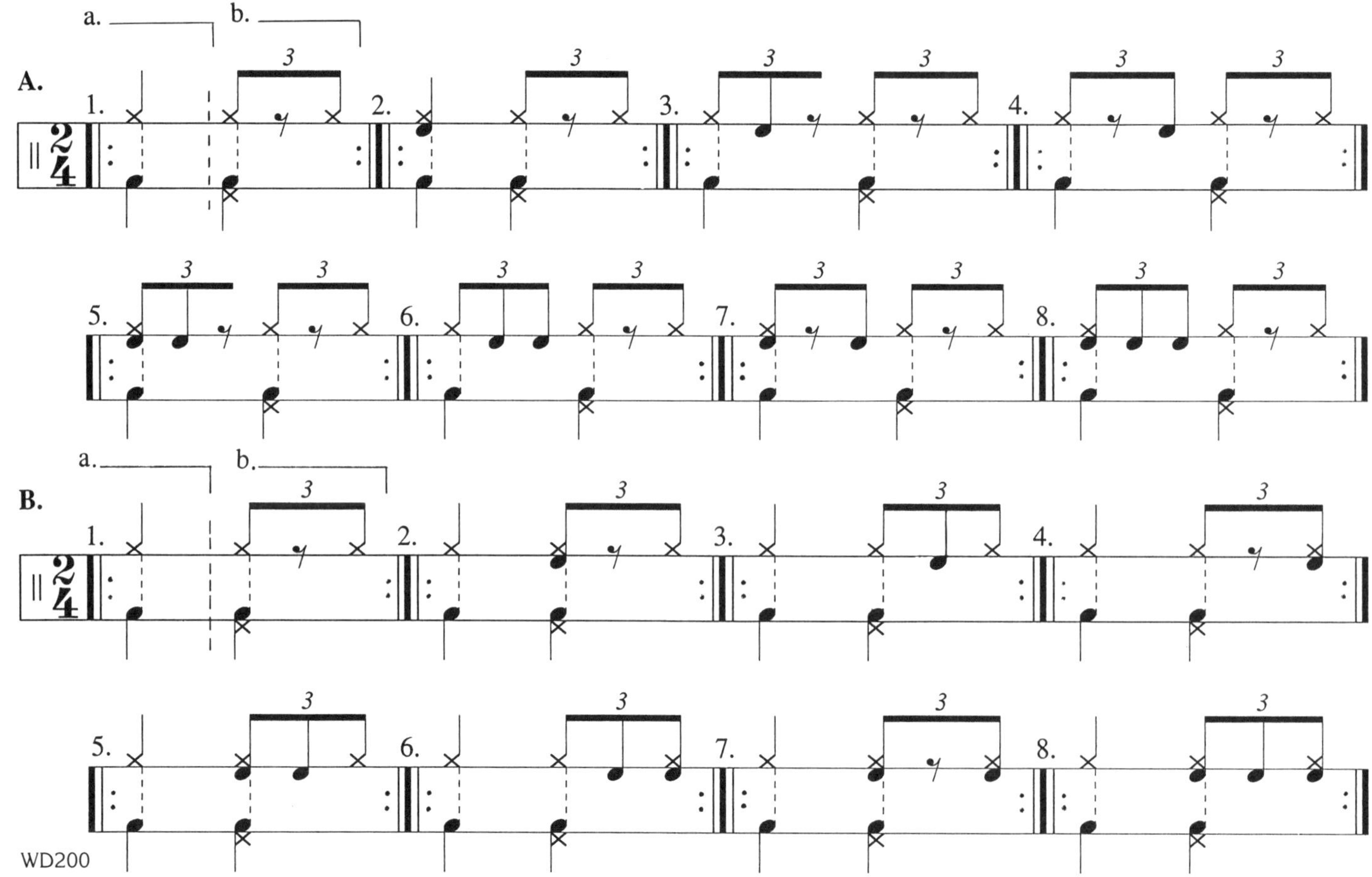

45 *Compound Meter Eighth Note Grooves I*

These grooves combine constant hi-hat ride, snare, and bass drum parts with various left foot hi-hat parts. Ride on the edge of the hi-hat cymbals with the shoulder of the stick to enhance the opening and closing effect.

Practice Options

- ☐ Omit the ride when the hi-hat closes. (In other words, do not strike the hi-hat with your stick when you are closing it with your foot.)
- ☐ Ride on a cymbal. Play the left foot hi-hat part on the bass drum using a double pedal or a second bass drum.
- ☐ Combine the first half of any pattern ("a.") with the second half of any other pattern ("b.").
- ☐ Repeatedly alternate pattern #1 with any other pattern.
- ☐ Combine any two patterns.

Variations

feet

- ☐ Substitute any of the following bass drum patterns.

- ☐ Play the bass drum when the hi-hat is open only.

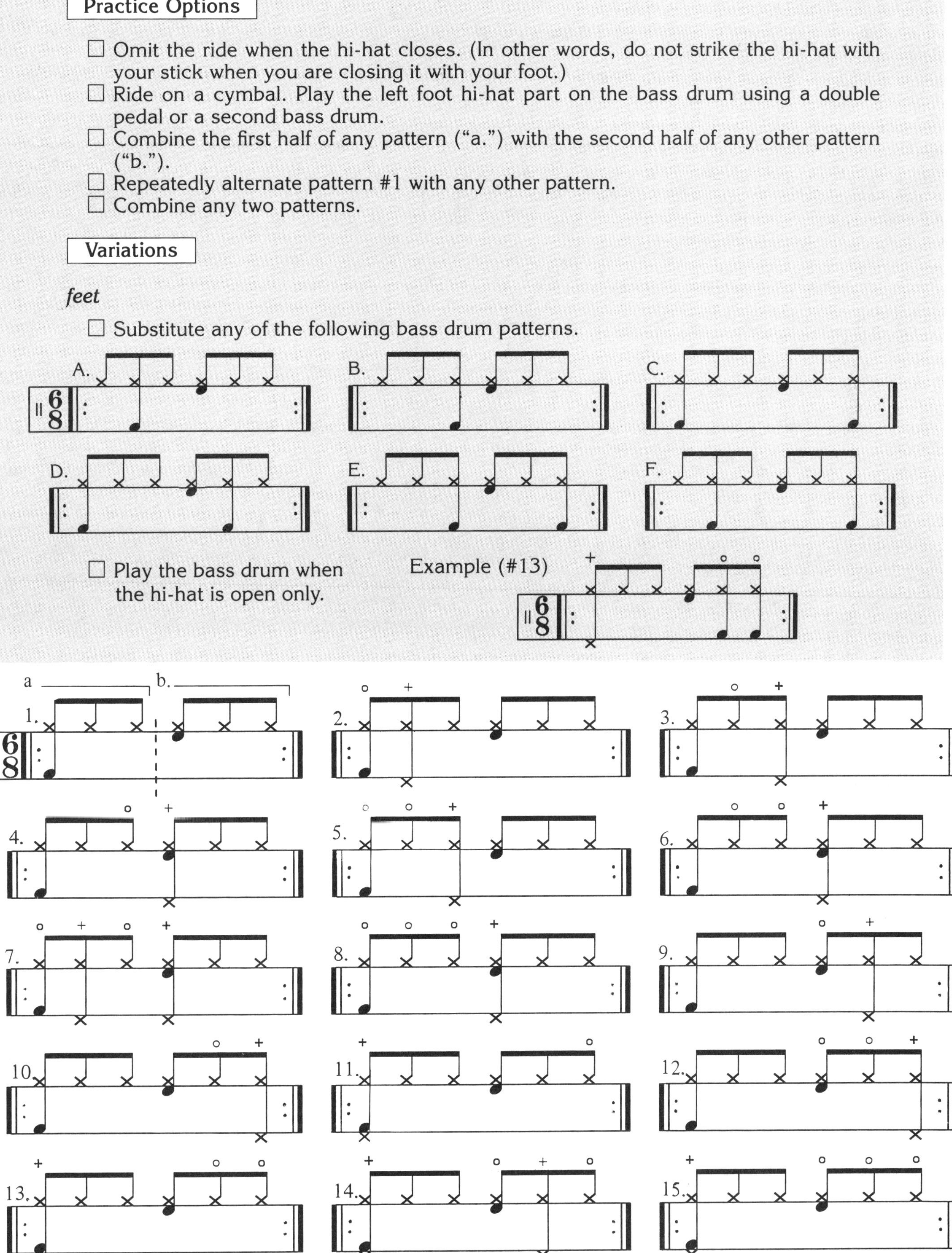

46 *Eighth Note Triplet Fill Patterns I*

Each of these fills uses the same simple alternate sticking pattern.

Practice Options

- ☐ Play each fill in the context of time (see p. 6).
- ☐ Combine any two fills.
- ☐ Play the fills in either section "A." or section "B." consecutively to create a sixteen measure solo.
- ☐ Substitute various appropriate hi-hat and feet patterns (see pp. 150–151).

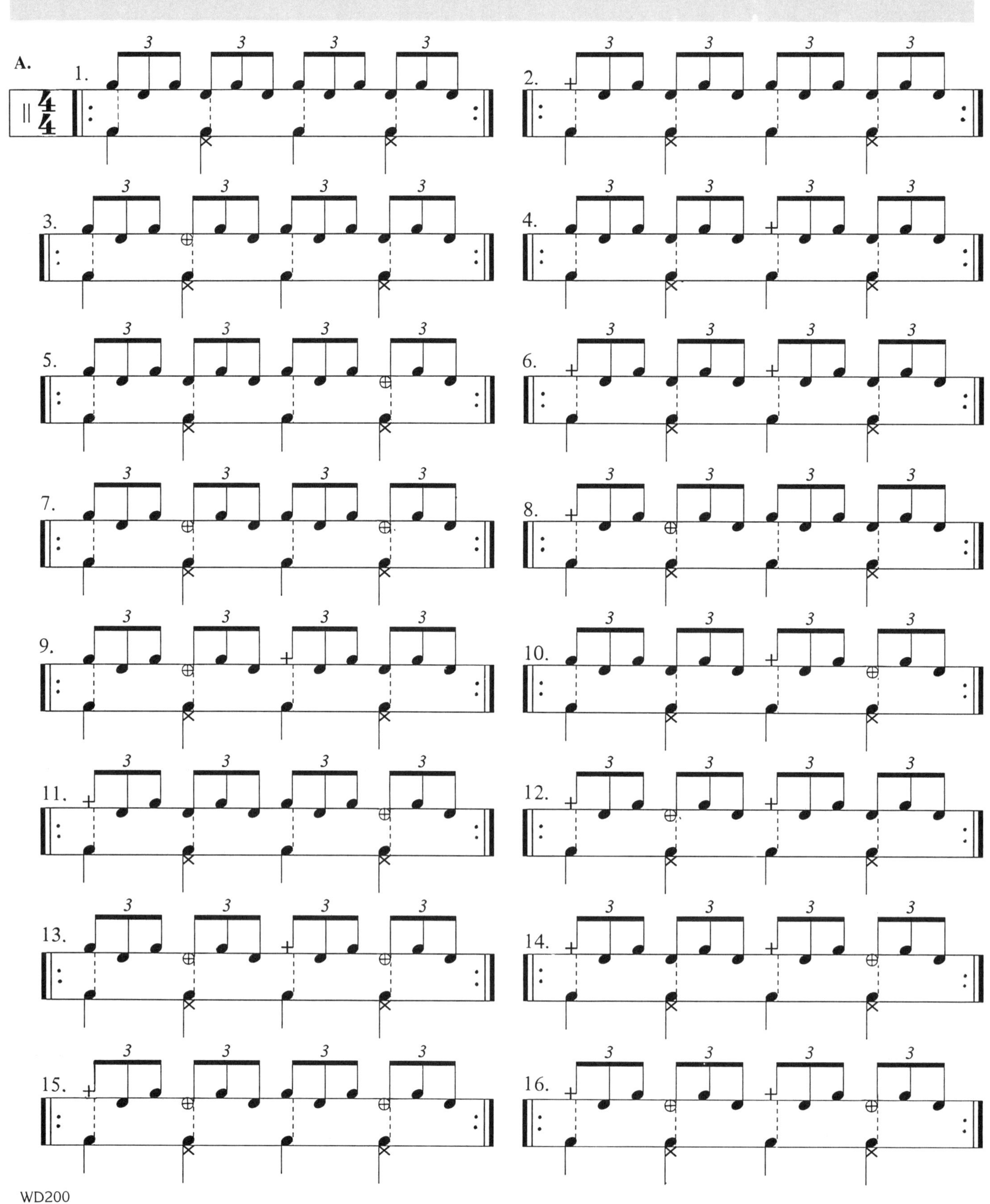

Variations

hands

☐ Play each tom note as an open double stroke.

Example (#B9)

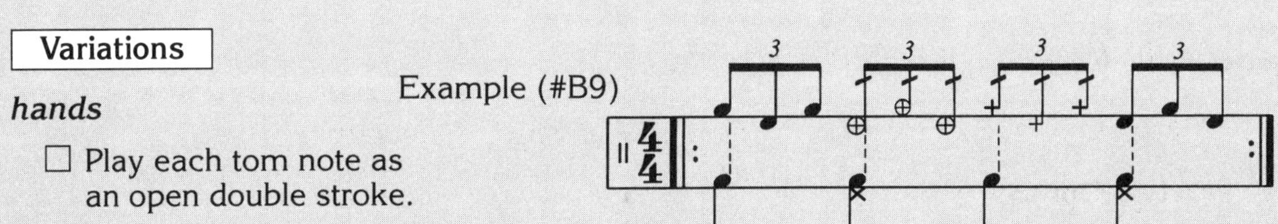

Also try playing each snare note, rather than each tom note, as an open double stroke.

hands and feet

☐ Interpret each pattern as sixteenth note triplets in $\frac{2}{4}$ time. Play quarter notes on the bass drum and hi-hat.

B.

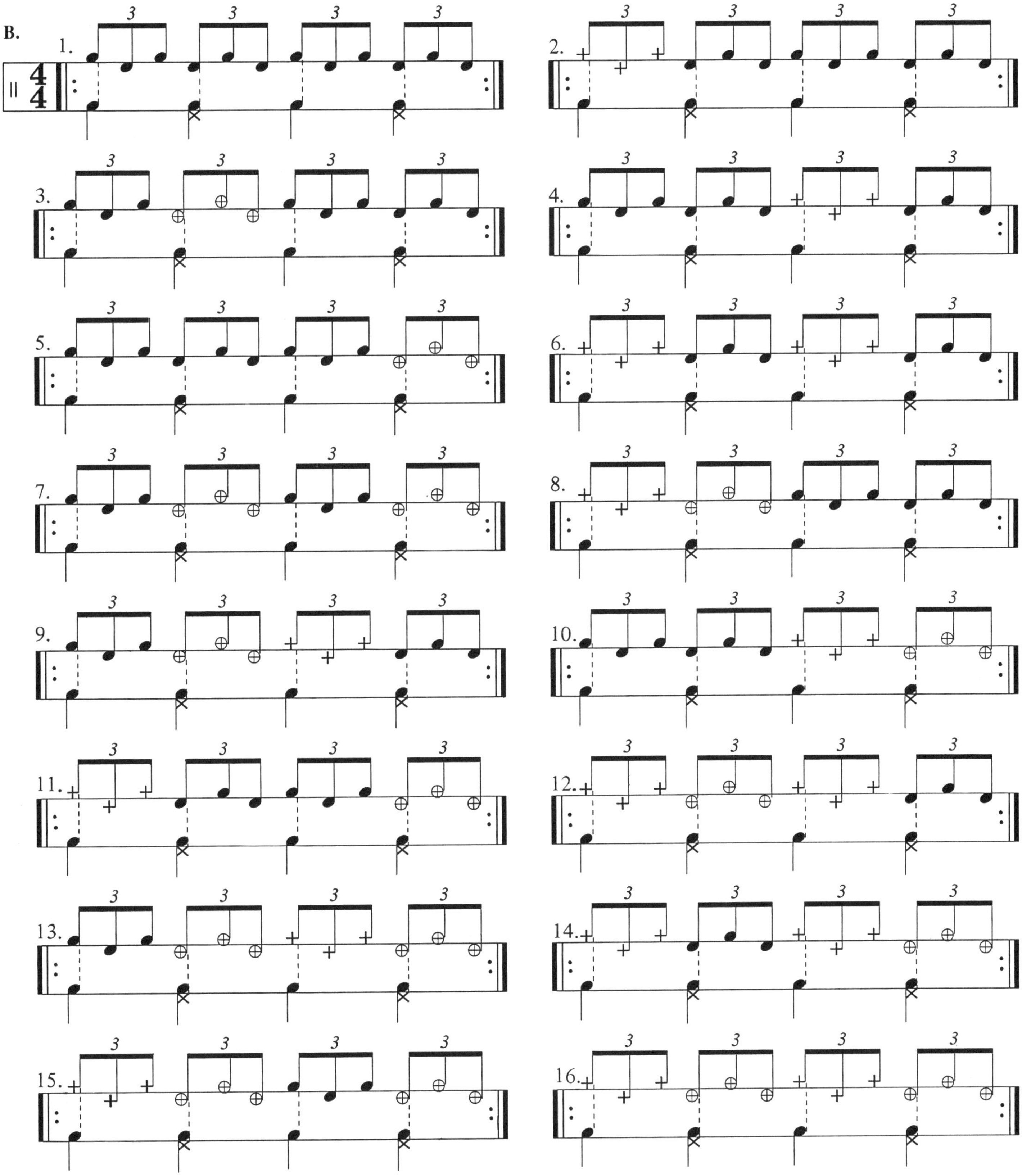

1.

2.

3.

4.

5.

6.

7.

8.

9.

10.

11.

12.

13.

14.

15.

16.

47 *Eighth Note Triplet Fill Patterns II*

In addition to functioning as phrase-ending fills, short triplet patterns such as these are ideal for use as part of big band/jazz ensemble set-ups/lead-ins. In this context, be sure that the fill ends on the beat before the ensemble figure (kick) you are setting up. The fill should end on the beat regardless of whether the figure is on or off the beat.

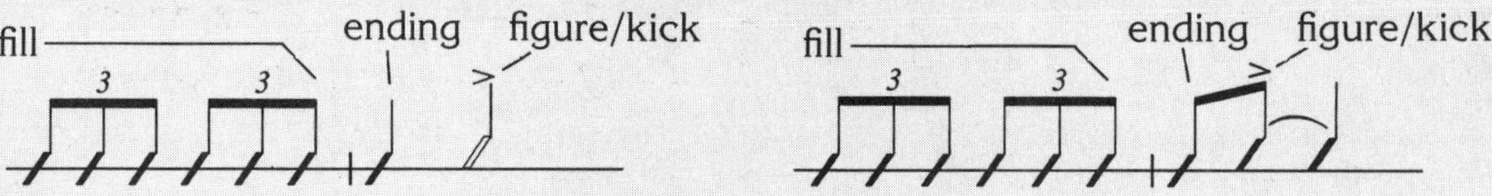

Practice Options

- ☐ Play each fill in the context of time (see p. 6) or as part of set-ups for various figures (see above).
- ☐ Combine the first half of any fill ("a.") with the second half of any other fill ("b.") within the same section ("A." or "B.").
- ☐ Combine any three halves ("a. - b. - a." or "b. - a. - b.") within the same section ("A." or "B.") to create 3/4 fills.
- ☐ Combine any two fills within the same section ("A." or "B.").
- ☐ Substitute various appropriate hi-hat and feet patterns (see pp. 150–151).

Variations

hands

- ☐ Interpret each triplet as any of the following eighth/sixteenth note combinations.

hands and feet

- ☐ Interpret each pattern as a one-measure 3/4 fill by playing each pair of triplets as three pairs of eighth notes. Use the following feet pattern.

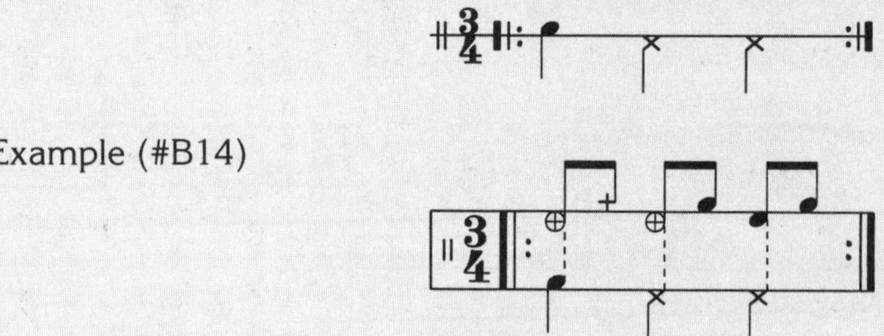

Example (#B14)

- ☐ Interpret each pattern as a one-measure 6/8 fill. Play each pair of triplets twice as six sixteenth notes. Use the following feet pattern.

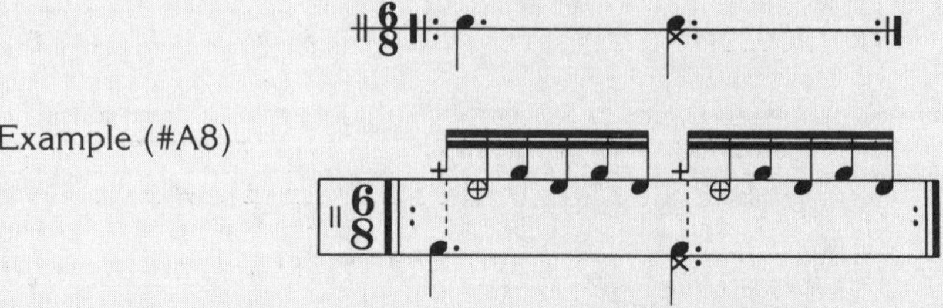

Example (#A8)

When playing 6/8 fills in the context of time, use grooves such as those found in Study #45, page 83.

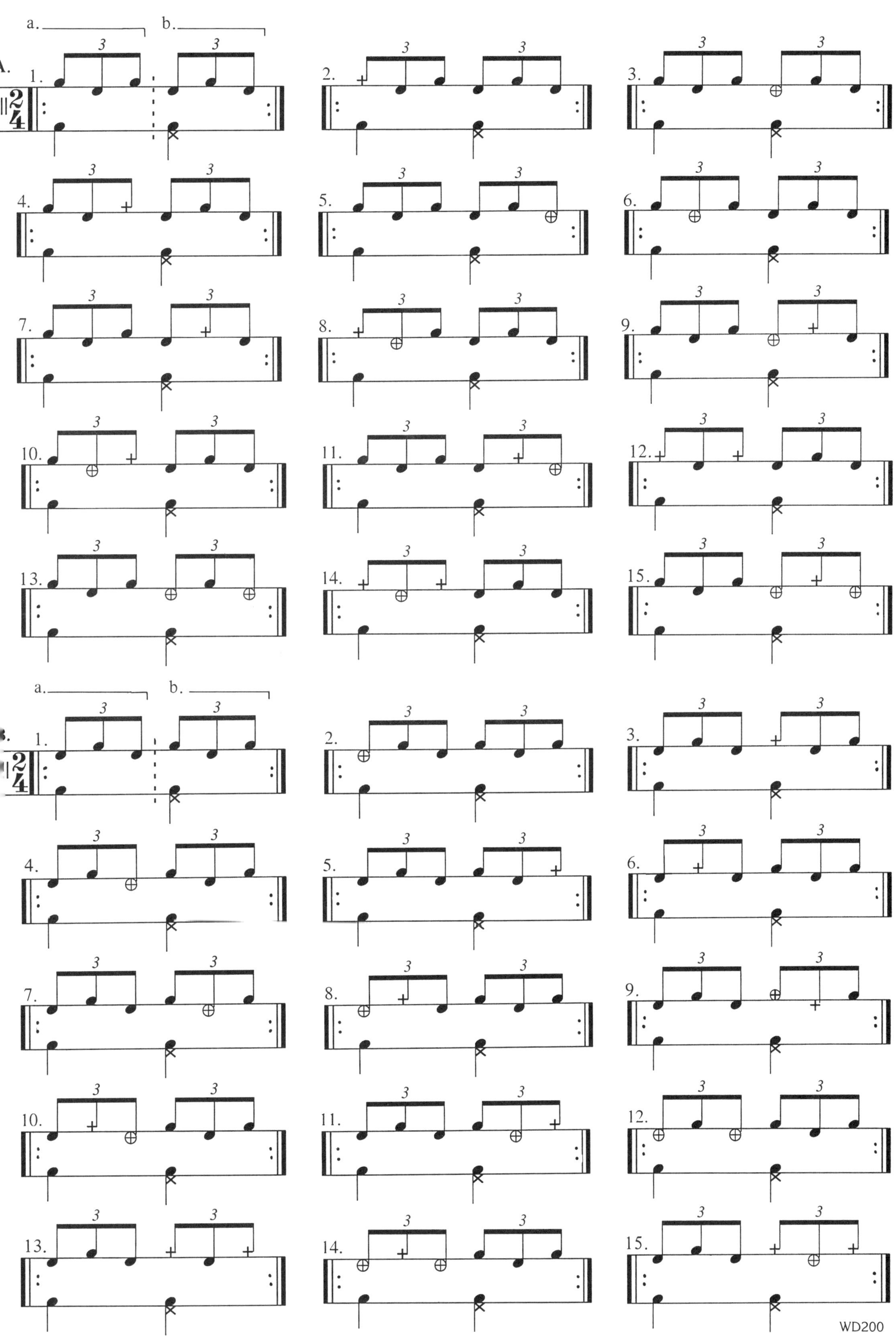
a.
b.
A.
1.
2.
3.
4.
5.
6.
7.
8.
9.
10.
11.
12.
13.
14.
15.
a.
b.
B.
1.
2.
3.
4.
5.
6.
7.
8.
9.
10.
11.
12.
13.
14.
15.

48 *Eighth Note Triplet Fill Patterns III*

Like the fills in Study #47, these fills are ideal for use as part of big band/jazz ensemble set-ups/lead-ins.

Practice Options

- ☐ Play each fill in the context of time (see p. 6) or as part of set-ups for various figures (see p. 86).
- ☐ Combine any two fills.
- ☐ Substitute various appropriate hi-hat and feet patterns (see pp. 150–151).

Variations

hands

- ☐ Play the last two strokes of each fill as either open double stroke or alternating single stroke sixteenth notes.

Examples (#5)

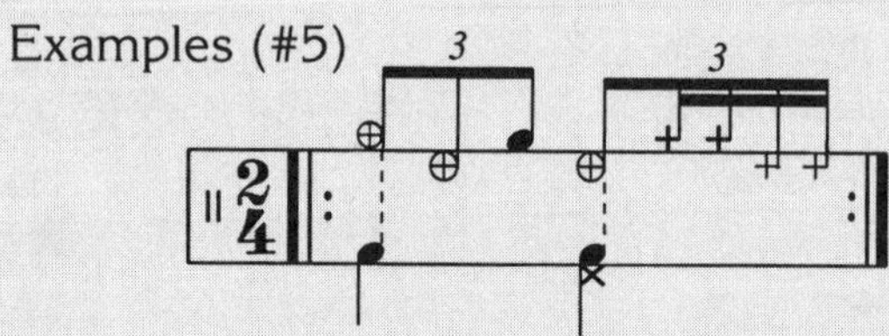

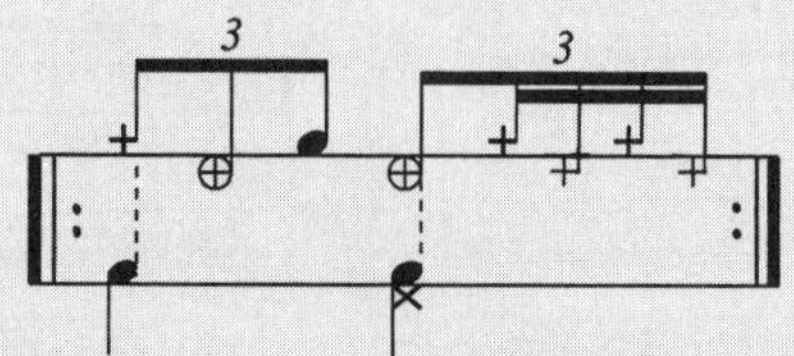

- ☐ Interpret each triplet as any of the following eighth/sixteenth note combinations.

A.  B.  C. 

hands and feet

- ☐ Interpret each pattern as a one-measure $\frac{3}{4}$ fill by playing each pair of triplets as three pairs of eighth notes. Use the following feet pattern.

Example (#1)

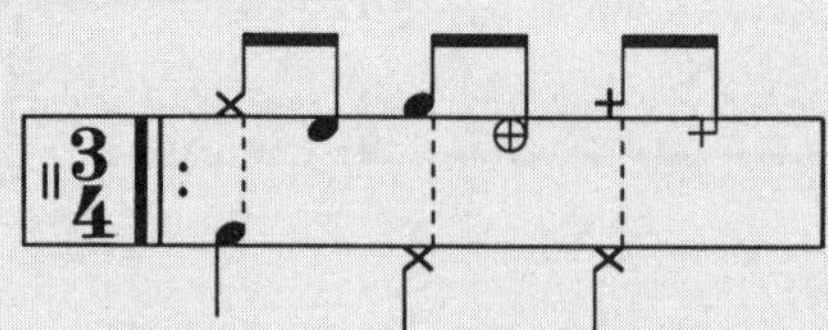

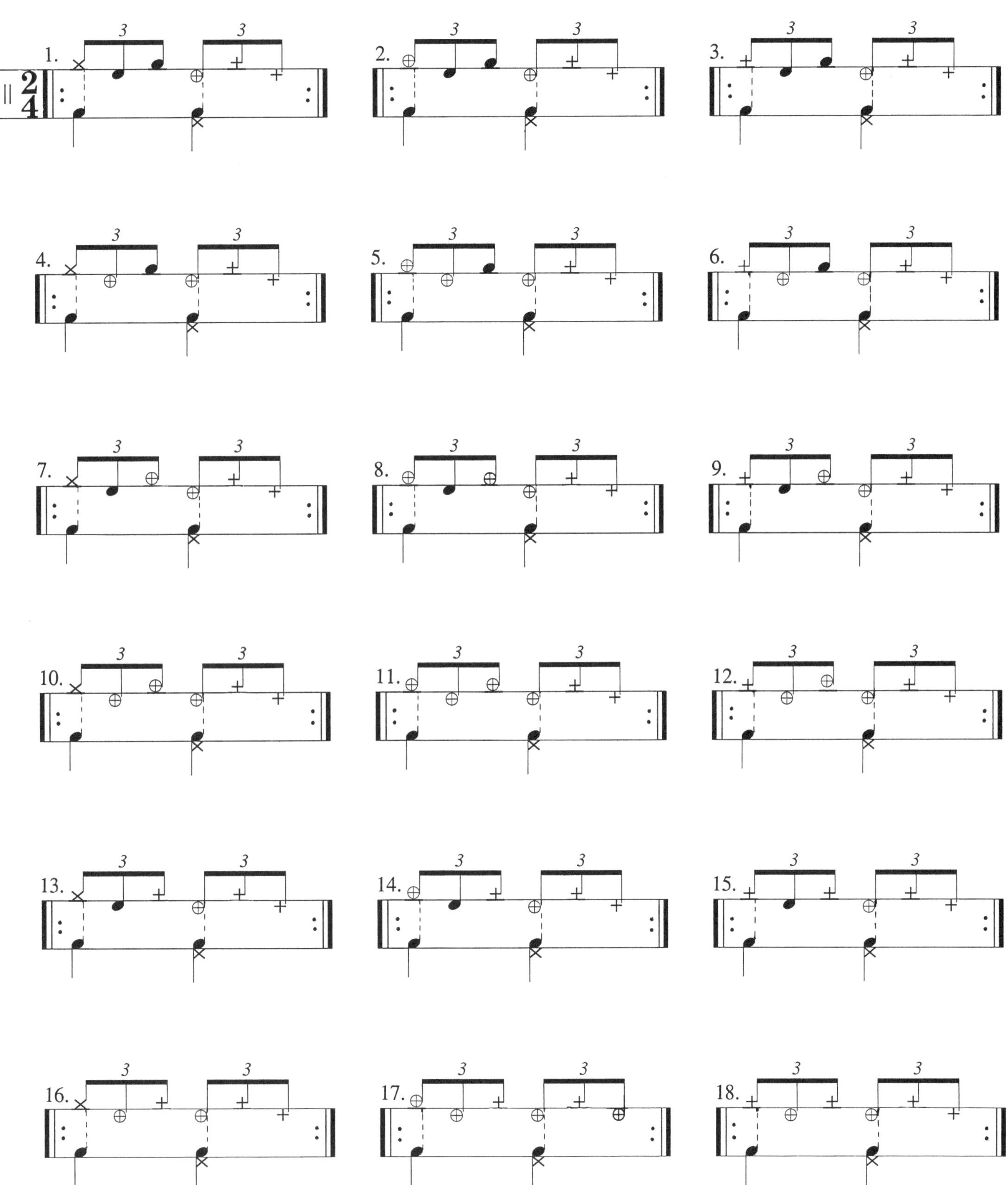
1.
2.
3.
4.
5.
6.
7.
8.
9.
10.
11.
12.
13.
14.
15.
16.
17.
18.

49 *Eighth Note Triplet Fill Patterns IV*

These fills consist of various triplet sticking patterns spread around the drum set. When playing consecutive notes with the same hand, be sure that you play each note with equal intensity.

Practice Options

- ☐ Play each fill in the context of time (see p. 6).
- ☐ Combine any two fills.
- ☐ Substitute various appropriate hi-hat and feet patterns (see pp. 150–151).

Variations

hands

☐ Following the indicated sticking, play each fill using the following surface combinations:
- — both right and left hand on snare drum.
- — right hand stationary on <u>one</u> tom, left hand on snare.
- — right hand moving from surface to surface, *ad lib.*; left hand stationary on snare.
- — Left hand moving from surface to surface, *ad lib.*; right hand stationary on snare or cymbal bell.
- — both hands moving from surface to surface, *ad lib.*

hands and feet

☐ Play the tom part on a cymbal bell, and double it with the bass drum. Close the hi-hat on beats 2 and 4 (omit the written bass drum part).

Example (#16)

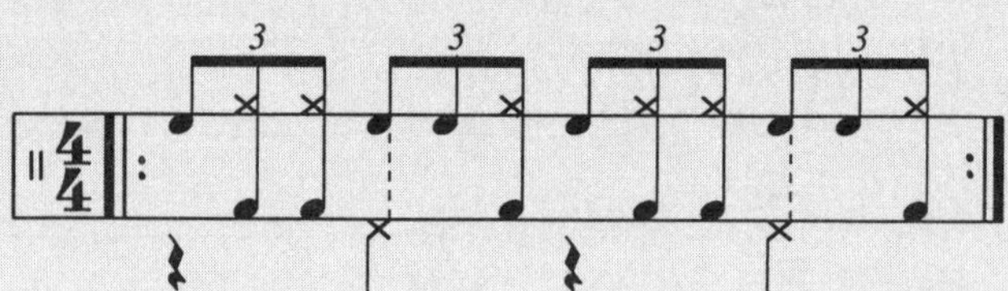

Play the tom part on the snare drum and the snare part on the hi-hat (loosely closed). With the bass drum, double the hand part played on the hi-hat (omit the written bass drum part).

Example (#16)

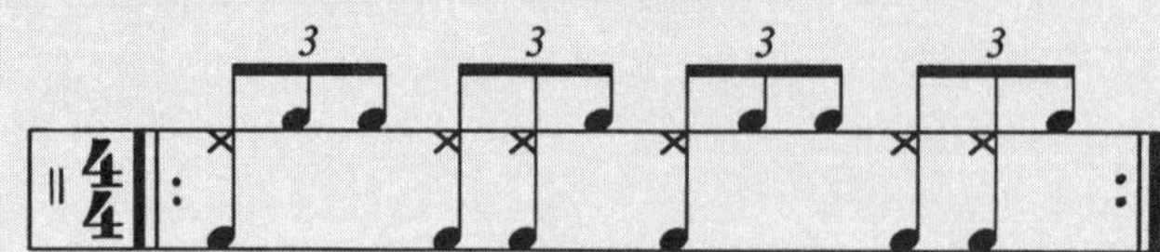

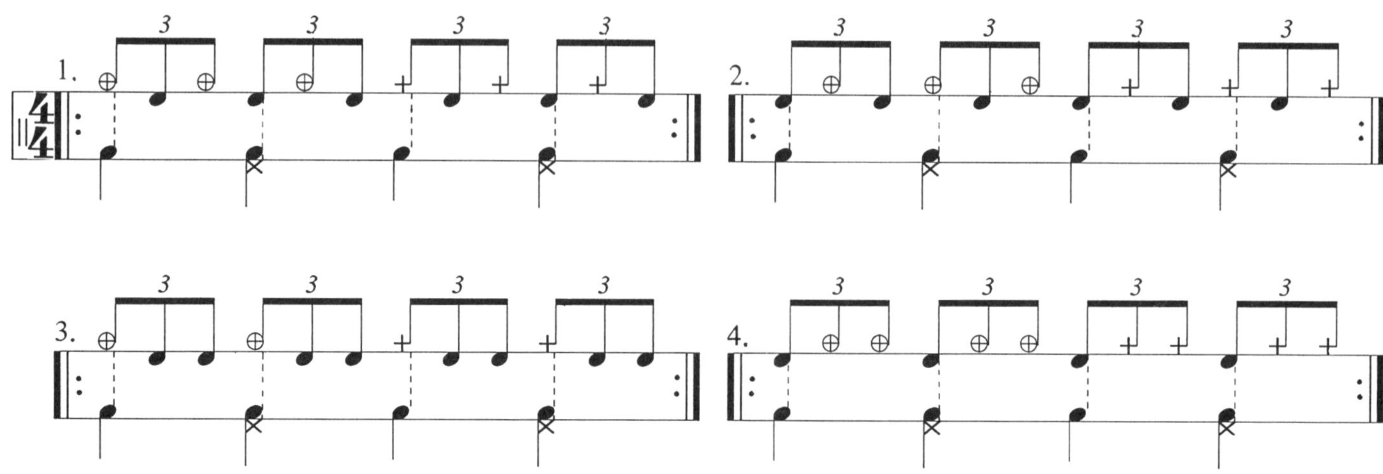

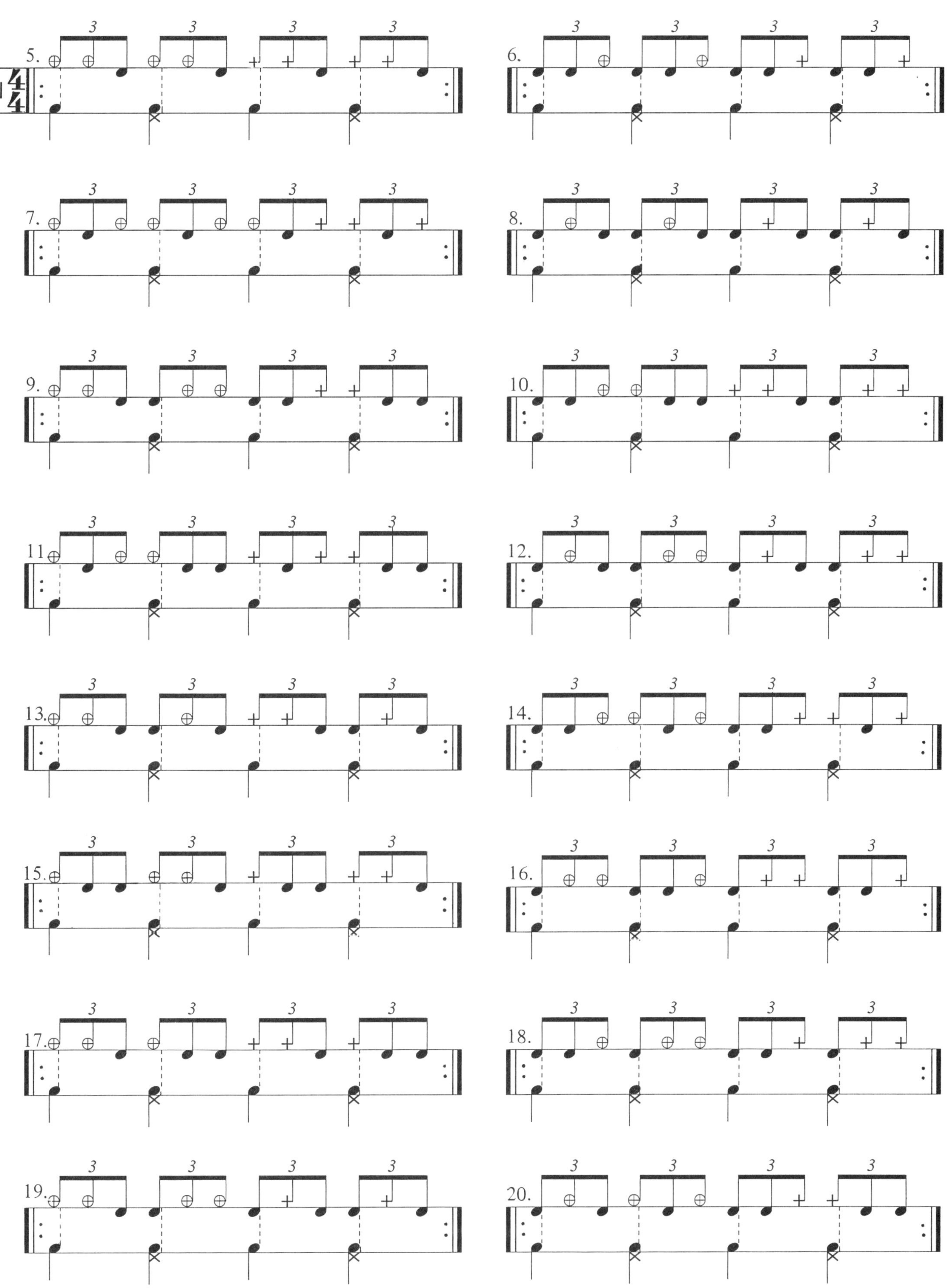
5.
6.
7.
8.
9.
10.
11
12.
13.
14.
15.
16.
17.
18.
19.
20.

50 *Eighth Note Triplet Fill Patterns V*

These fills consist of various sticking patterns spread around the drum set. When playing consecutive notes with the same hand, be sure that you play each note with equal intensity.

Practice Options

- ☐ Play each fill in the context of time (see p. 6).
- ☐ Combine any two fills.
- ☐ Substitute various appropriate hi-hat and feet patterns (see pp. 150–151).

Variations

hands and feet

- ☐ Delete either tom part and play the bass drum in its place (omit the written bass drum part).

Examples (#22)

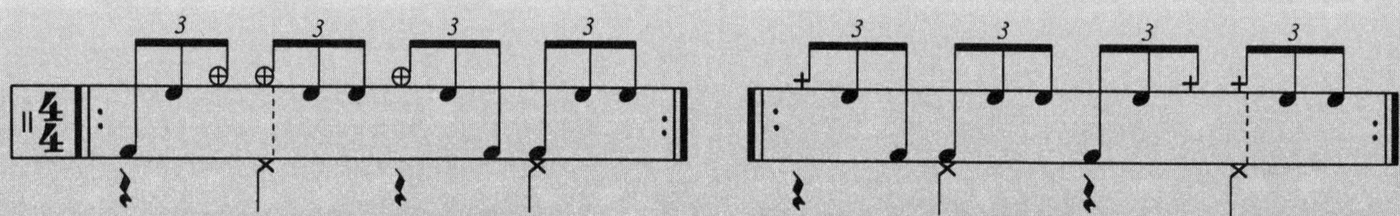

- ☐ Play the snare drum part with your feet. Play notes above the top line on the bass drum and notes below the top line on the hi-hat. Either play the snare drum in unison with the feet or omit some or all of the snare drum notes.
- ☐ Interpret each pattern as sixteenth note triplets. Play quarter notes on the bass drum and hi-hat.

9.
3
10.
11.
12.
13.
14.
15.
16.
17.
18.
19.
20.
21.
22.
23.
24.

51 *Eighth Note Triplet Fill Patterns VI*

These fills use four note groupings in a triplet setting to create an asymmetrical three against four feel.

Practice Options

- ☐ Play each fill in the context of time (see p. 6).
- ☐ Play tom notes on various cymbals or a loosely closed hi-hat.
- ☐ Combine any "a." with any "b." with any "c." Also try slitting "a.," "b.," or "c.," playing each half in a different portion of the measure.

Example (½#12"a." - #5"b." - #4"c." - ½#12"a.")

- ☐ Combine any two fills.
- ☐ Substitute various appropriate hi-hat and feet patterns (see pp. 150–151).

Variations

hands

- ☐ Play any snare note or any tom note as an open double stroke.

Examples (#8)

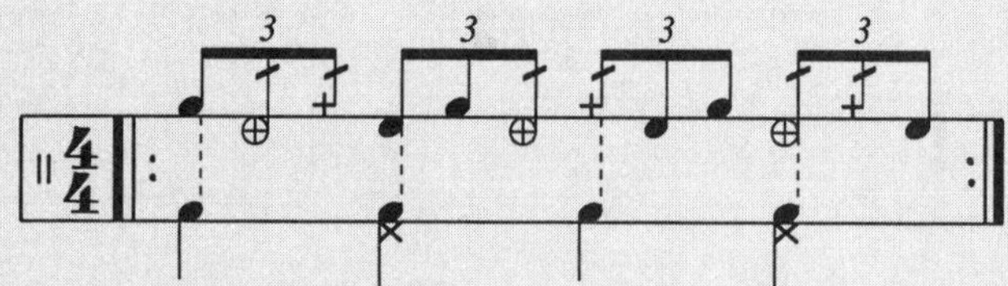

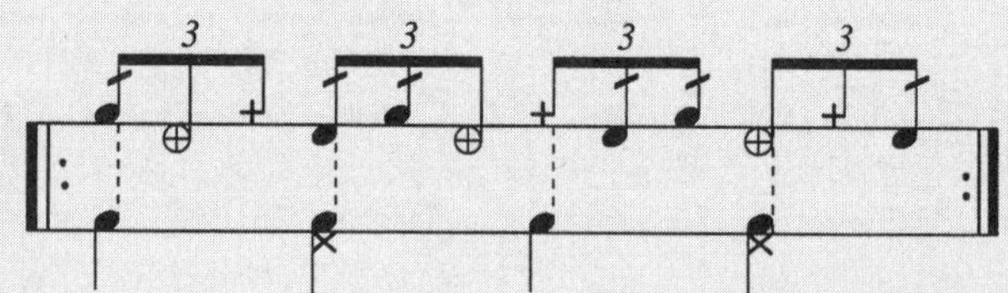

hands and feet

- ☐ Delete either the large tom notes, the small tom notes, or both, and replace them with bass drum notes (omit the written bass drum part).

Examples (#10)

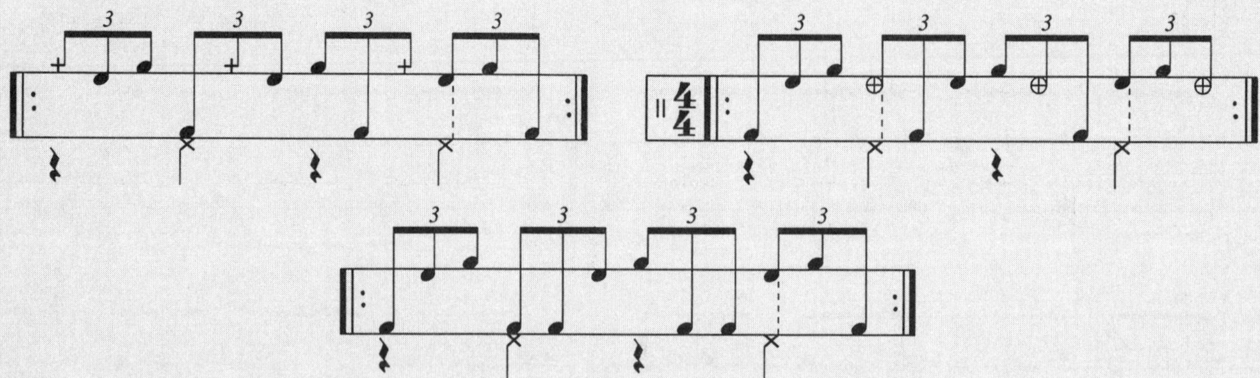

Delete the snare drum notes played by either or both hands, and replace them with bass drum notes (omit the written bass drum part).

Example (#10)

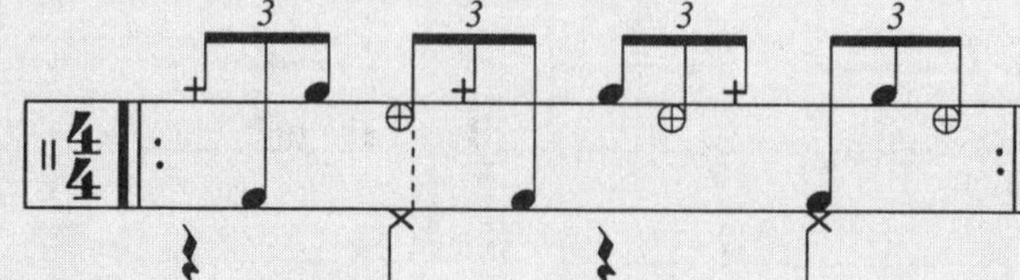

- ☐ Interpret each pattern as sixteenth note triplets. Play quarter notes on the bass drum and hi-hat.

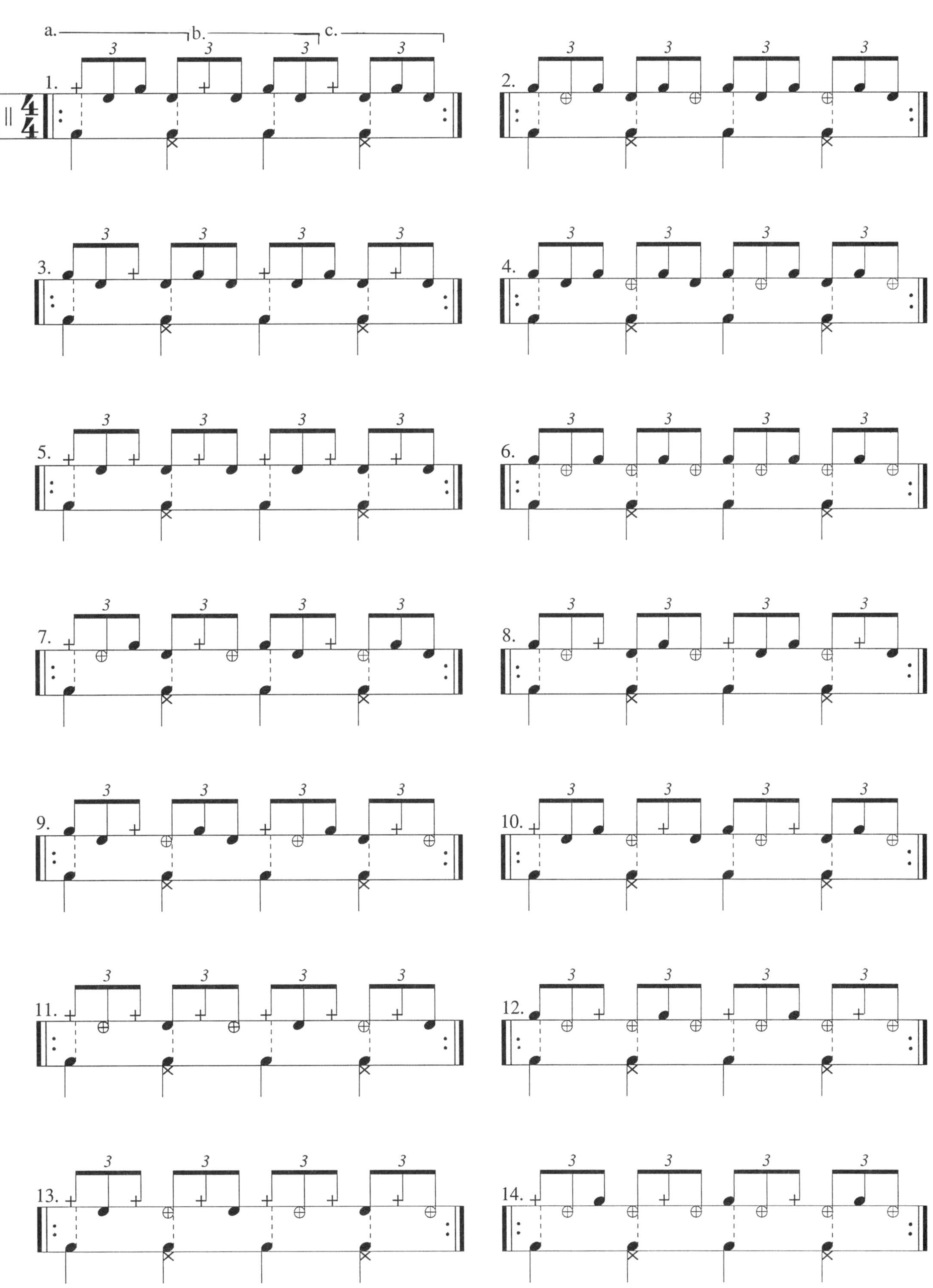
a.
b.
c.
1.
2.
3.
4.
5.
6.
7.
8.
9.
10.
11.
12.
13.
14.

52 *Eighth Note Triplet Grooves II*

These grooves combine a constant hi-hat and "three against two" ride with various snare and bass parts. Despite the way the grooves are broken up between the limbs, you should feel a "linear" eighth note triplet pulse throughout.

Practice Options

- ☐ Omit the snare drum part on the first half ("a.") or second half ("b.") of each pattern.
- ☐ Combine the first half of any pattern ("a.") with the second half of any other pattern ("b.").
- ☐ Combine the second half of any pattern with the first half of any other pattern so that "b." falls on beat 1 and "a." falls on beat 2. Close the hi-hat on beat 2 only.
- ☐ Combine any two patterns.
- ☐ Substitute various appropriate hi-hat patterns (see pp. 150–151).

Variations

hands

- ☐ Substitute any of the following ride patterns.

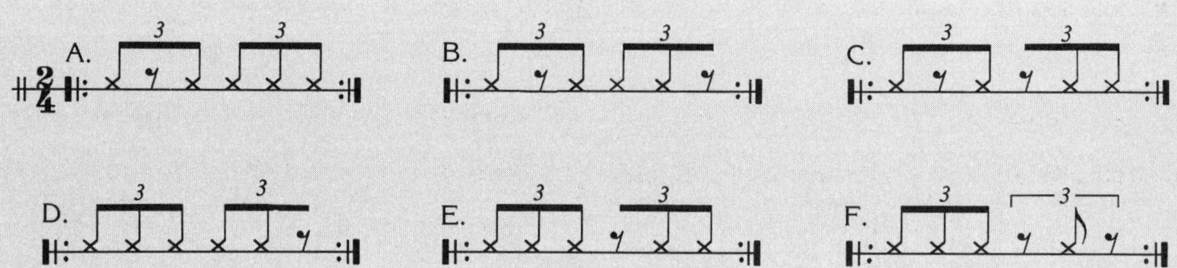

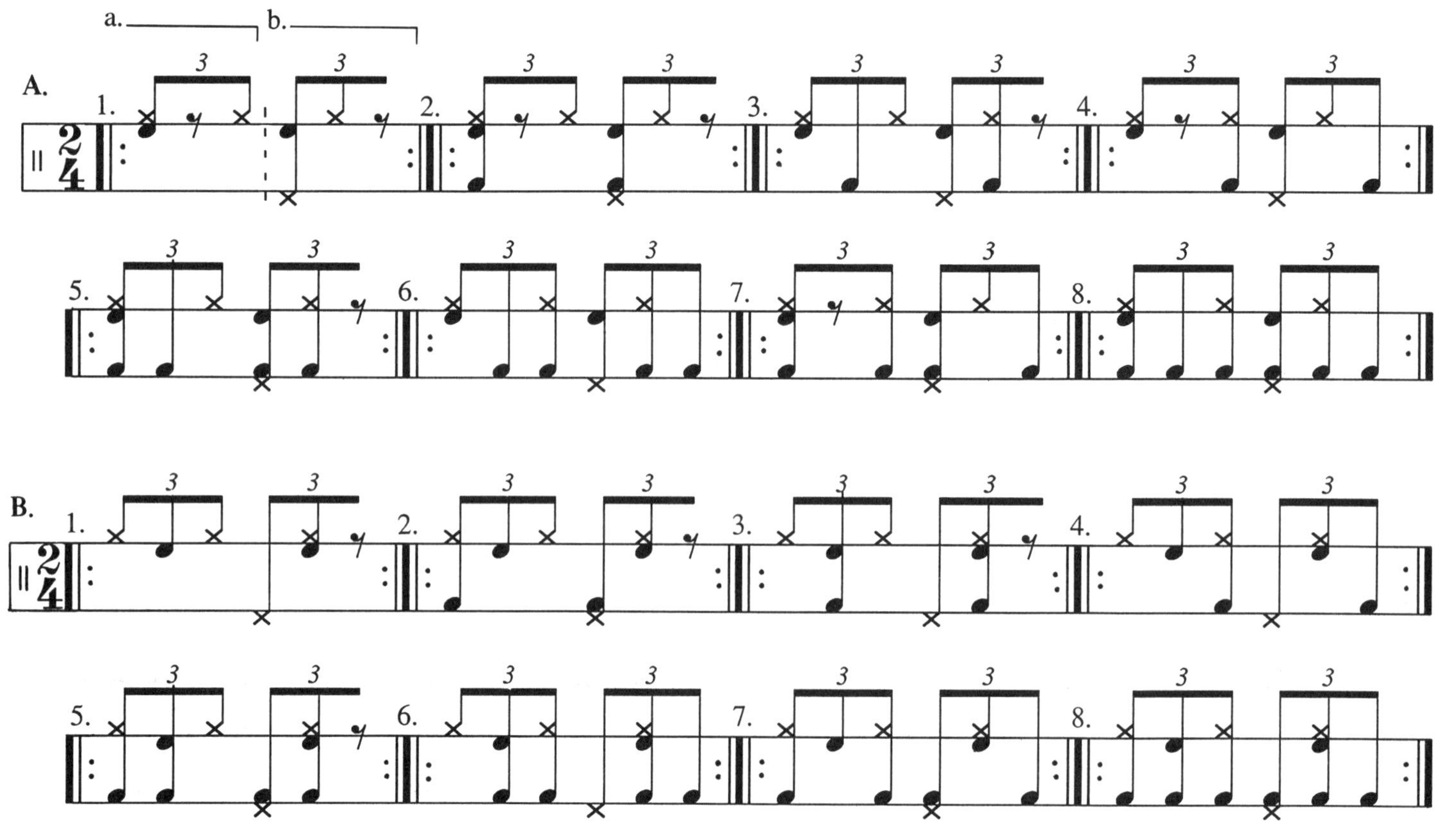

C.
1.
2.
3.
4.
5.
6.
7.
8.
D.
E.
F.
G.

53 *Compound Meter Eighth Note Grooves II*

These grooves combine a constant cymbal/back-beat hand part and constant feet part with another hand part which varies from pattern to pattern. Play the constant cymbal part on the edge of the hi-hat cymbals with the shoulder of your stick to increase the opening and closing effect.

Practice Options

- ☐ In section "A.," play the cymbal parts above the top line on a cymbal bell.
- ☐ Combine the first half of any pattern ("a.") with the second half of any other pattern ("b.") within the same section ("A." or "B.").
- ☐ Repeatedly alternate pattern #1 with any other pattern within the same section ("A." or "B.").

Variations

feet

- ☐ Substitute any of the following feet patterns.

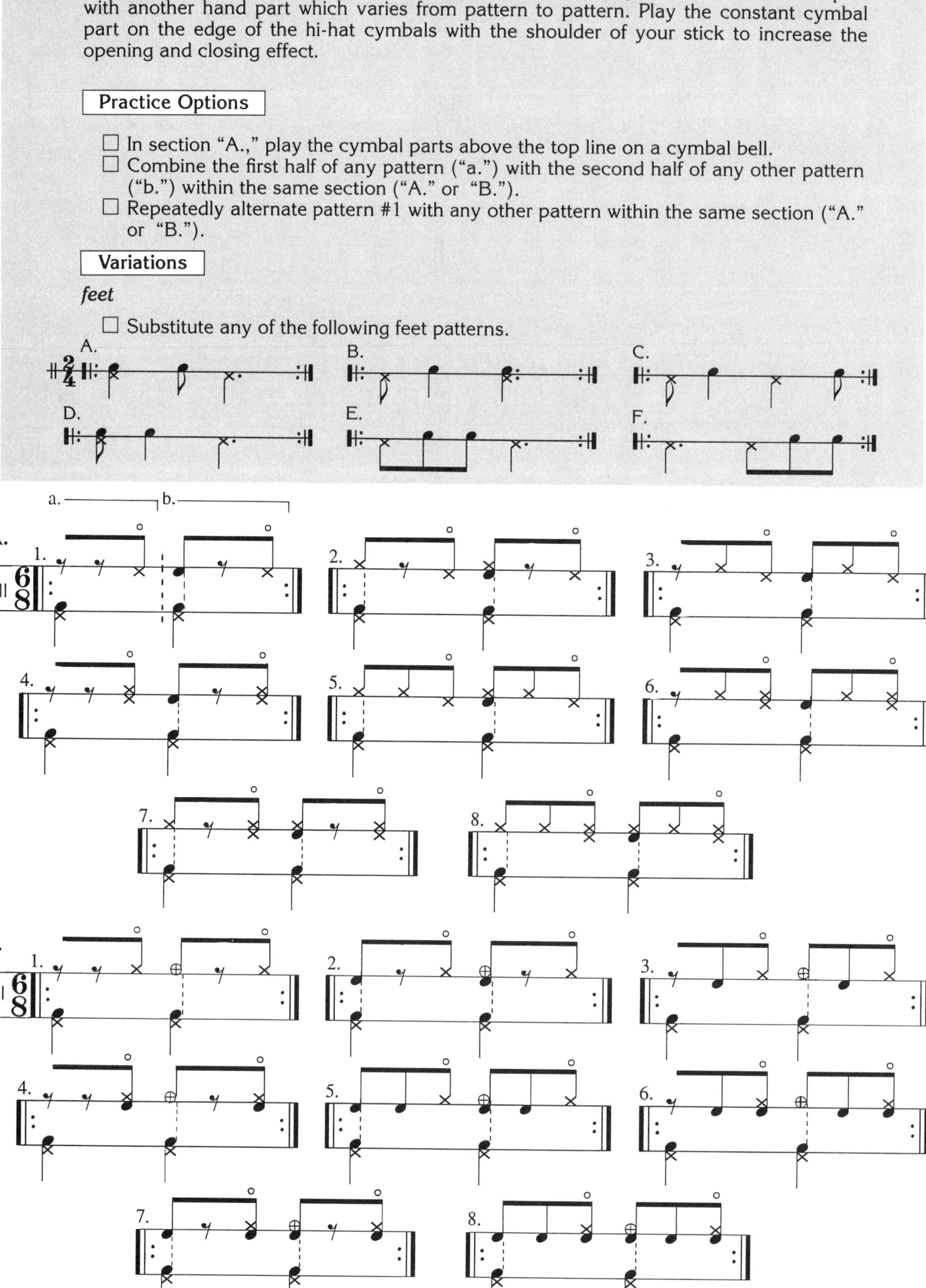

54 *Compound Meter Eighth Note Grooves III*

In these patterns, only the bass drum remains constant. Play the cymbal parts on the edge of the hi-hat cymbals with the shoulder of your stick to increase the opening and closing effect.

Practice Options

- ☐ Combine two, three, four, or five patterns to create $\frac{6}{8}$, $\frac{9}{8}$, $\frac{12}{8}$, and $\frac{15}{8}$ grooves.
- ☐ Play each pattern as a fill in the context of time (see p. 6).

Variations

hands

- ☐ Play constant eighth notes in either or both hands.

Examples (#16)

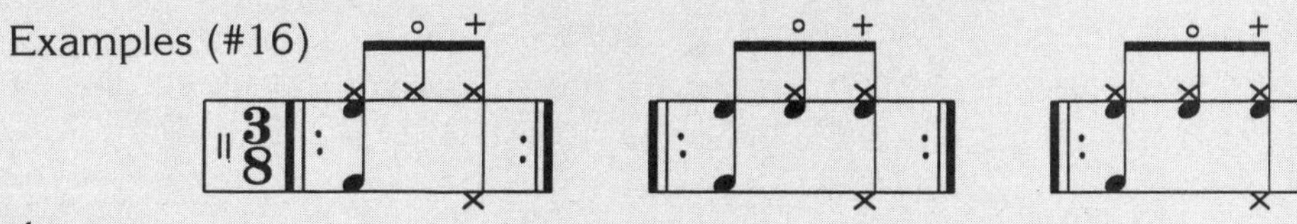

feet

- ☐ Play the bass drum when the hi-hat is open only.
- ☐ Play the bass drum when the hi-hat closes only.

Example (#19) Example (#19)

hands and feet

- ☐ Combine any two patterns, interpreting the combination as three groups of two eighth notes in $\frac{3}{4}$ time.

Example (#4-#5)

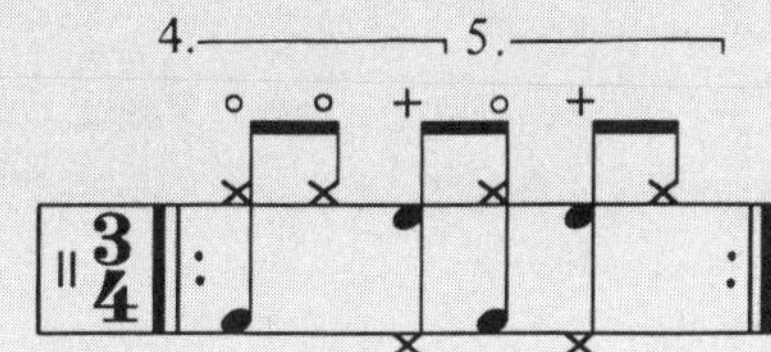

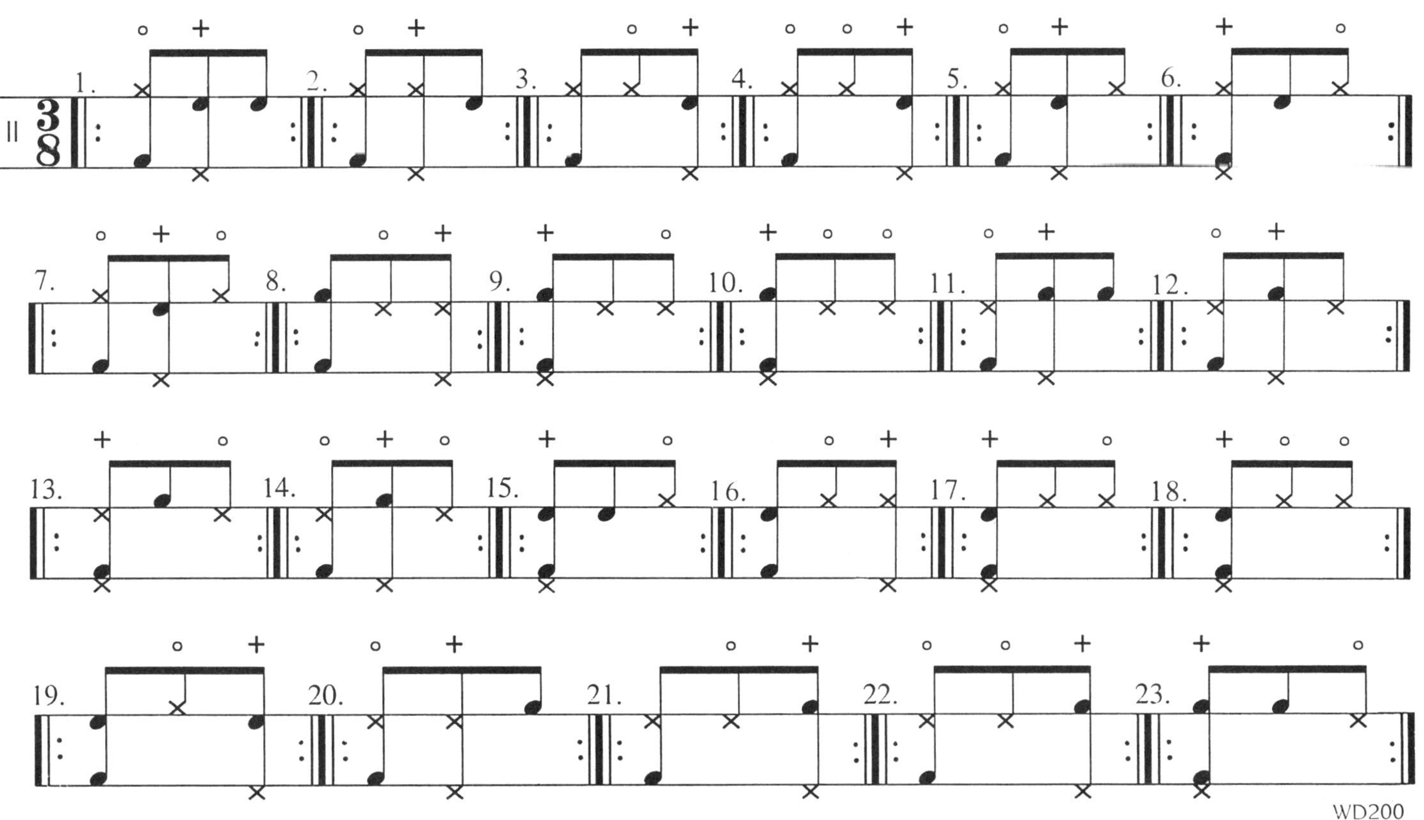

55 *Eighth Note Triplet Fill Patterns VII*

These fills contain movement between the hands and bass drum. Play the double-stops using either open or closed (flat) flams.

Practice Options

- ☐ Play each fill in the context of time (see p. 6).
- ☐ Add a crescendo to each fill.
- ☐ Combine any two fills.
- ☐ Substitute various appropriate hi-hat patterns (see p. 151).

Variations

hands

- ☐ Play each fill using various surface combinations.
- ☐ Play each doublestop as two independent 16th notes, beginning with either hand.

Examples (#20)

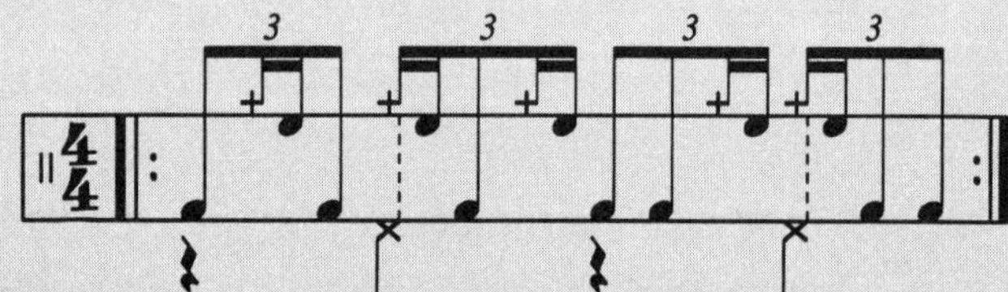

- ☐ Interpret each triplet as any of the following eighth/sixteenth note combinations.

A.  B.  C.  D. 

Try combining these rhythms within fills.

feet

- ☐ Close the hi-hat in unison with the bass drum (omit the written hi-hat part).

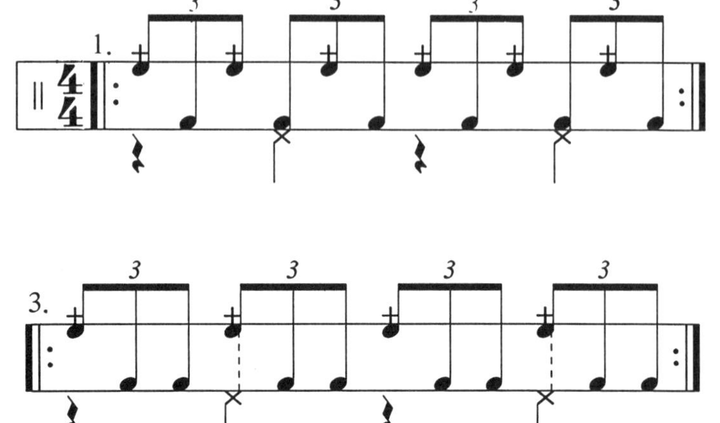

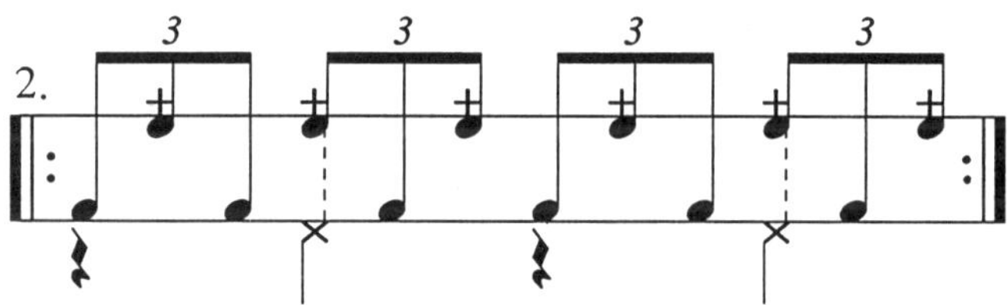

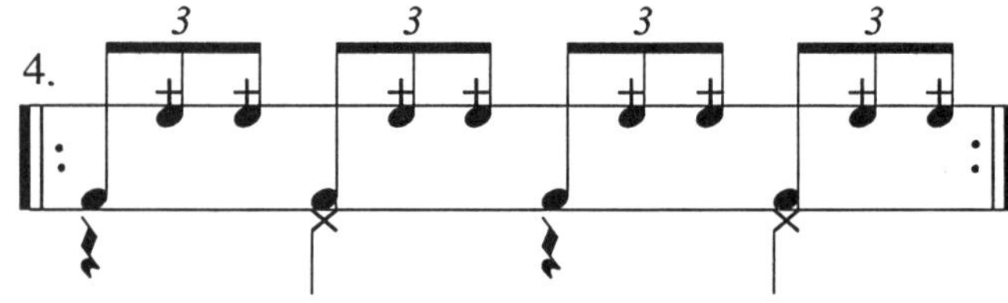

5.
6.
7.
8.
9.
10.
11.
12.
13.
14.
15.
16.
17.
18.
19.
20.

56 *Eighth Note Triplet Fill Patterns VIII*

These fills contain movement between the hands and bass drum. Played repeatedly at a rapid or gradually accelerated tempo, they make effective extended solo licks.

Practice Options

- ☐ Play each fill in the context of time (see p. 6).
- ☐ Combine any "a." with any "b." with any "c." with any "d." Also combine two, three, and five beats to create $\frac{2}{4}$, $\frac{3}{4}$, and $\frac{5}{4}$ fills.
- ☐ Play the fills within sections "A.," "B.," or "C." consecutively to create sixteen measure solos.
- ☐ Substitute various appropriate hi-hat patterns (see p. 151).

Variations

hands

- ☐ Play the tom notes on other surfaces.
- ☐ Play any snare drum note as an open double stroke.
- ☐ Omit notes played by the hands *ad lib.*, creating broken figures.
- ☐ Interpret each triplet as any of the following eighth/sixteenth note combinations.

A. B. C. D.

Try combining these rhythms within fills.

feet

- ☐ Close the hi-hat in unison with the bass drum (omit the written hi-hat part).

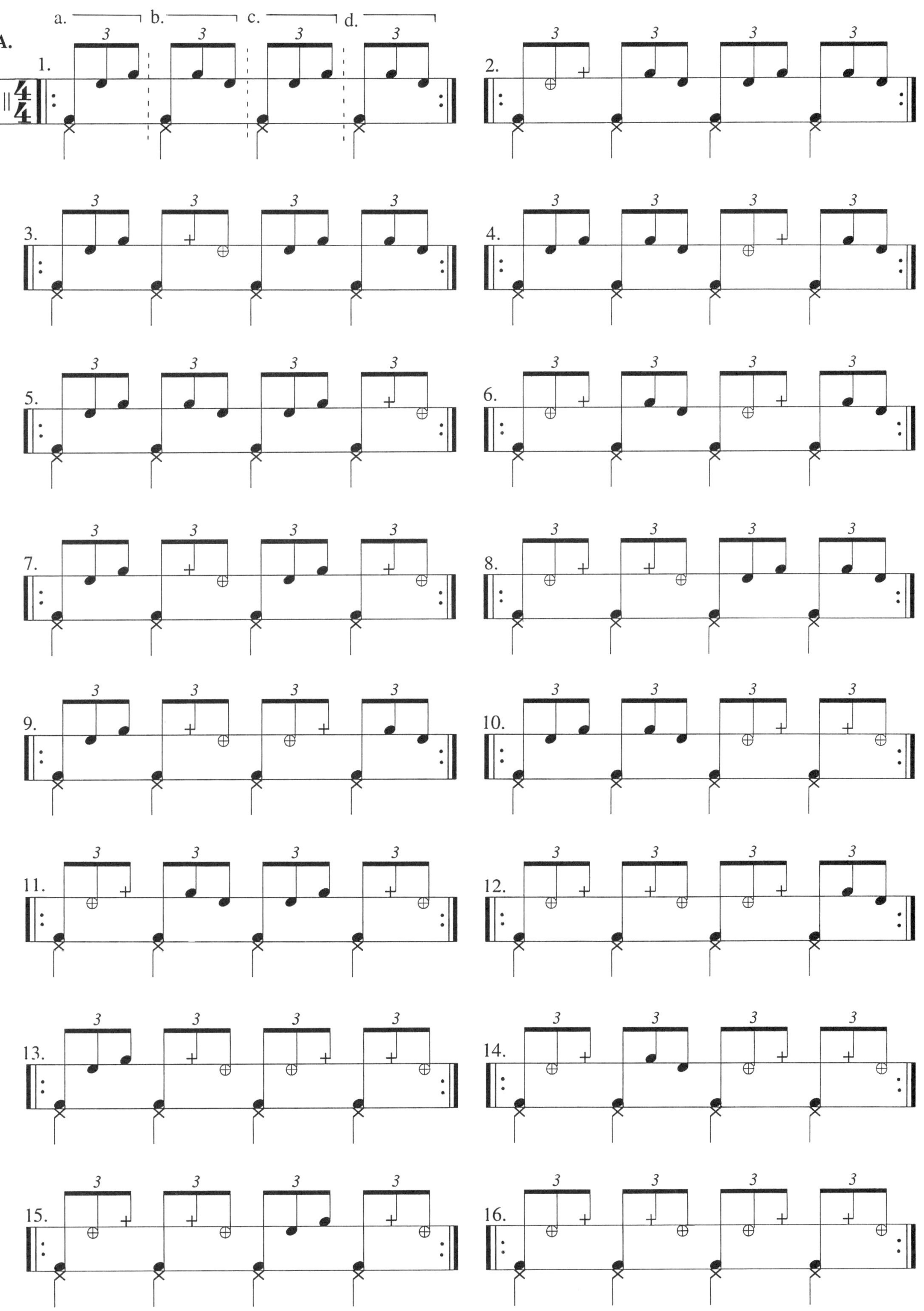

A.
a.
b.
c.
d.
1.
2.
3.
4.
5.
6.
7.
8.
9.
10.
11.
12.
13.
14.
15.
16.

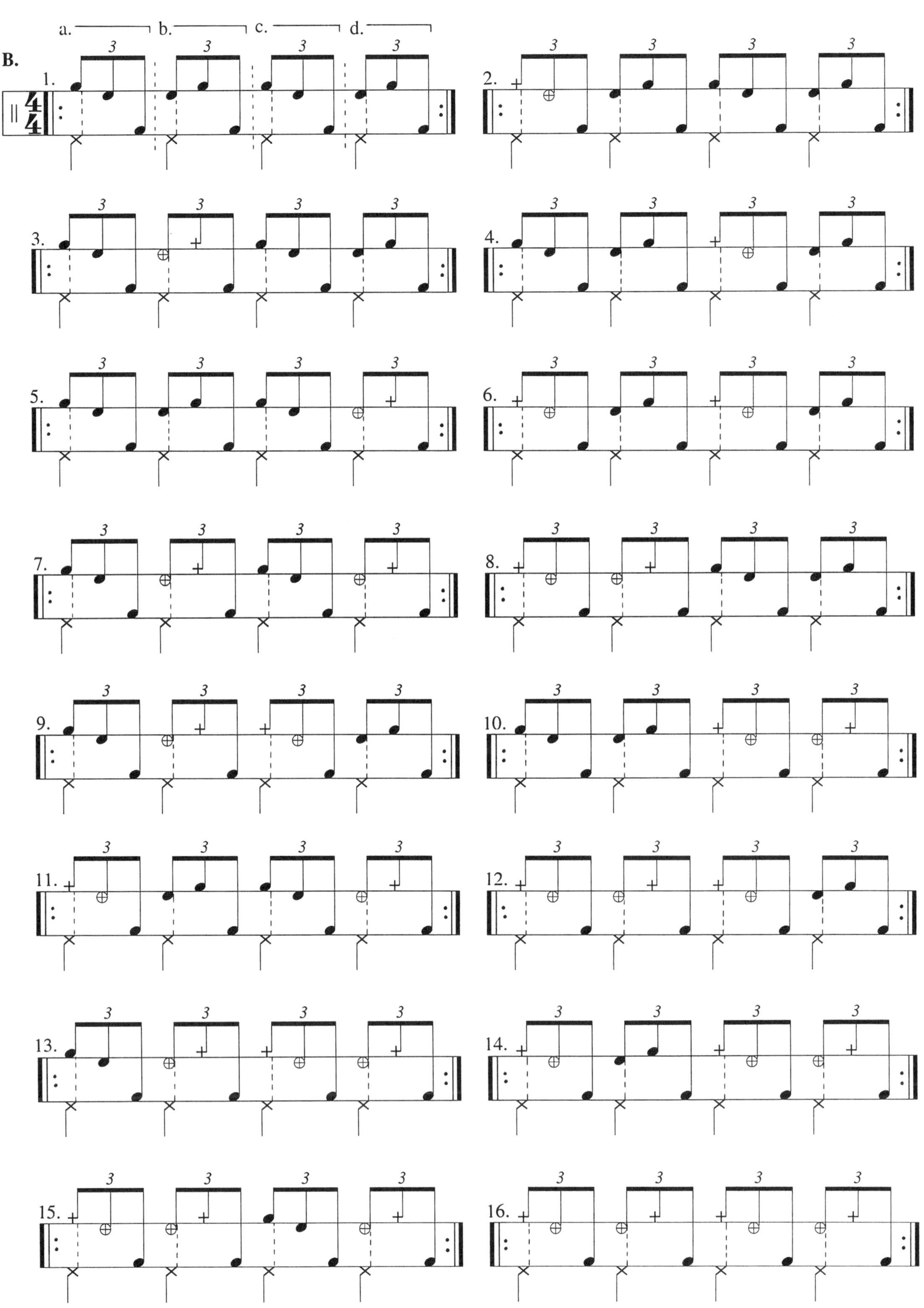
a.
b.
c.
d.
B.
1.
2.
3.
4.
5.
6.
7.
8.
9.
10.
11.
12.
13.
14.
15.
16.

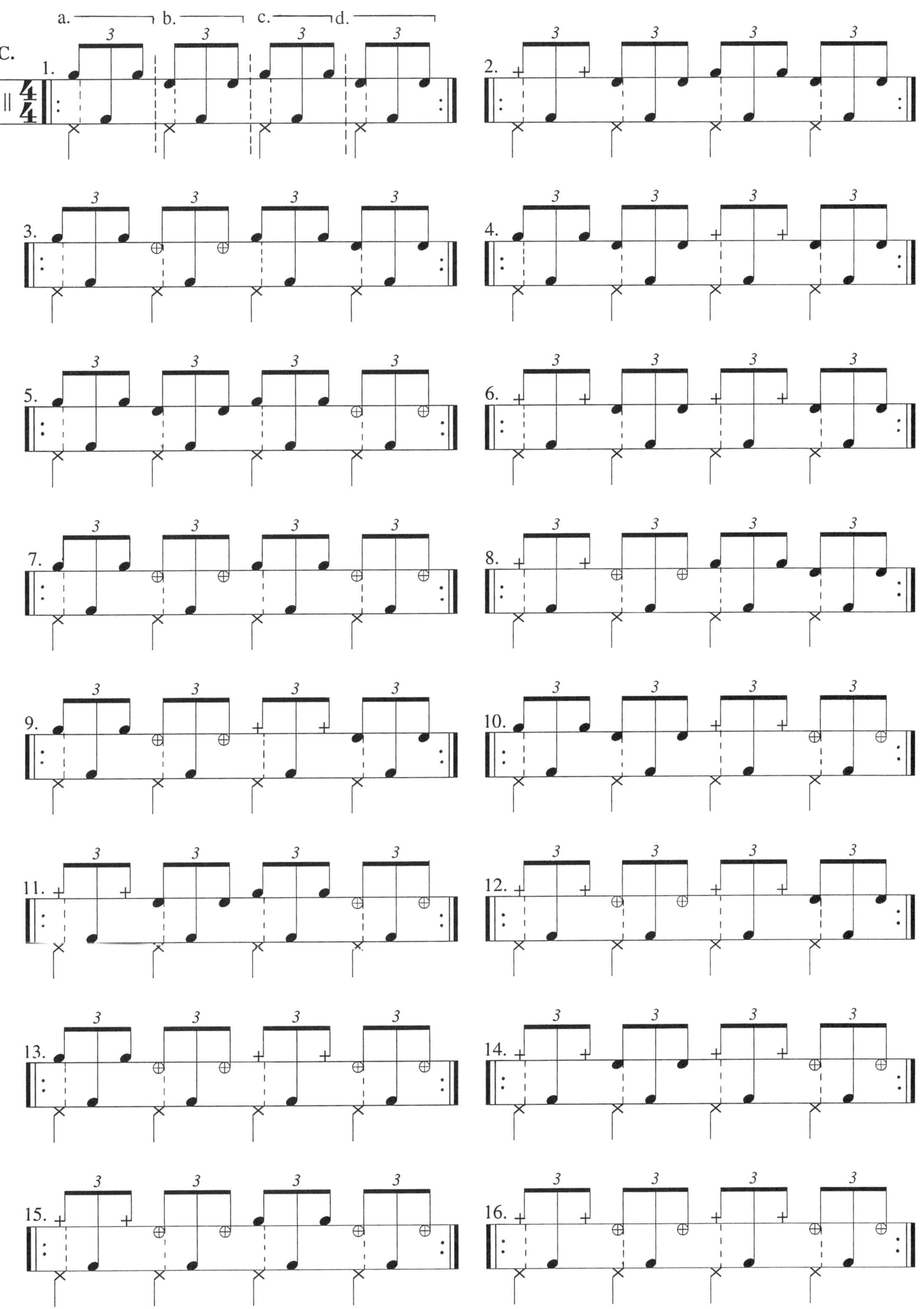
a.
b.
c.
d.
C.
1.
2.
3.
4.
5.
6.
7.
8.
9.
10.
11.
12.
13.
14.
15.
16.

57 *Eighth Note/Eighth Note Triplet Groove/Fill Patterns*

These linear patterns involve movement between the hands and feet. Note that within each section, the feet are constant. The feet part is written to allow several interpretations.

— play the feet part on the bass drum and hi-hat in unison.

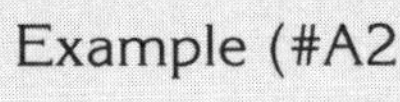
Example (#A2)

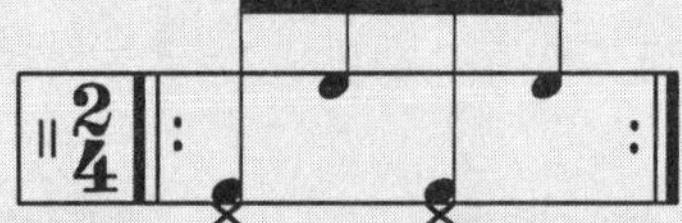

— play the feet part on the bass drum and keep time with the hi-hat.

Example (#A2)

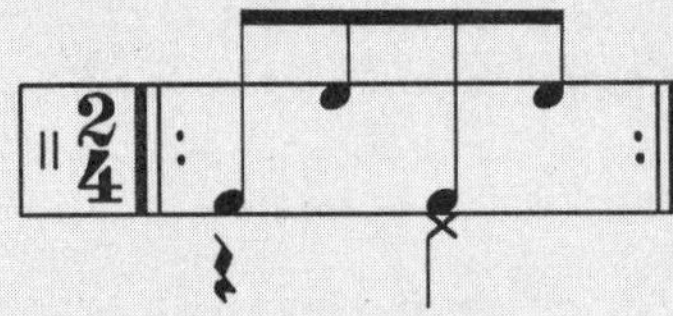

— play the feet part on the hi-hat and keep time with the bass drum.

Example (#A2)

Practice Options

☐ Play each pattern in the context of time (see p. 6).
☐ Combine patterns within and between sections "A." and "B." and within and between sections "C." and "D."

Variations

hands

☐ Following the indicated sticking, play each pattern using various surface combinations:
- Both right and left hand on snare drum.
- Right hand moving from surface to surface, *ad lib.*; left hand stationary on snare.
- Left hand moving from surface to surface, *ad lib.*; right hand stationary on cymbal, snare, or tom.
- Both hands moving from surface to surface, *ad lib.*

☐ Play any right or left hand note as two sixteenth notes.

hands and feet

☐ Play each pattern in sections "A." and "B." three times, interpreting the combination as four triplets in 4/4 time. Play the feet part on the bass drum and close the hi-hat on beats 2 and 4 or all four beats.

Example (#B3)

Also try combining three <u>different</u> patterns.

☐ Play each pattern in sections "C." and "D." two times, interpreting the combination as three groups of four sixteenth notes in 3/4 time. Play the feet part on the bass drum and close the hi-hat on beats 2 and 3 or all three beats.

Example (#C6)

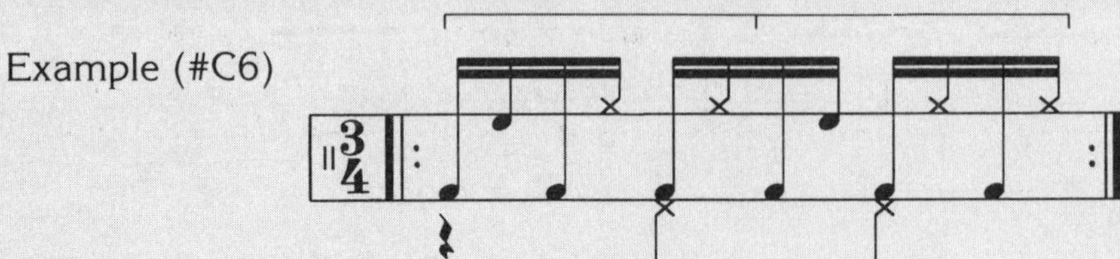

Also try combining two <u>different</u> patterns.

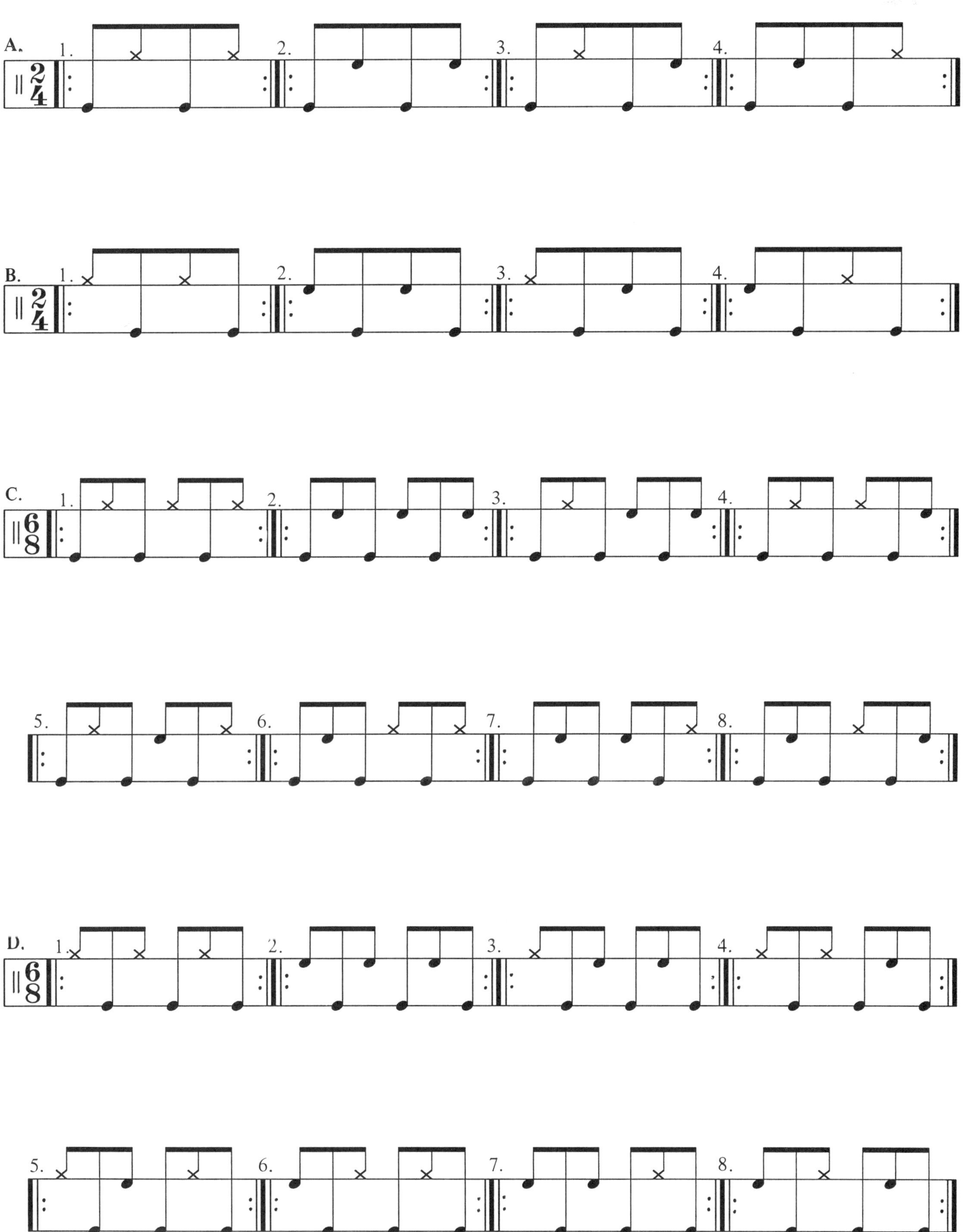
A.
1.
2.
3.
4.
B.
1.
2.
3.
4.
C.
1.
2.
3.
4.
5.
6.
7.
8.
D.
1.
2.
3.
4.
5.
6.
7.
8.

58 *Eighth Note Triplet Fill Patterns IX*

These fills involve linear movement between the hands and bass drum.

Practice Options

- ☐ Play each fill in the context of time (see p. 6).
- ☐ Combine any two fills.
- ☐ Substitute various appropriate hi-hat patterns (see p. 151).

Variations

hands

- ☐ Following the indicated sticking, play each fill using various surface combinations:
  - — right hand on tom, left hand on snare.
  - — right hand on cymbal bell or special effects cymbal, left hand on snare.
  - — right hand moving from surface to surface, *ad lib.*; left hand stationary on snare.
  - — left hand moving from surface to surface, *ad lib.*; right hand stationary on snare.
  - — both hands moving from surface to surface, *ad lib.*
- ☐ Randomly omit notes played by the hands, creating broken figures.
- ☐ Play any note as a flam.

feet

- ☐ Play the bass drum part with both the bass drum and hi-hat in unison (omit the written hi-hat part).
- ☐ Play the bass drum part with the hi-hat. At the same time, play the bass drum on beat 1 only, beat 3 only, beats 1 and 3, or the back-beats.
- ☐ Omit the written feet part, and substitute feet patterns 1–5 or 39–49 on page 150.

hands and feet

- ☐ Accent any note or notes.
- ☐ Interpret each pattern as sixteenth note triplets. Play quarter notes on the hi-hat.
- ☐ Interpret each pattern as three groups of four sixteenth notes in $\frac{3}{4}$ time.

9.
10.
11.
12.
13.
14.
15.
16.
17.
18.
19.
20.
21.
22.
23.
24.

25.
26.
27.
28.
29.
30.
31.
32.
33.
34.
35.
36.
37.
38.
39.
40.

41.
42.
43.
44.
45.
46.
47.
48.
49.
50.
51.
52.
53.
54.
55.
56.

59 *Compound Meter Eighth Note Fill Patterns*

In these linear fills, the feet remain constant within each lettered section; only the surfaces struck by the hands change.

Practice Options

- ☐ Play each fill in the context of time (see p. 6).
- ☐ Substitute various appropriate hi-hat patterns (see p. 151).

Variations

hands

- ☐ Play any stroke as an open double stroke or flam.

hands and feet

- ☐ Play each pattern two times, interpreting the combination as three groups of four sixteenth notes in $\frac{3}{4}$ time. Close the hi-hat on beats 2 and 3 or all three beats.

Example (#E2)

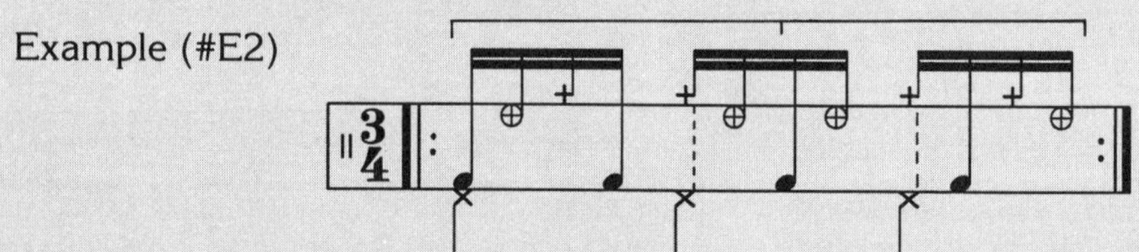

Also try combining two different patterns.

A. 1. 2. 3. 4. 5. 6. 7. 8.

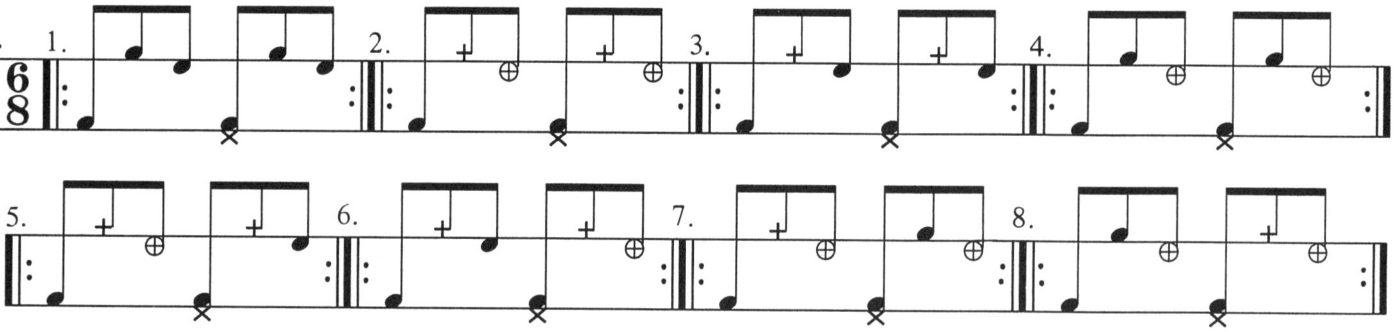

B. 1. 2. 3. 4. 5. 6. 7. 8.

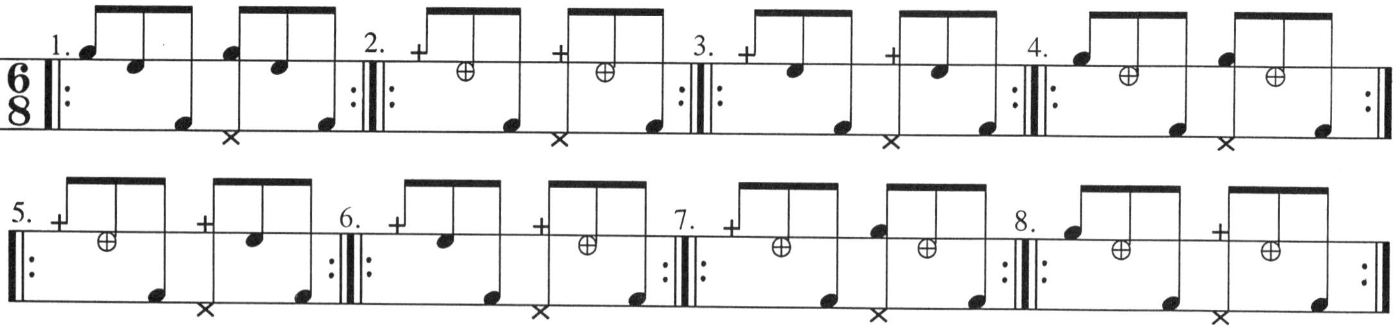

C. 1. 2. 3. 4. 5. 6. 7. 8.

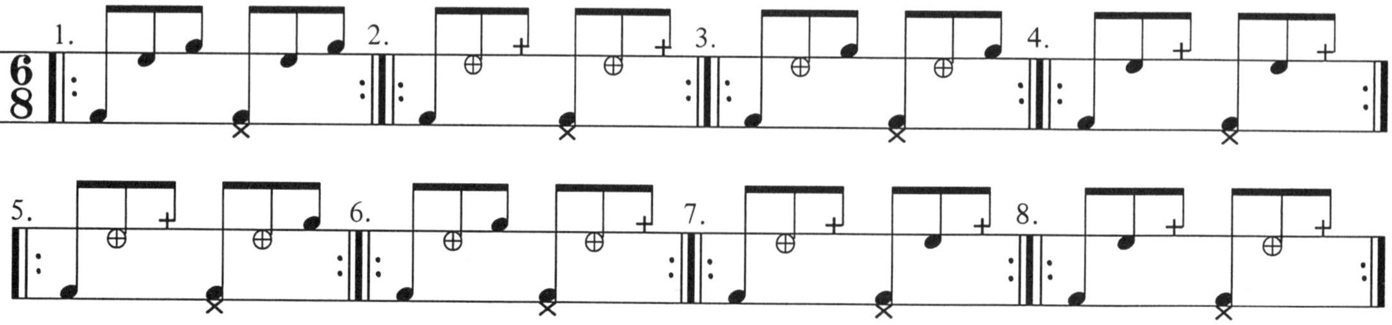

D.
1.
2.
3.
4.
5.
6.
7.
8.
E.
1.
2.
3.
4.
5.
6.
7.
8.
F.
1.
2.
3.
4.
5.
6.
7.
8.
G.
1.
2.
3.
4.
H.
1.
2.
3.
4.
I.
1.
2.
3.
4.

60 *Compound Meter Eighth Note Groove/Fill Patterns I*

These linear patterns involve movement between the hands and feet. Notice that sections "A." and "C." mirror one another, as do sections "B." and "D." The feet part is written on a single line staff to allow several interpretations.

— Play the feet part on the bass drum and hi-hat in unison.

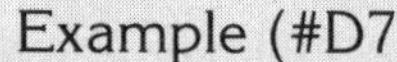
Example (#D7)

— Play the feet part on the bass drum and keep time with the hi-hat.

Example (#D7)

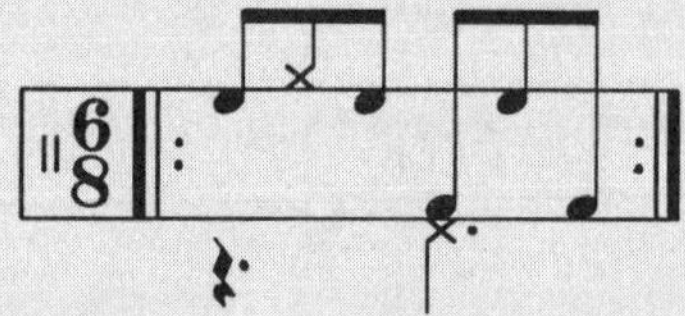

— Play the feet part on the hi-hat and keep time with the bass drum.

Example (#D7)

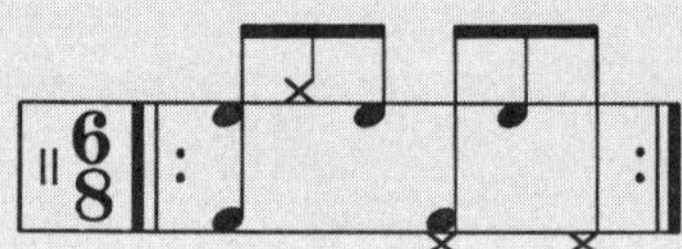

Practice Options

☐ Play each pattern in the context of time (see p. 6).
☐ Play the cymbal part on a cymbal bell or closed hi-hat (omit the left foot part).
☐ Combine patterns within and between sections "A." and "B." and within and between sections "C." and "D."

Variations

hands

☐ Following the indicated sticking, play each pattern using various surface combinations:
— both right and left hand on snare drum.
— right hand moving from surface to surface, *ad lib.*; left hand stationary on snare.
— left hand moving from surface to surface, *ad lib.*; right hand stationary on cymbal, snare, or tom.
— both hands moving from surface to surface, *ad lib.*
☐ Play any right or left hand note as two sixteenth notes.

hands and feet

☐ Play each pattern two times, interpreting the combination as three groups of four sixteenth notes in $\frac{3}{4}$ time. Play the feet part on the bass drum and close the hi-hat on beats 2 and 3 or all three beats.

Example (#C3)

Also try combining two different patterns.

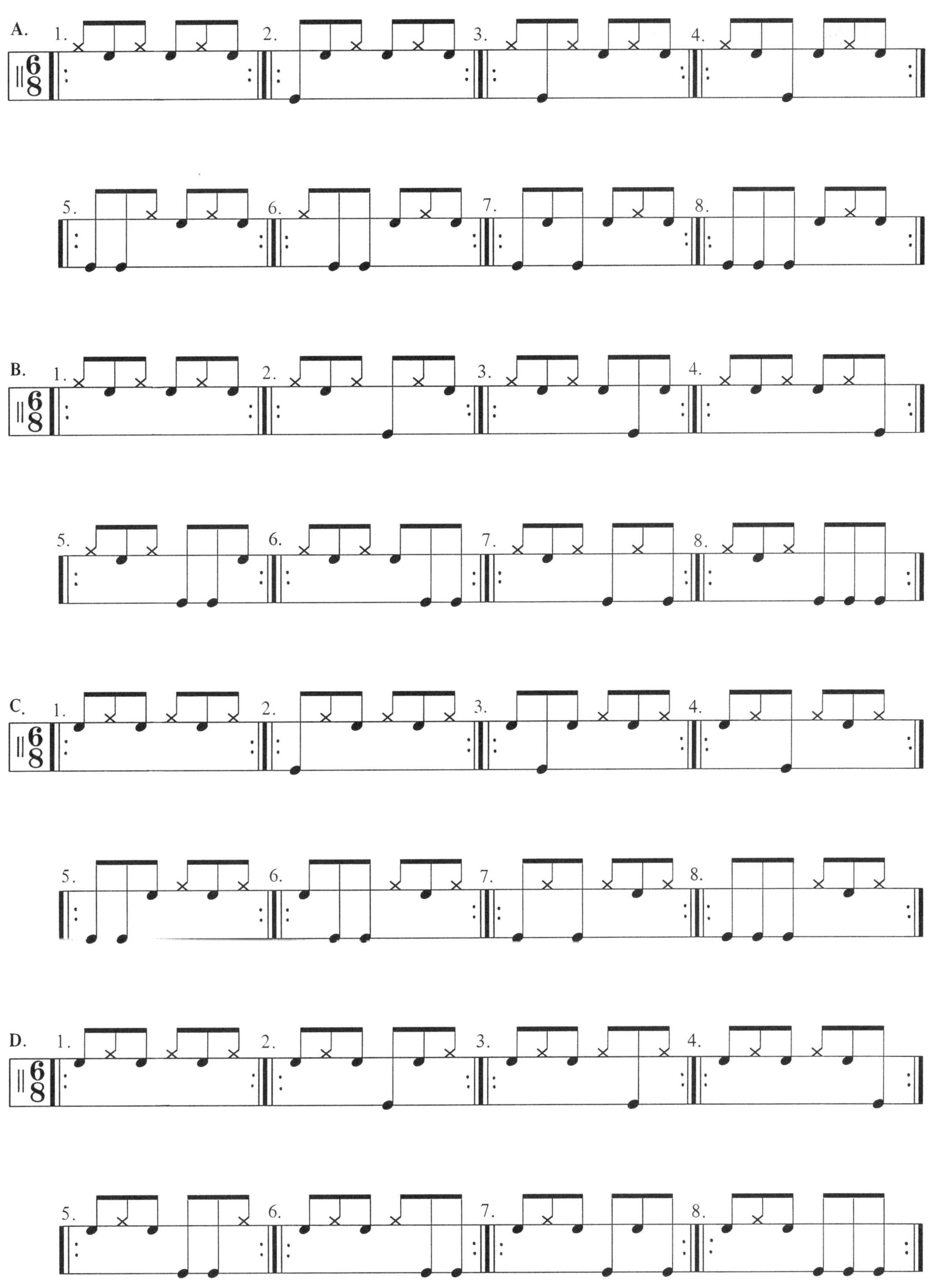
A.
1.
2.
3.
4.
5.
6.
7.
8.
B.
1.
2.
3.
4.
5.
6.
7.
8.
C.
1.
2.
3.
4.
5.
6.
7.
8.
D.
1.
2.
3.
4.
5.
6.
7.
8.

61 *Eighth Note Triplet Fill Patterns X*

This study provides interesting fills that can be played without interrupting the time. Notice that a constant ride floats above active linear interplay between the snare drum and bass drum.

Practice Options

- ☐ Play each fill in the context of time (see p. 6).
- ☐ Play only the first three beats of any pattern ("a.") to create a $\frac{3}{4}$ fill.
- ☐ Substitute various appropriate hi-hat patterns (see p. 151).

Variations

hands

- ☐ Play some or all of the snare drum notes on other surfaces.
- ☐ Omit the snare drum part.
- ☐ Play the snare drum on the back-beats only.
- ☐ Substitute any of the following ride patterns. (When using ride "G." or "H.," count sixteenth note triplet subdivisions as you play each fill).

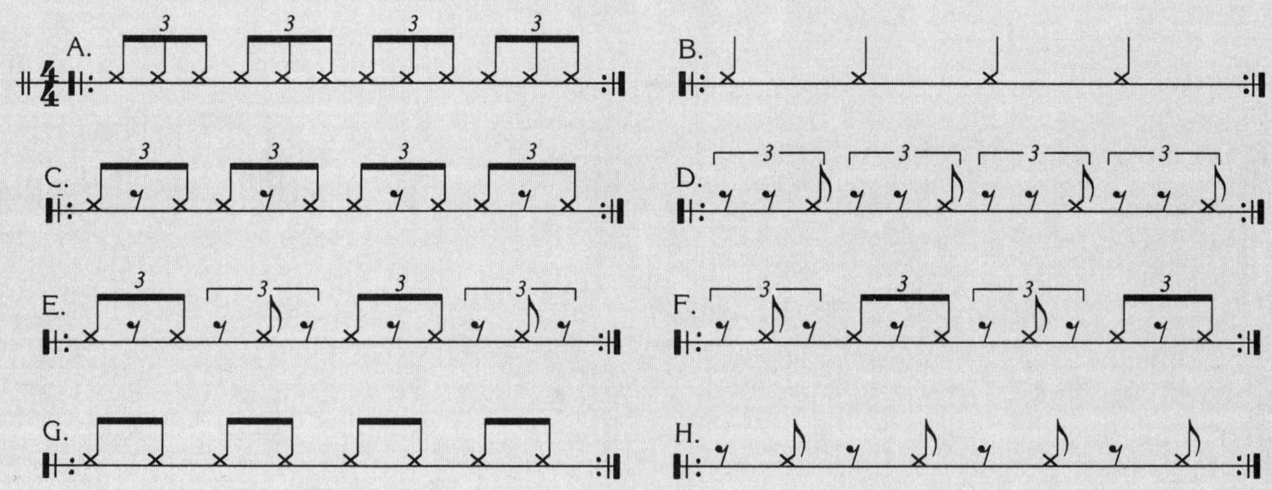

feet

- ☐ Omit the bass drum part.
- ☐ Substitute any of the following p. 150 feet patterns: #1–#5, #39–#49.

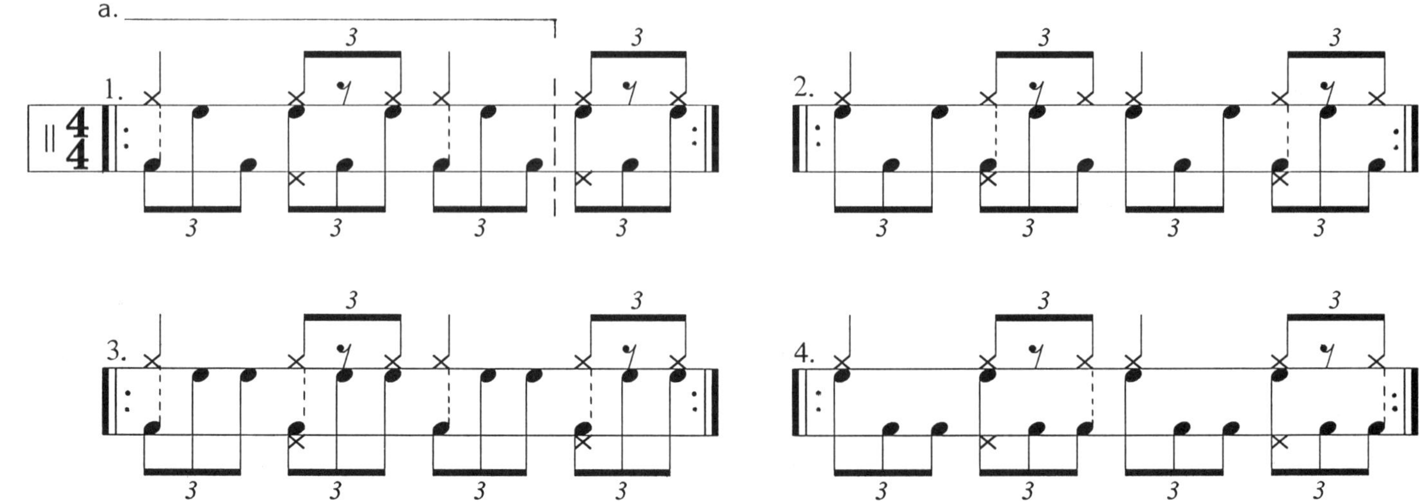

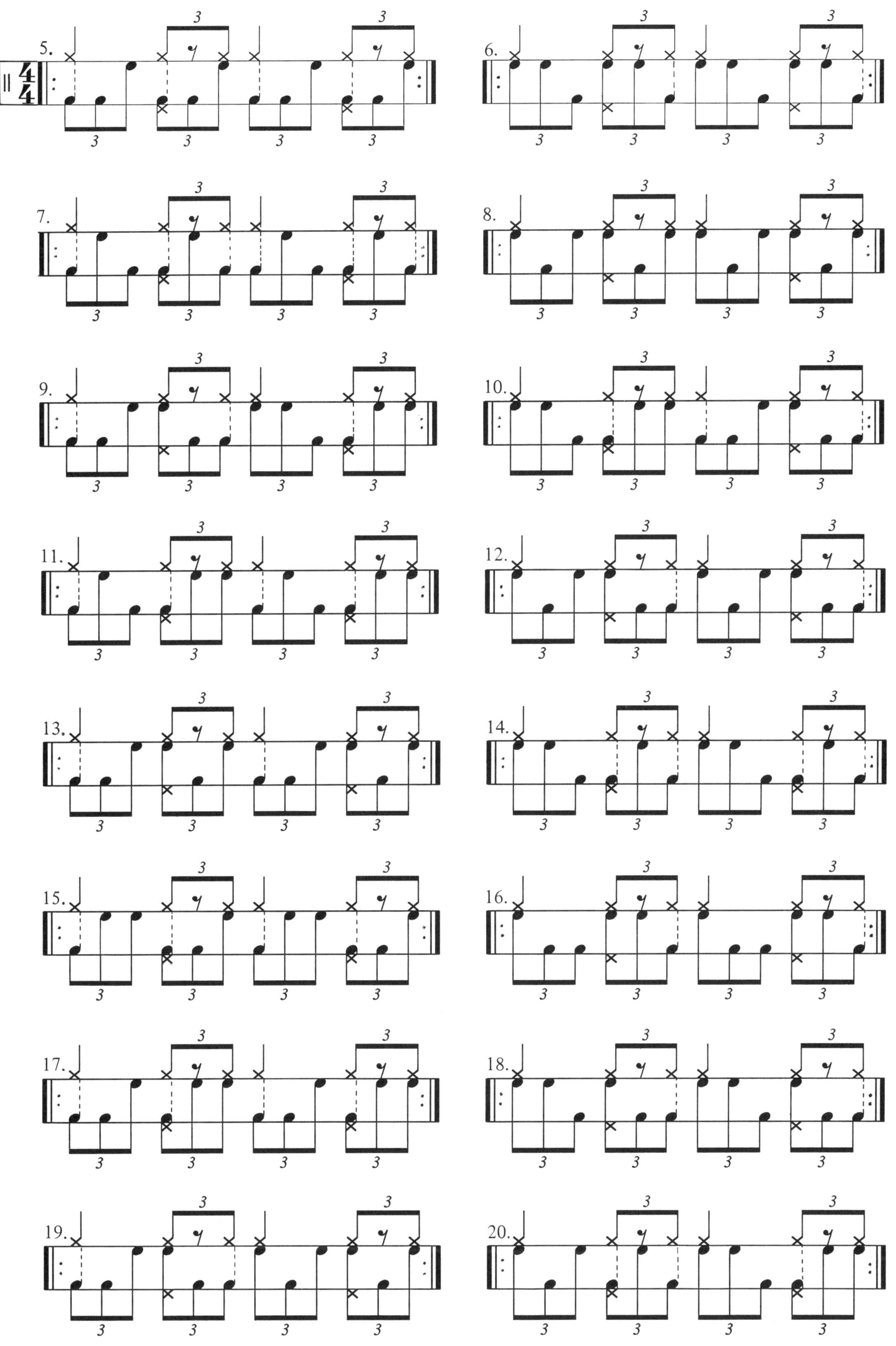
5.
6.
7.
8.
9.
10.
11.
12.
13.
14.
15.
16.
17.
18.
19.
20.

62 *Compound Meter Eighth Note Groove/Fill Patterns II*

These patterns involve movement between the hands and feet. Notice that the hands mirror one another in sections "A." and "B." Likewise, the hands mirror one another in sections "C." and "D." The feet part is written on a single line staff to allow several interpretations.

— Play the feet part on the bass drum and hi-hat in unison.

Example (#C2)

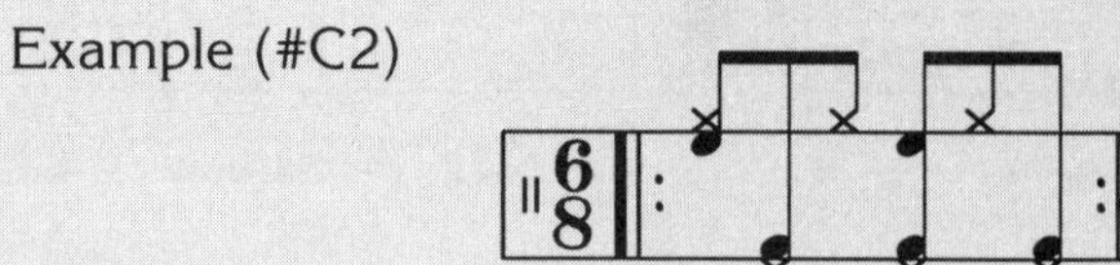

— Play the feet part on the bass drum and keep time with the hi-hat.

Example (#C2)

— Play the feet part on the hi-hat and keep time with the bass drum.

Example (#C2)

Practice Options

☐ Play each pattern in the context of time (see p. 6).
☐ Combine the first half of any pattern ("a.") with the second half of any other pattern ("b.").
☐ Combine patterns within and between sections "A." and "B." and within and between sections "C." and "D."

Variations

hands

☐ Play the snare drum notes on other surfaces.

hands and feet

☐ Play each pattern two times, interpreting the combination as three groups of four sixteenth notes in 3/4 time. Play the feet part on the bass drum and close the hi-hat on beats 2 and 3 or all three beats.

Example (#B4)

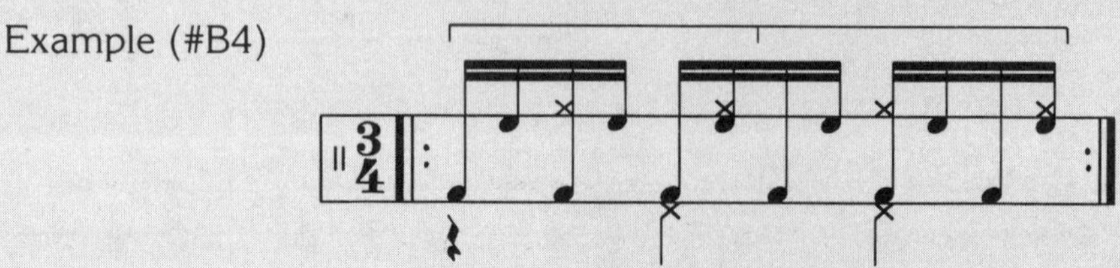

Also try combining two different patterns.

A.
a.
b.
1.
2.
3.
4.
5.
6.
7.
8.
B.
C.
D.
6
8

63 *Eighth Note Triplet Grooves III*

Within each lettered section, patterns #2, #3, and #4 are variations on pattern #1.

Practice Options

- ☐ Play the cymbal part on a cymbal bell.
- ☐ Play the cymbal part on a closed hi-hat (omit the left foot part).
- ☐ Repeatedly alternate pattern #1 with any other pattern within the same lettered section
- ☐ Combine any two patterns within the same lettered section.
- ☐ Substitute various appropriate hi-hat patterns (see p. 151).

Variations

hands

- ☐ Play some or all of the snare drum notes on other surfaces.
- ☐ Play some or all of the cymbal notes on other surfaces.

hands and feet

- ☐ Interpret each pattern as three groups of two eighth notes in $\frac{3}{4}$ time.

Example (#F2)

- ☐ Interpret each pattern as three groups of two eighth notes in $\frac{3}{4}$ time. Substitute any of the $\frac{3}{4}$ hi-hat patterns on p. 151.

Example (#F2)—with $\frac{3}{4}$ hi-hat pattern "A." from p. 151

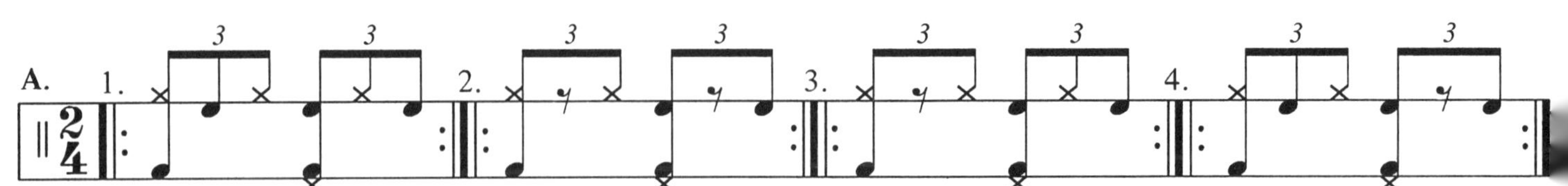

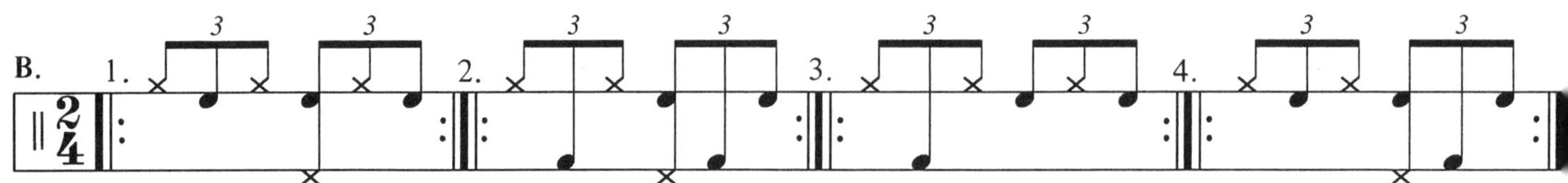

C.
1.
2.
3.
4.
D.
E.
F.
G.
H.

64 *Compound Meter Eighth Note Grooves IV*

These patterns combine the hands and feet to create a variety of grooves. Play the cymbal part on the hi-hat (closed unless otherwise indicated), and exaggerate the snare drum back-beat accents.

Practice Options

- ☐ Play the cymbal part on a cymbal bell (omit the written hi-hat parts in patterns #10–#18), and add various appropriate hi-hat patterns from page 151.
- ☐ Combine any two patterns.

Variations

hands

- ☐ Play some of the snare drum or cymbal notes on toms.

hands and feet

- ☐ Interpret each pattern as three groups of four sixteenth notes in $\frac{3}{4}$ time.

Example (#1)

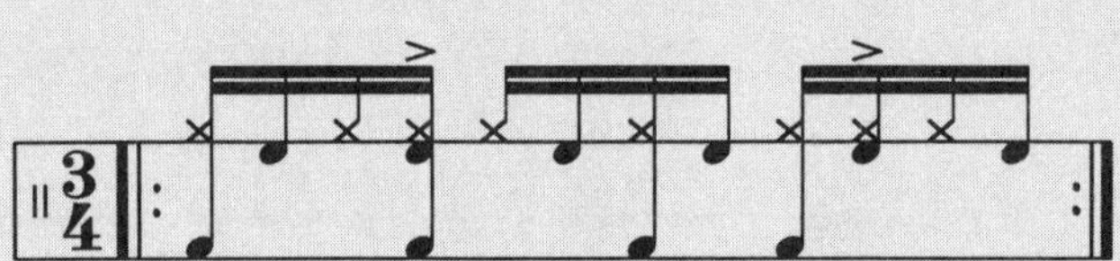

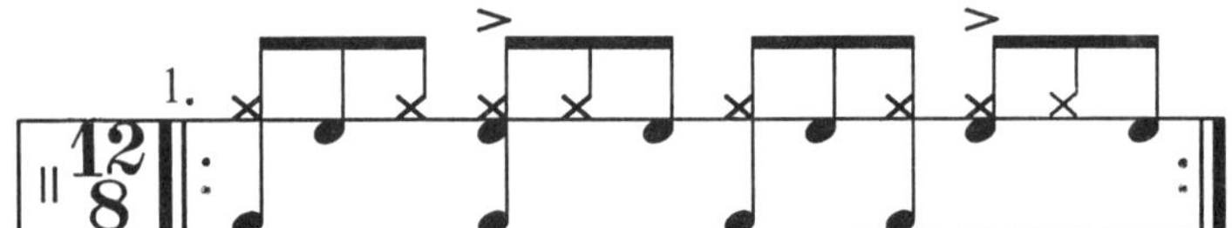

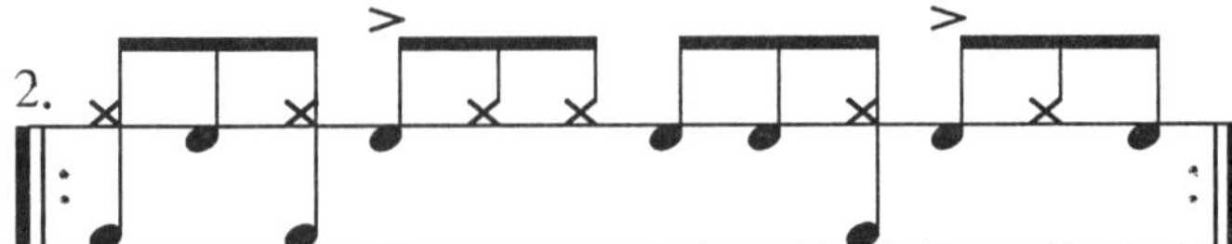

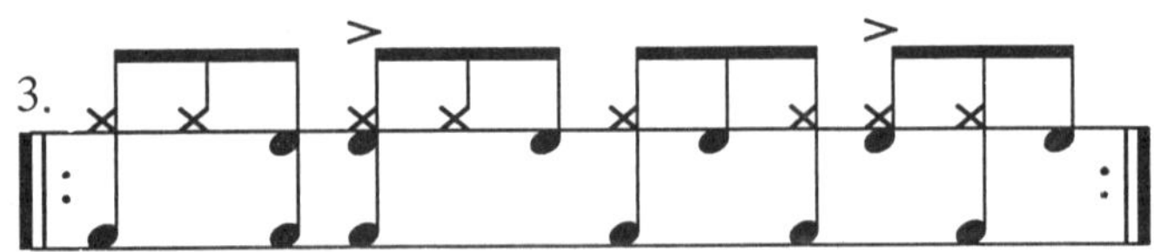

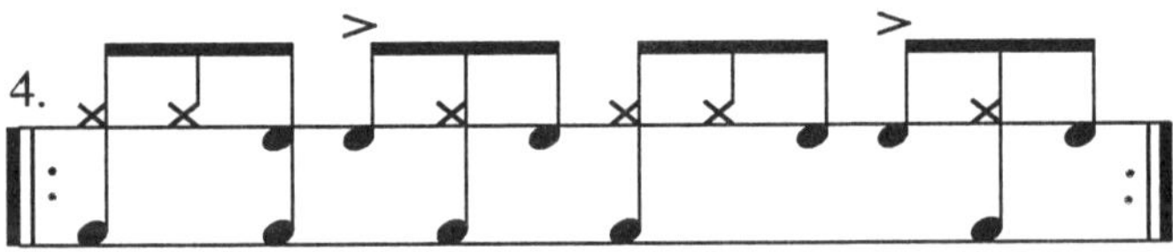

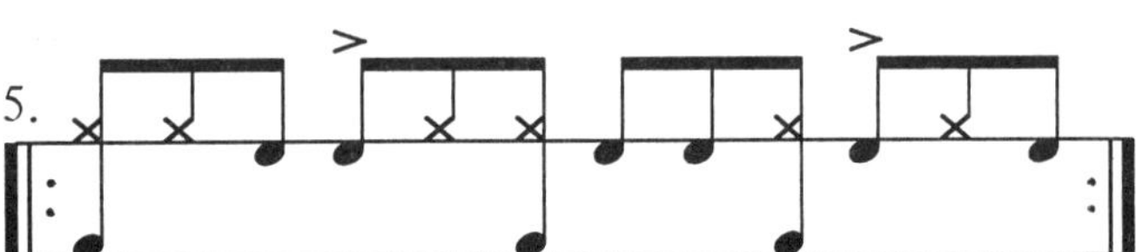

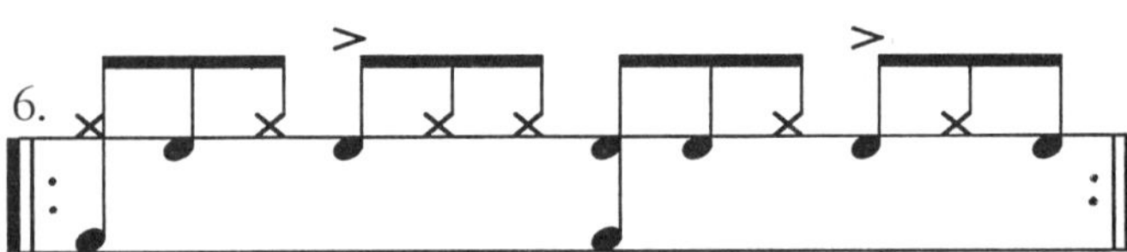

7.
12
8
8.
9.
10.
11.
12.
13.
14.
15.
16.
17.
18.

65 *Sixteenth Note Triplet Fill Patterns I*

These fills are based on various triplet sticking patterns.

Practice Options

- ☐ Play each fill in the context of time (see p. 6).
- ☐ Substitute various appropriate hi-hat and feet patterns (see pp. 150–151).

Variations

hands

- ☐ Following the indicated sticking, play each fill using various surface combinations:
  - — both right and left hand on snare drum.
  - — right hand on tom, left hand on snare.
  - — right hand moving from surface to surface, *ad lib.*; left hand stationary on snare.
  - — left hand moving from surface to surface, *ad lib.*; right hand stationary on snare.
  - — both hands moving from surface to surface, *ad lib.*

hands and feet

- ☐ Double the cymbal part with the bass drum.

Example (#15)

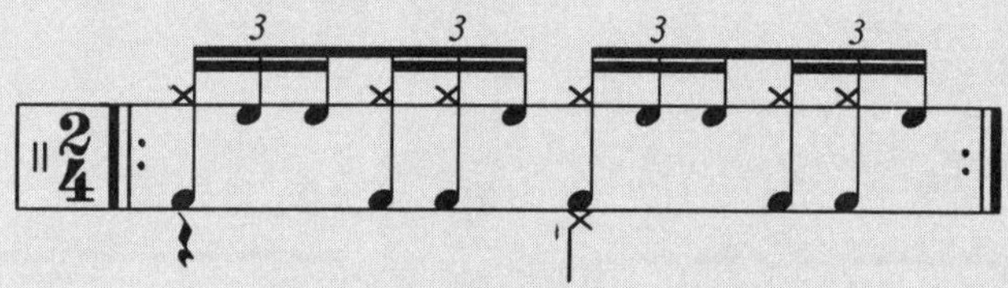

- ☐ Play the cymbal part on the snare drum and the snare drum part on the hi-hat loosely closed. Double the cymbal with the bass drum.

Example (#15)

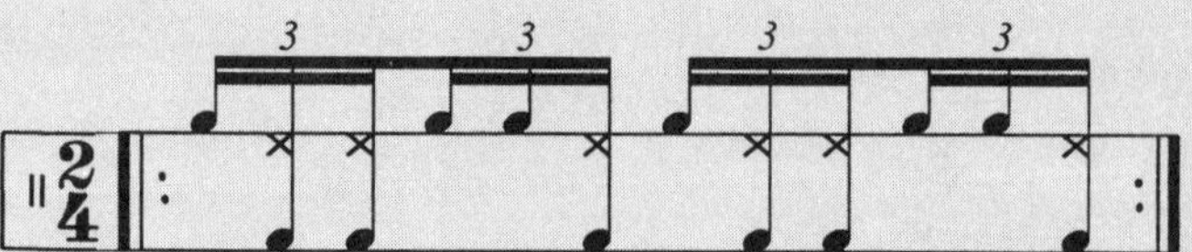

- ☐ Interpret each pattern as three groups of four sixteenth notes in 3/4 time. Use an appropriate 3/4 feet pattern (see p. 151).

Example (#18)

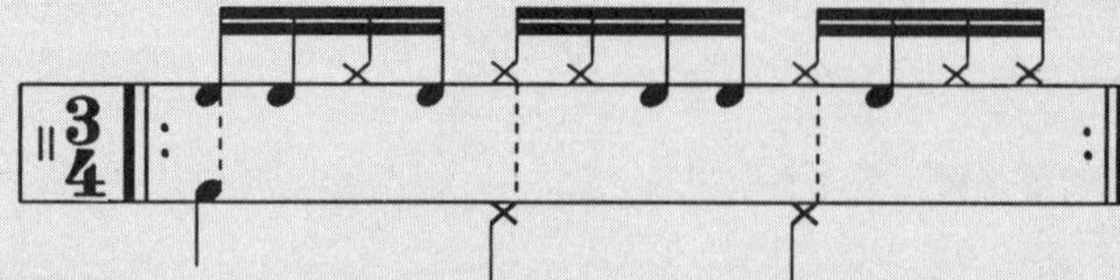

- ☐ Interpret each pattern in 4/4 time. Play each pattern as three groups of four sixteenth notes, followed by four alternating sixteenth notes to complete the measure. Use an appropriate 4/4 feet pattern (see p. 150).

Example (#12)

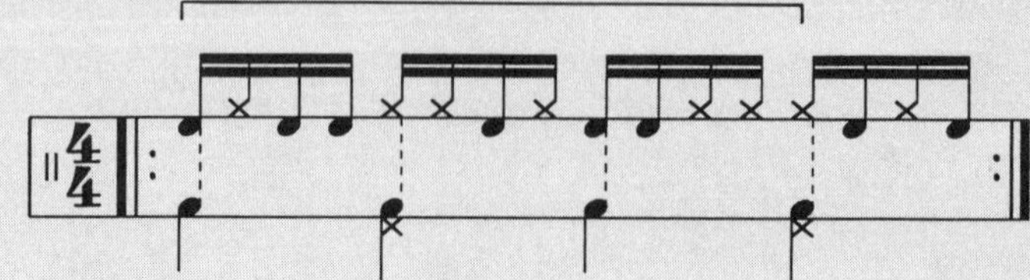

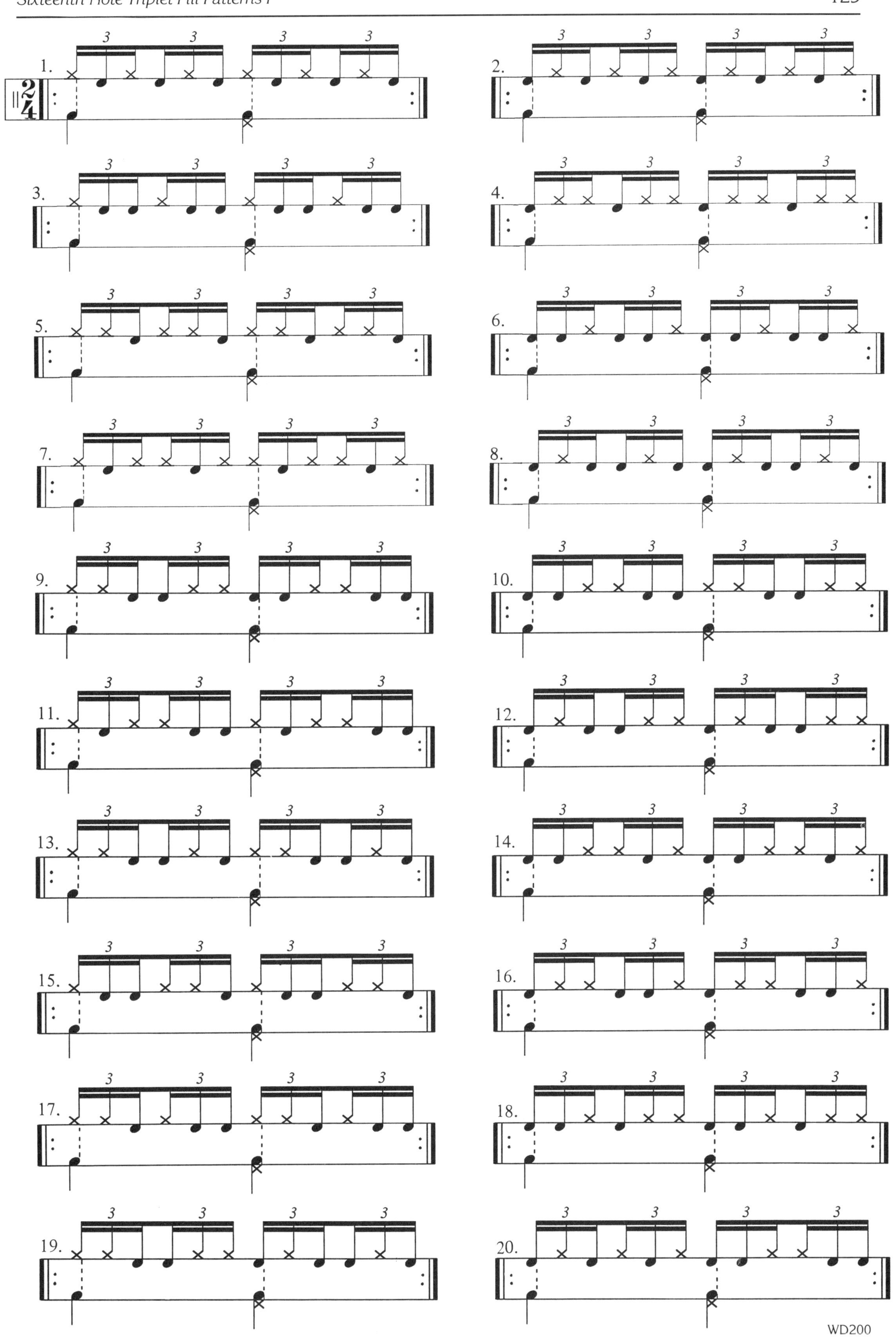
1.
2.
3.
4.
5.
6.
7.
8.
9.
10.
11.
12.
13.
14.
15.
16.
17.
18.
19.
20.

66 *Sixteenth Note Triplet Grooves*

These grooves combine linear cymbal/bass drum parts with a constant snare drum/ hi-hat back-beat. To add extra rhythmic momentum, strongly accent the snare drum back-beat.

Practice Options

- ☐ Play the cymbal part on a closed hi-hat (omit the left foot part).
- ☐ Combine the first half of any pattern ("a.") with the second half of any other pattern ("b.").

Variations

hands

- ☐ Substitute either of the following cymbal patterns for the written cymbal part.

A.

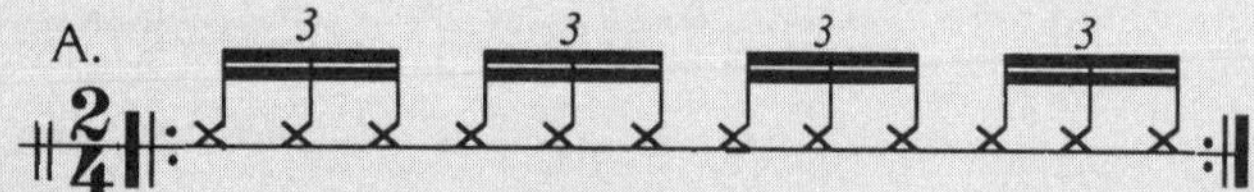

B.

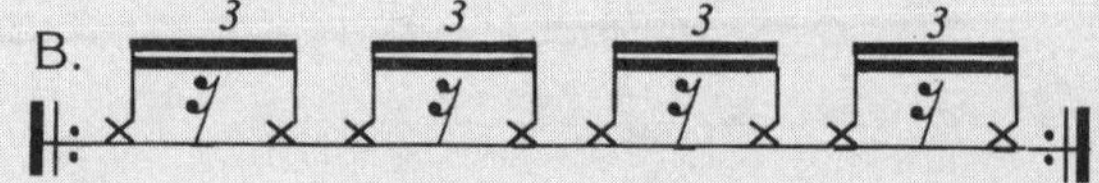

feet

- ☐ Substitute any of the following hi-hat patterns (left foot).

A.

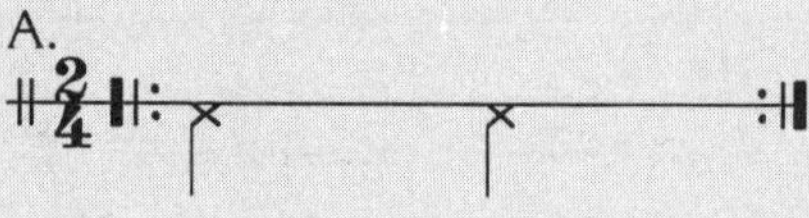

B.

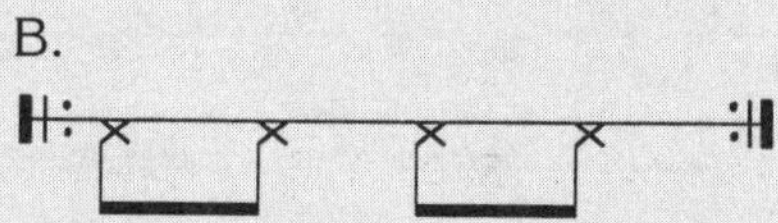

C.

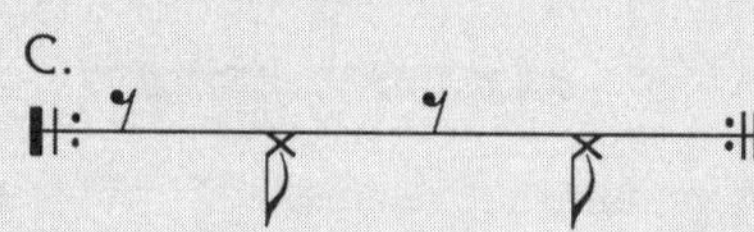

D.

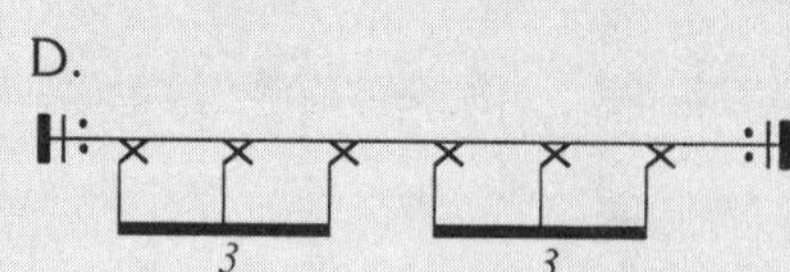

- ☐ Play the bass drum part on the hi-hat with the left foot. Keep time with the bass drum.

Example (#2)

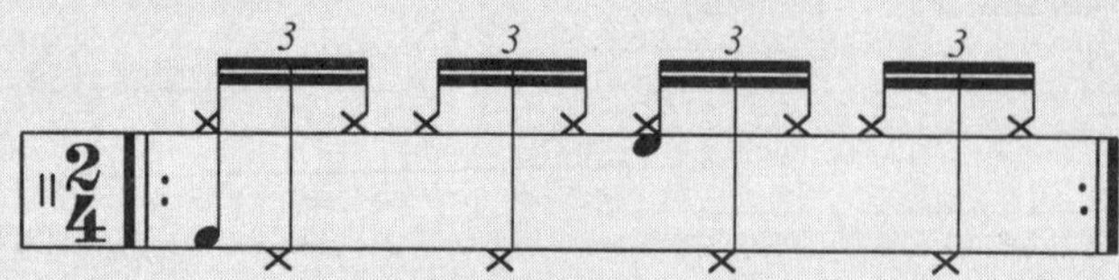

- ☐ When using double bass drums, omit the hi-hat part and alternate the feet on consecutive sixteenth notes in the bass drum part. Play individual sixteenth notes with either foot.

Examples (#5)

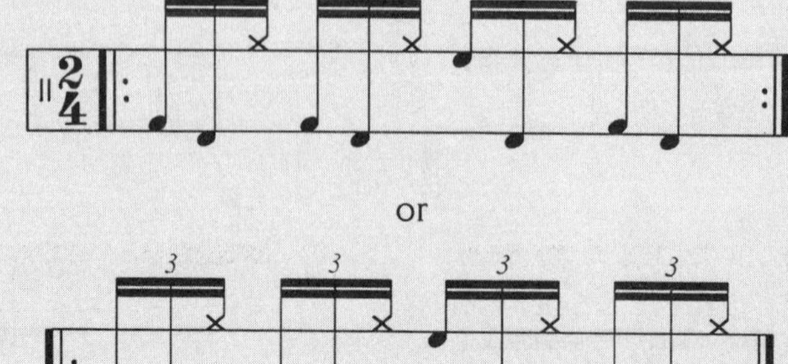

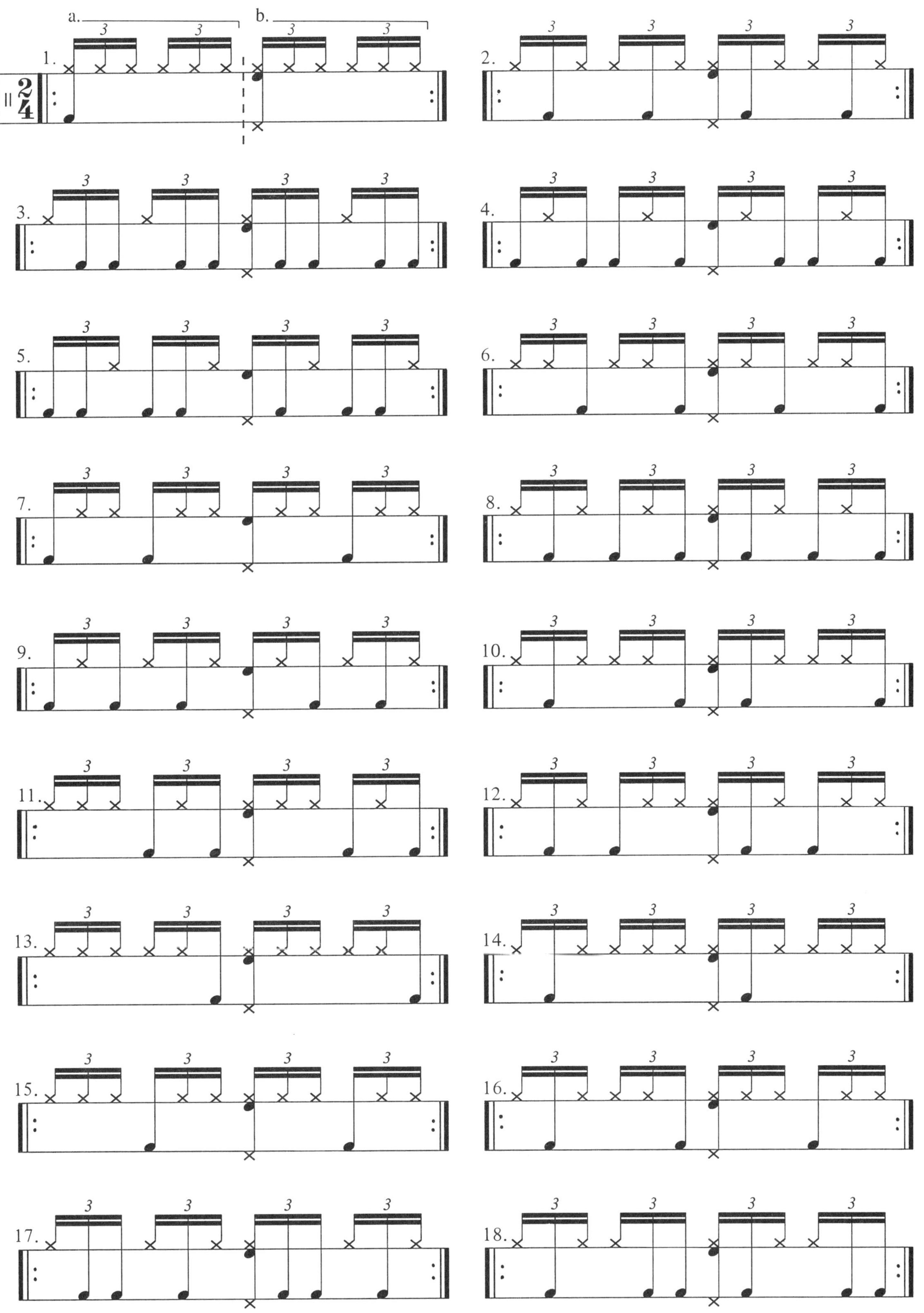
a.
b.
1.
2.
3.
4.
5.
6.
7.
8.
9.
10.
11.
12.
13.
14.
15.
16.
17.
18.

67 *Sixteenth Note Triplet Fill Patterns II*

In these patterns, a constant ride floats above linear snare drum/bass drum parts.

Practice Options

- ☐ Play each fill in the context of time (see p. 6). Use the same ride and hi-hat pattern for both the time and the fill itself.
- ☐ Play the ride part on a cymbal bell.
- ☐ Combine the first half of any pattern ("a.") with the second half of any other pattern ("b.").
- ☐ Combine any two patterns.
- ☐ Substitute various appropriate hi-hat patterns (see p. 151).

Variations

hands

- ☐ Play some of the snare drum notes on other surfaces.
- ☐ Substitute a sixteenth note triplet shuffle ride, played either on a closed hi-hat (omit the left foot part) or cymbal.

Example (#1)

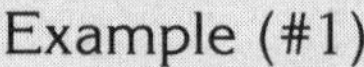

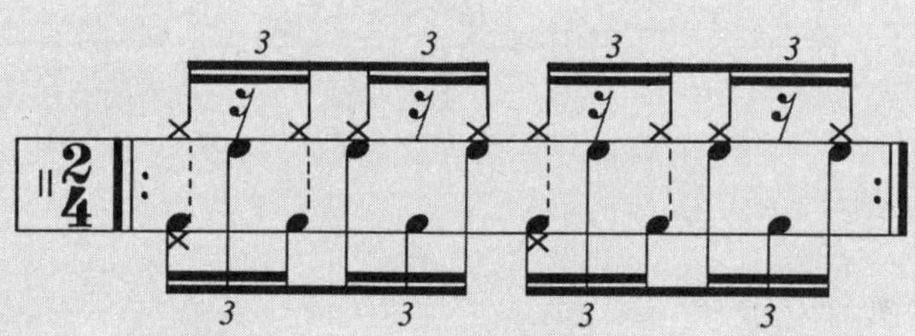

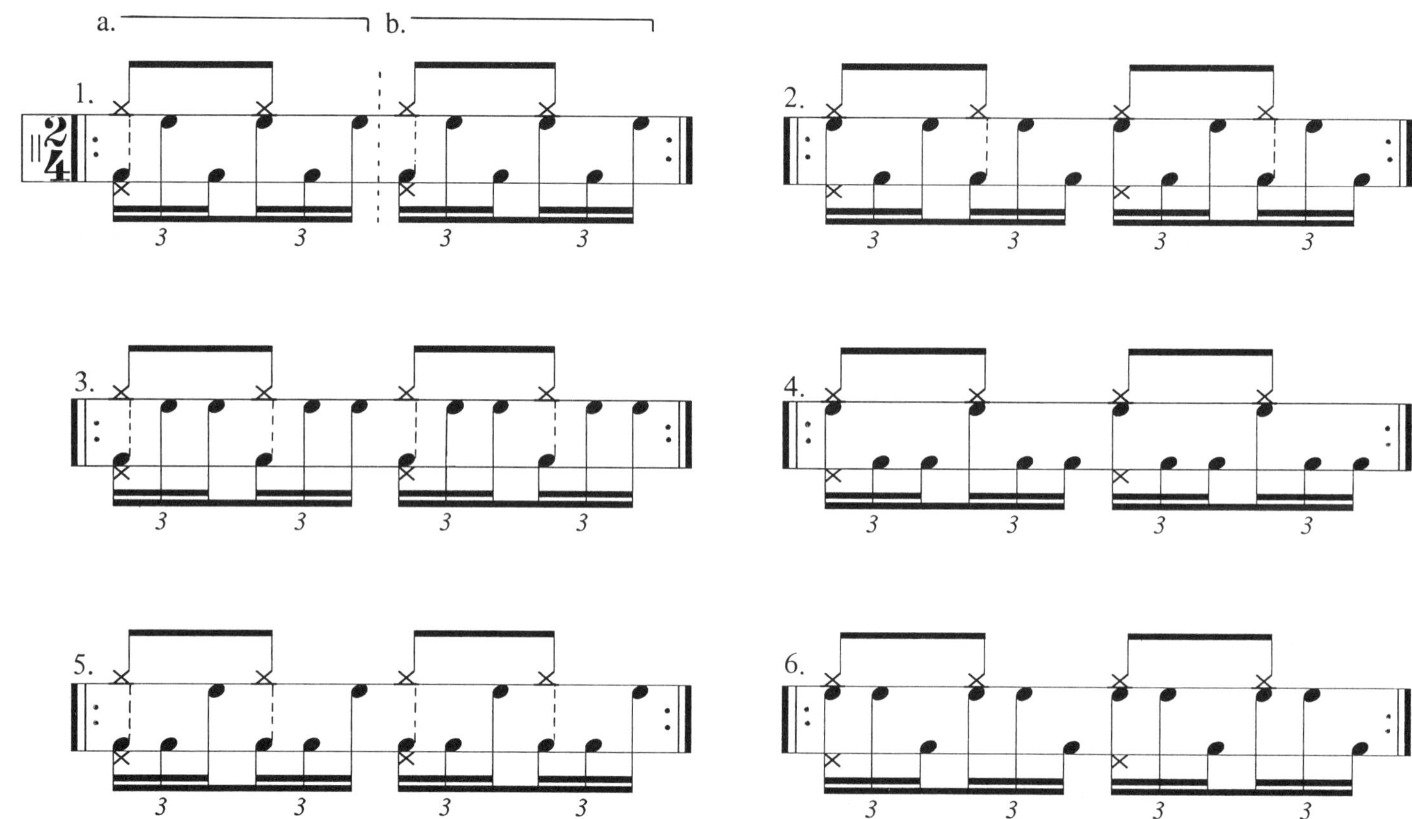

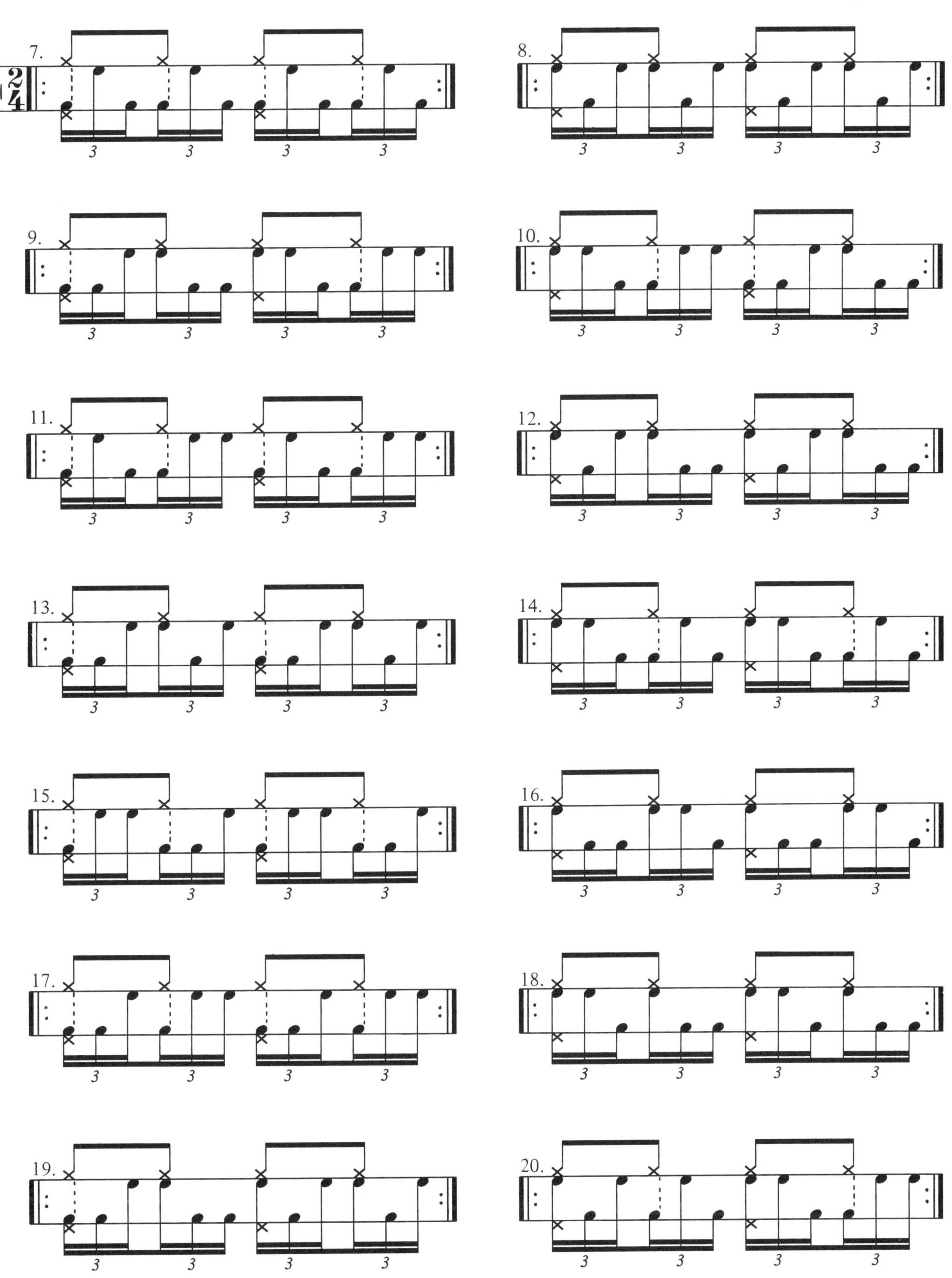
7.
8.
9.
10.
11.
12.
13.
14.
15.
16.
17.
18.
19.
20.

68 *Double Stroke Grooves*

These double stroke grooves use accents to create various feels.

Practice Options

- ☐ Play cymbal accents on the bell, and snare accents as rim shots.
- ☐ Combine any two patterns.
- ☐ Swing the eighth notes (♫ = ♩♪)
- ☐ Substitute various appropriate hi-hat and feet patterns (see pp. 150–151).

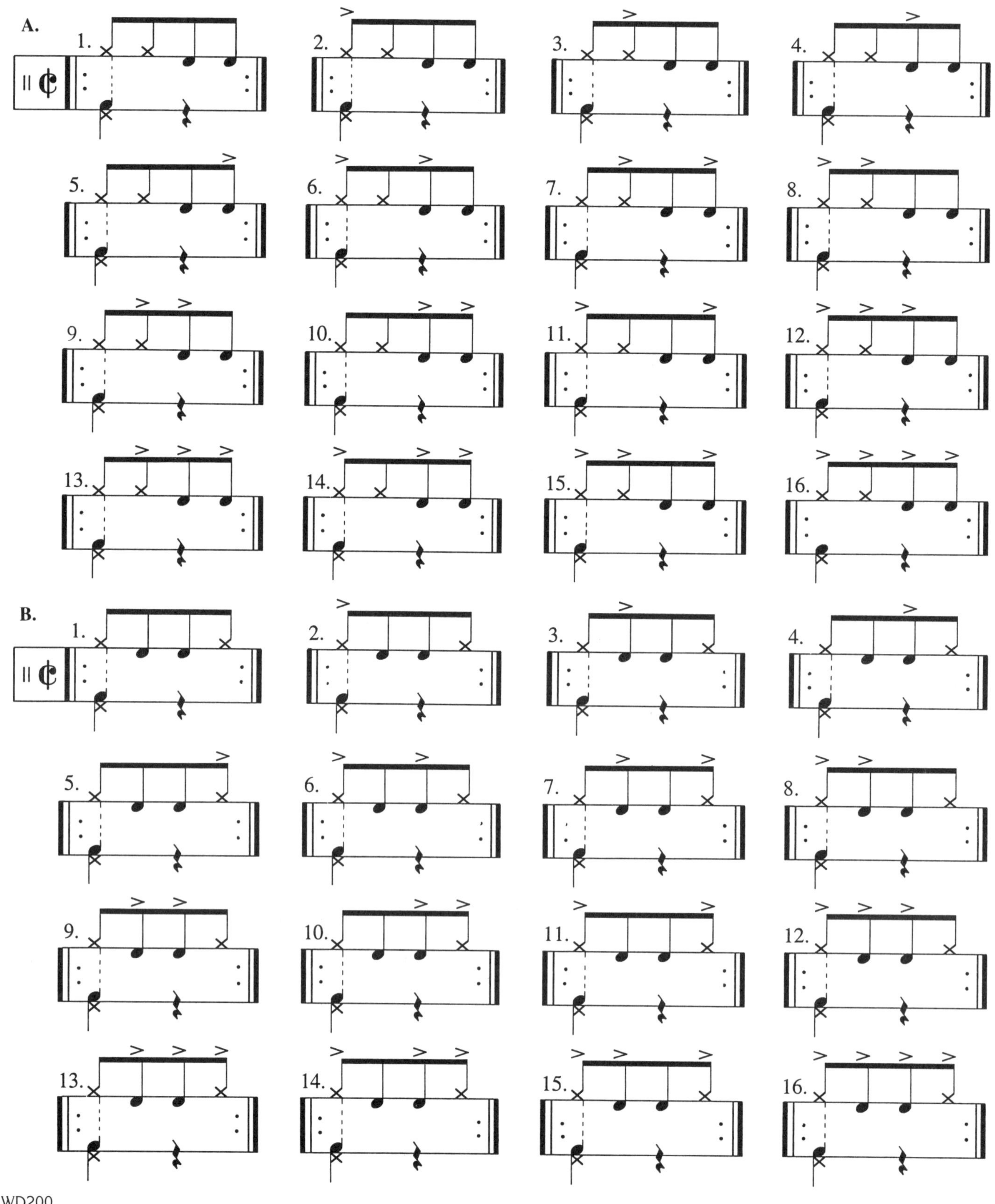

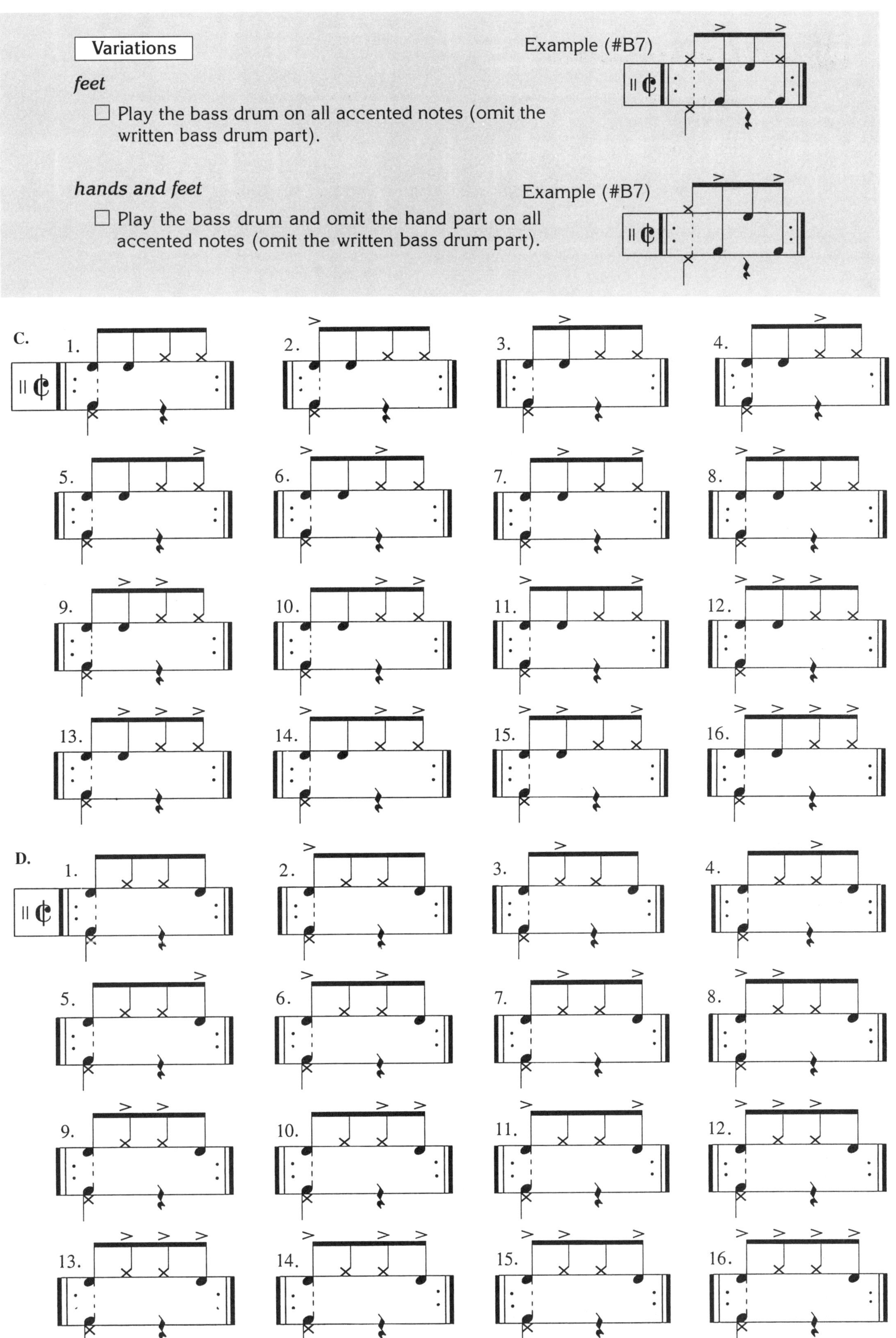
Variations
feet
☐ Play the bass drum on all accented notes (omit the written bass drum part).
Example (#B7)
hands and feet
☐ Play the bass drum and omit the hand part on all accented notes (omit the written bass drum part).
Example (#B7)
C.
1.
2.
3.
4.
5.
6.
7.
8.
9.
10.
11.
12.
13.
14.
15.
16.
D.
1.
2.
3.
4.
5.
6.
7.
8.
9.
10.
11.
12.
13.
14.
15.
16.

69 *Half Time Grooves*

These grooves create a half-time feel.

Practice Options

- ☐ Play the ride part on a closed hi-hat (omit the left foot part).
- ☐ Combine any two patterns.
- ☐ Combine the first half of any section "A." pattern ("a.") with the second half of any section "B." pattern ("b.").
- ☐ Repeatedly alternate any pattern with the following "four-feel" groove:

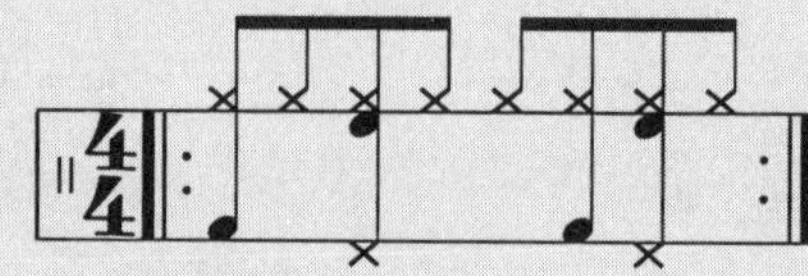

- ☐ Swing the eighth notes (♫ = ♩♪ triplet).
- ☐ Substitute various appropriate hi-hat and feet patterns (see pp. 150–151).

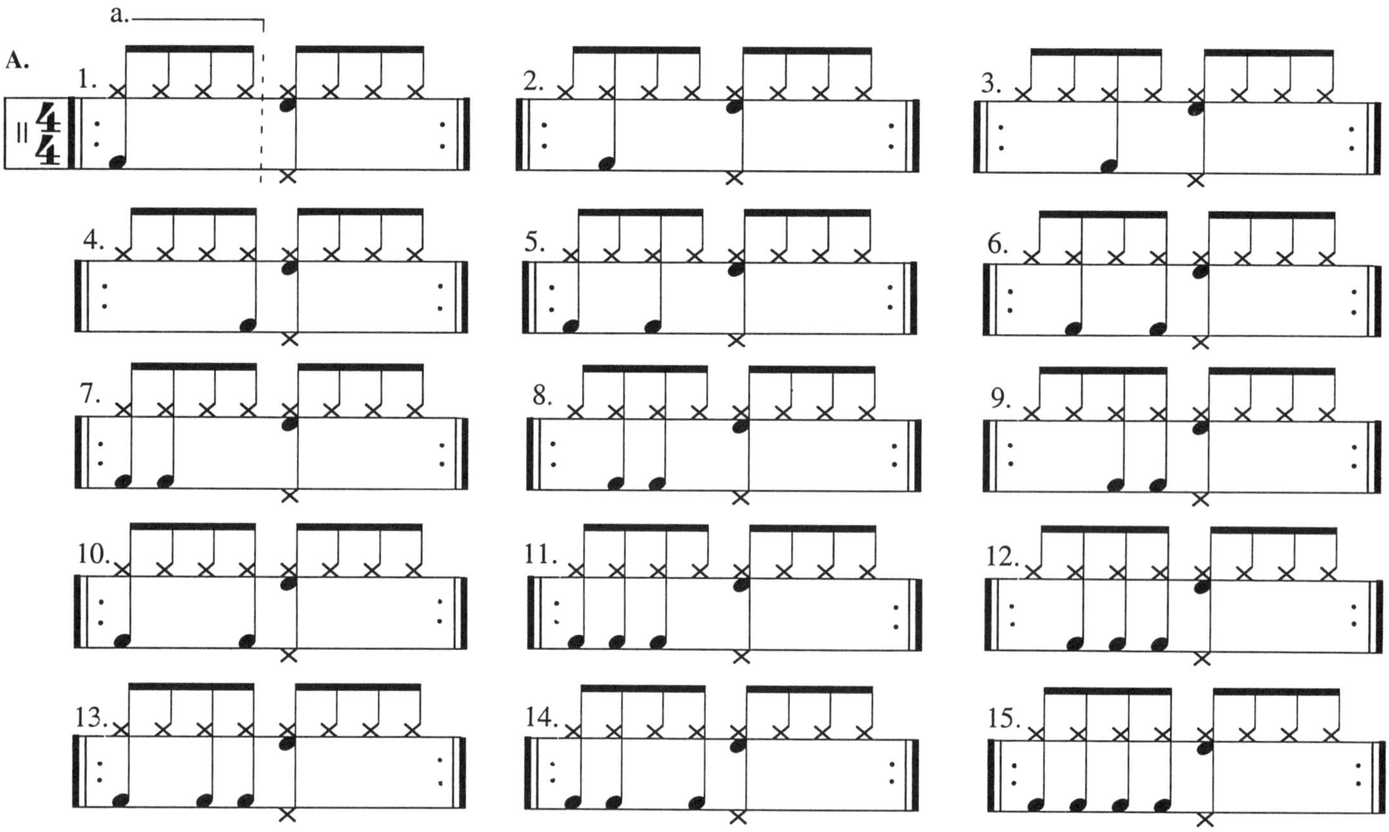

A. a.

1. 2. 3. 4. 5. 6. 7. 8. 9. 10. 11. 12. 13. 14. 15.

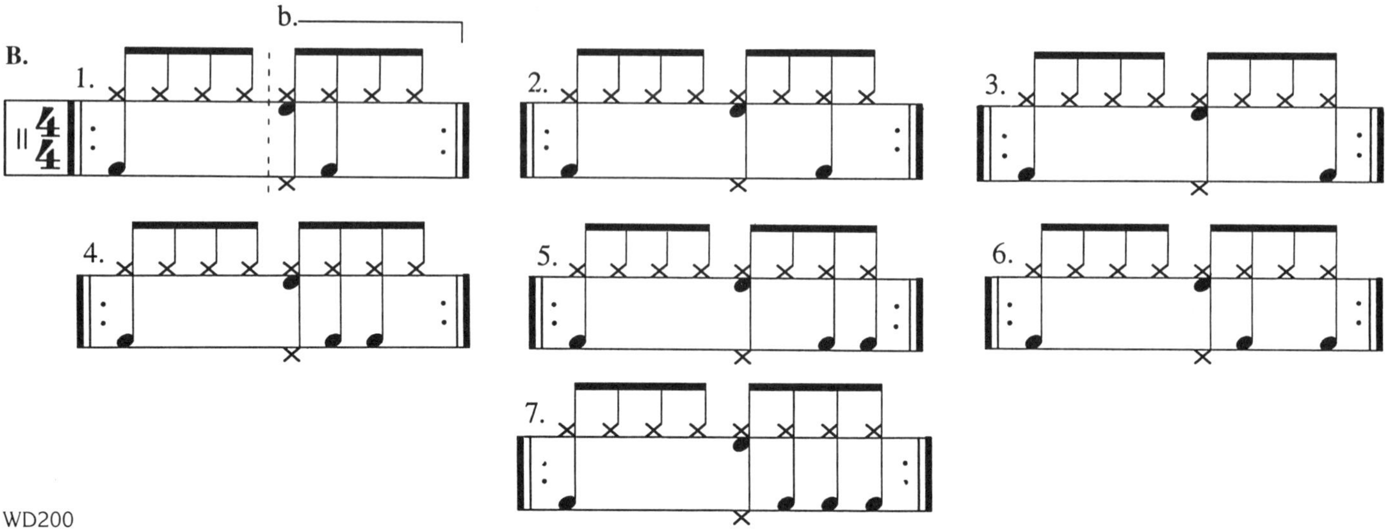

B. b.

1. 2. 3. 4. 5. 6. 7.

70 *More Moves and Grooves*

Below are several of the author's favorite grooves and fills in various styles. Try applying the same kinds of variations to these as you have to other patterns throughout this book.

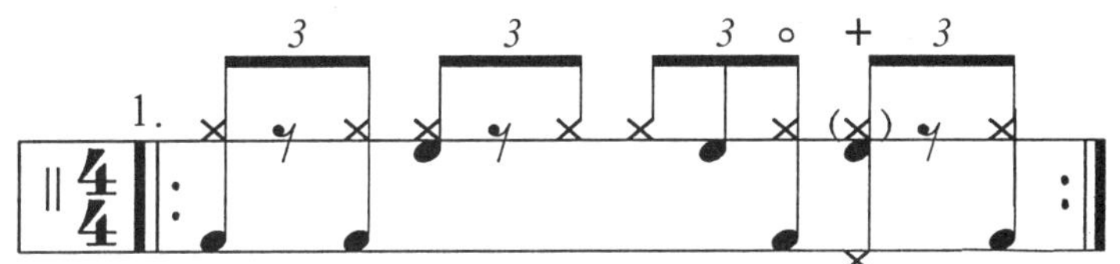

2.

3.

4.

5.

6.

7.

8.

9.

10.

11.

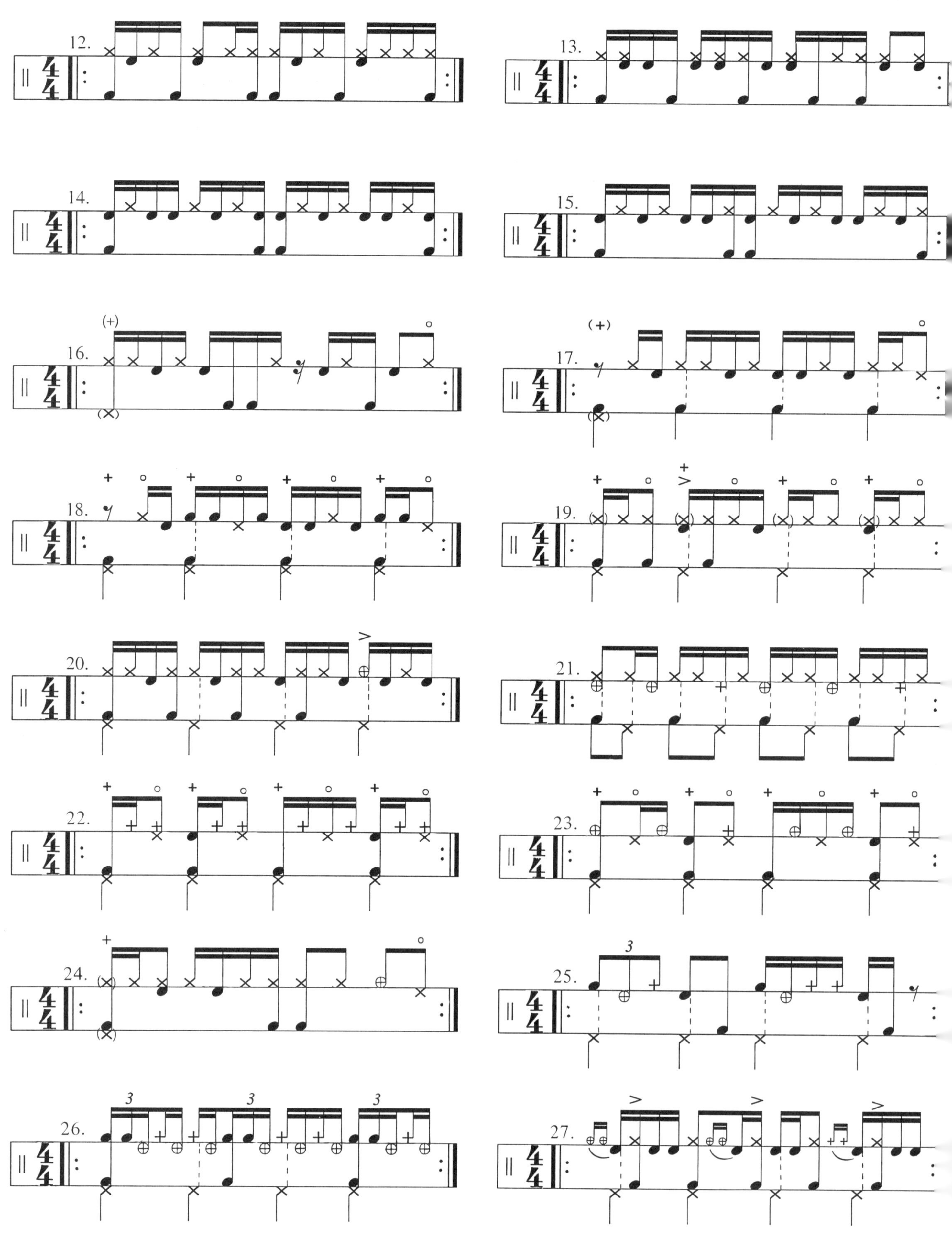
12.
13.
14.
15.
16.
17.
18.
19.
20.
21.
22.
23.
24.
25.
26.
27.

APPENDICES I - II

LEAD SHEETS

As a drummer reading charts or in a strictly improvisatory situation, you are faced with the task of applying specific rhythmic patterns to your time playing or fill playing. For example, in a jazz ensemble setting, your charts may include the words "jazz time" along with small rhythms printed atop the staves, and nothing more. In a small group setting, you may have no written part at all, but there will be certain rhythmic elements you hear in the tune that you will want to reflect in your playing. How does a drummer handle such situations?

The lead sheets found in Appendices I and II provide many common rhythmic figures you may encounter. **Practice Options** and **Variations** suggest ways to apply these figures in the context of grooves and fills just as you might in the above scenarios. When interpreting the figures as fills, play each fill in the context of time (see p. 6).

APPENDIX I: *Eighth Note Lead Sheet*

This lead sheet (found on p. 139) contains one measure eighth note based rhythmic figures. Internalize each rhythm to the point that you can look at the entire measure as a whole and immediately think or play the rhythm (in the same way you can look at a word made up of several letters and say or think it immediately).

Practice Options

- ☐ Play each figure repeatedly on the snare drum using right hand lead, left hand lead, and alternate sticking. Once you master the hands alone, add any appropriate feet pattern (see pp. 150–151).
- ☐ Play each figure on the bass drum both as written and as an accent pattern in one measure of eighth notes.

Example (#B13) as accent pattern in one measure of eighth notes

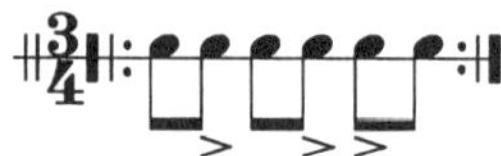

- ☐ Play each figure on the snare drum as a fill (in the context of time). Add any appropriate feet pattern (see pp. 150–151).
- ☐ Swing the eighth notes (♫ = ♩♪ triplet).
- ☐ Combine any two figures or parts of figures to create new figures in various meters.

Variations

groove context

- ☐ Play one of the following ride patterns with one hand (or any other appropriate ride pattern):

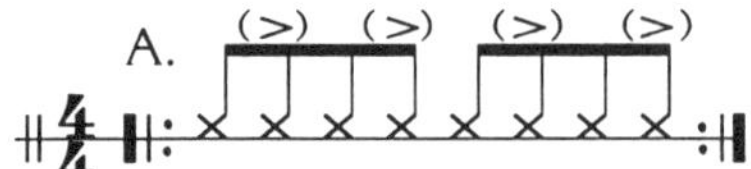

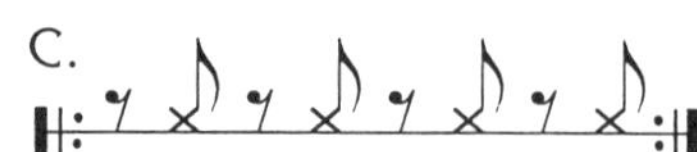

(Use only the first three beats when playing in $\frac{3}{4}$.)

Add:

— each figure, played by the other hand on the snare drum. Use any appropriate feet pattern (see pp. 150–151).

Example (#A24) - hands shown only

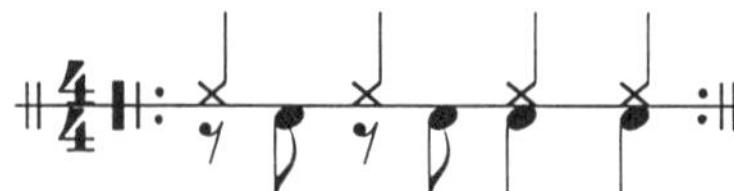

— each figure, played on the bass drum. Play back-beats on the snare drum. Close the hi-hat on all four beats or beats 2 and 3 in $\frac{3}{4}$ time.

Example (#A24)

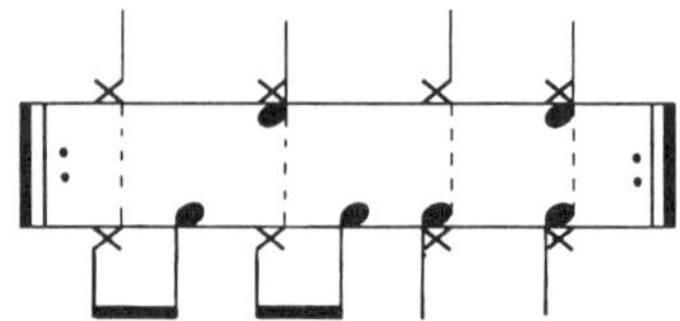

☐ Play one of the following jazz ride patterns with one hand:

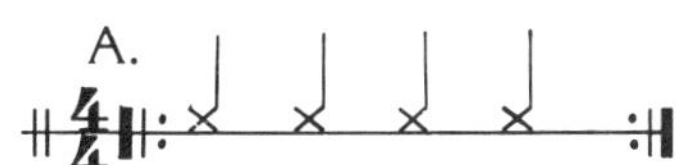

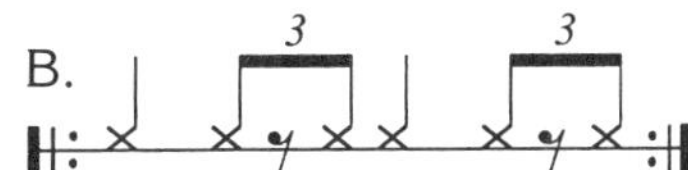

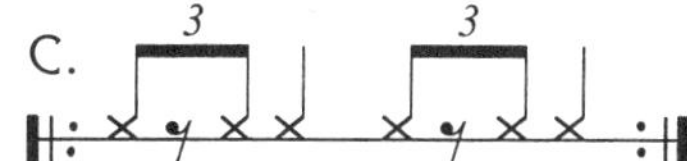

(Use only the first three beats when playing in $\frac{3}{4}$.)

Add:

— each figure, played by the other hand on the snare drum. Swing the eighth notes and close the hi-hat on the back-beats or beats 2 and 3 in $\frac{3}{4}$ time. (The right foot should rest.)

Example (#A12)
- hands shown only

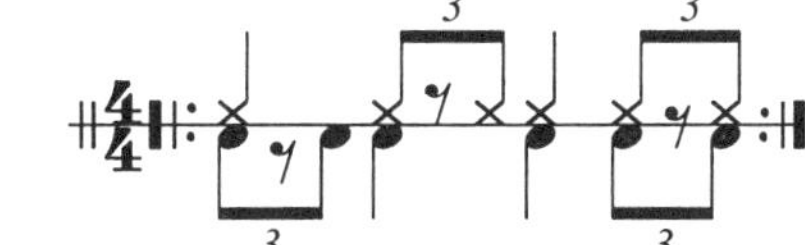

— each figure, played on the bass drum. Swing the eighth notes and close the hi-hat on the back-beats or beats 2 and 3 in $\frac{3}{4}$ time. (The left hand should rest.)

Example (#A12)

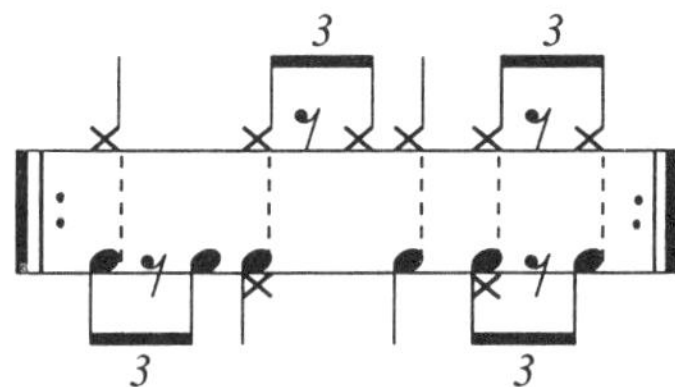

— each figure, played by alternating strokes between the snare drum and bass drum (beginning with either limb). Swing the eighth notes and close the hi-hat on the back-beats or beats 2 and 3 in $\frac{3}{4}$ time.

Example (#A12)

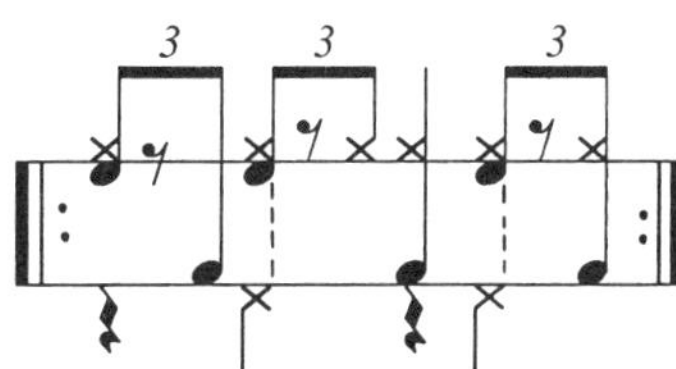

☐ Using either straight or swung eighth notes, play each figure as a ride on a cymbal. Add the snare drum on the back-beats in $\frac{4}{4}$ time, or on beats 2 and 3 or only beat 2 in $\frac{3}{4}$ time. Use any appropriate feet pattern (see pp. 150–151).

Examples (#B13) - hands shown only

straight

swing

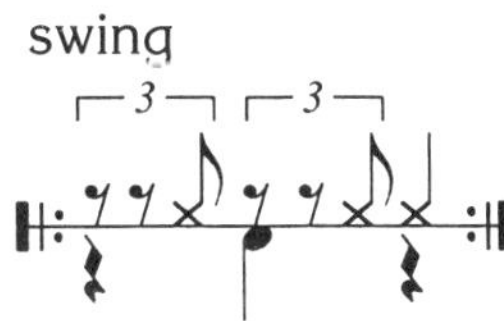

☐ Play the closed hi-hat/snare drum pattern shown in the examples and play each figure on the bass drum.

Examples (#A28)

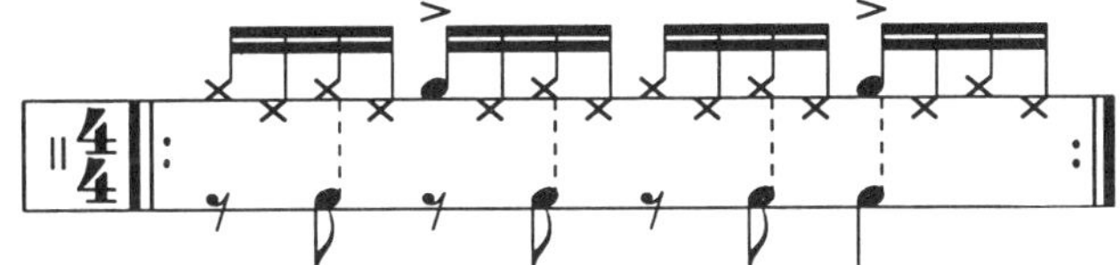

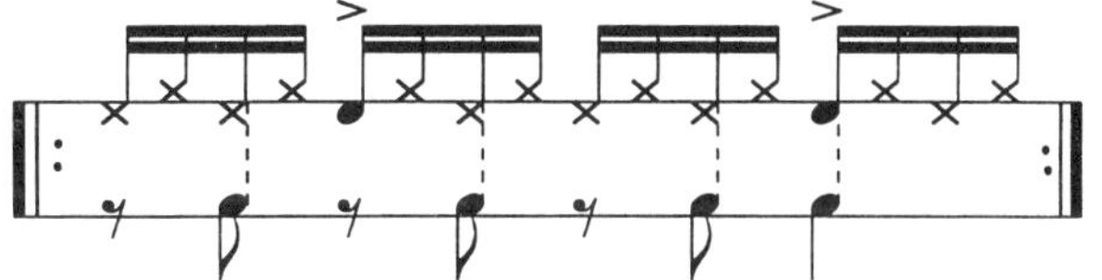

(In $\frac{3}{4}$ time, omit beat 3 of the given closed hi-hat/snare drum pattern.)

fill context

☐ Using either straight or swung eighth notes, play each figure as a fill. Incorporate various surfaces including the bass drum and hi-hat.

☐ Play each figure as a fill on the snare drum, allowing the figure to serve only as an accent pattern in one measure of eighth or sixteenth notes. Begin with either hand. Add any appropriate feet pattern (see pp. 150–151).

Examples (#A22) - hands shown only

Following a similar approach, play the accented notes on various non-snare surfaces. Add any appropriate feet pattern (see pp. 150–151).

Examples (#A22) - hands shown only

Following a similar approach, play the accented notes on a closed hi-hat doubled by the bass drum.

Examples (#A22)

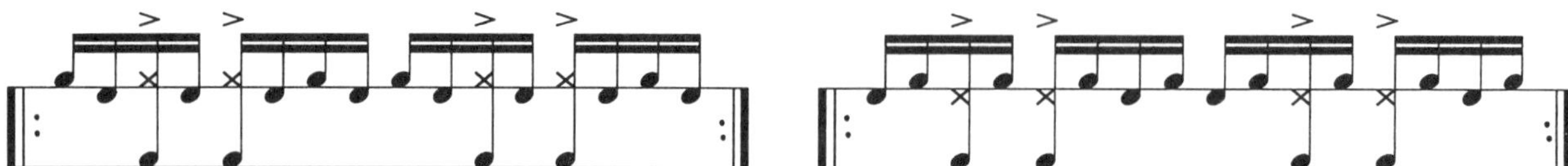

Following a similar approach, play the accented notes on the bass drum only, deleting the hand when the bass drum plays. Close the hi-hat on the back-beats or all four beats in $\frac{4}{4}$ time, or on beats 2 and 3 in $\frac{3}{4}$ time.

Examples (#A22)

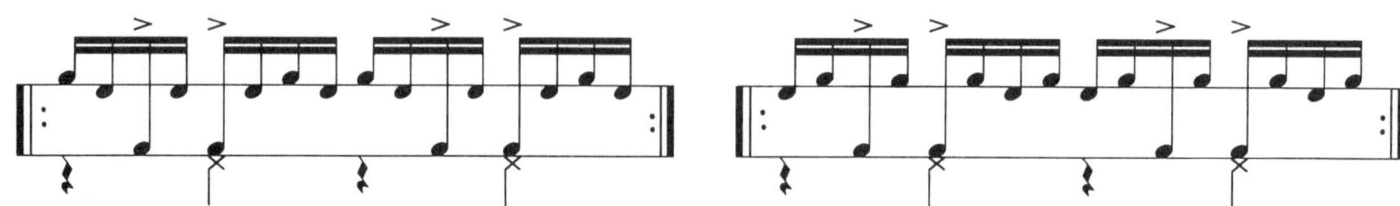

A.
1.
2.
3.
4.
5.
6.
7.
8.
9.
10.
11.
12.
13.
14.
15.
16.
17.
18.
19.
20.
21.
22.
23.
24.
25.
26.
27.
28.
29.
30.
31.
B.
1.
2.
3.
4.
5.
6.
7.
8.
9.
10.
11.
12.
13.
14.
15.

APPENDIX II: *Sixteenth Note Lead Sheet*

This lead sheet (found on p. 143) contains one measure sixteenth note based rhythmic figures. Internalize each rhythm to the point that you can look at the entire measure as a whole and immediately think or play the rhythm.

Practice Options

☐ Play each figure repeatedly on the snare drum using right hand lead, left hand lead, and alternate sticking. Once you master the hands alone, add any appropriate feet pattern (see pp. 150–151).

Examples (#A18)

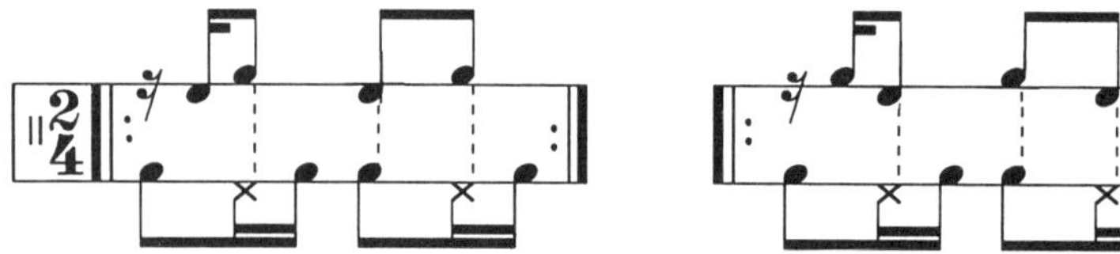

☐ Play each figure on the bass drum. Once you master the bass drum alone, add any appropriate hi-hat pattern (see p. 151).
☐ Play each figure on the snare drum as a fill (in the context of time). Add any appropriate feet pattern (see pp. 150–151).
☐ Play each figure on various surfaces as a fill (in the context of time). Add any appropriate feet pattern (see pp. 150–151).
☐ Combine any two figures or parts of figures to create new figures in various meters.

Variations

groove context

☐ Play either of the closed hi-hat/snare drum patterns shown in the examples, and play each figure on the bass drum.

Examples (#A20)

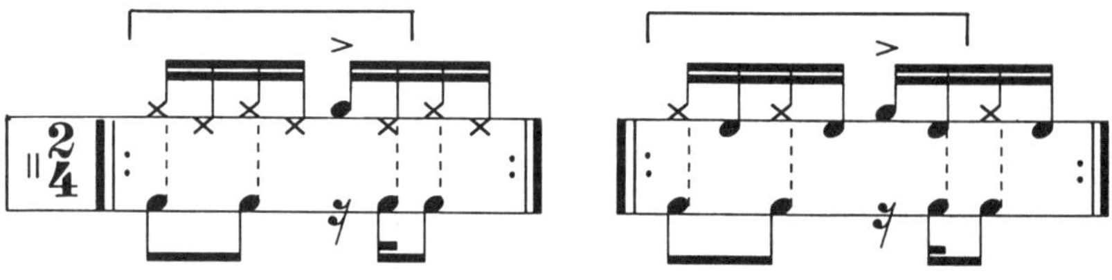

When using the section "B." $\frac{3}{8}$ figures, omit the last two sixteenth notes of the given closed hi-hat/snare patterns (see brackets above).

☐ Play the ride, snare drum, and bass drum parts shown in the examples. Open and close the hi-hat using the figures as a guide (play the ride part on the hi-hat).

Example (#A5) Example (#A29)

Example (#B10)

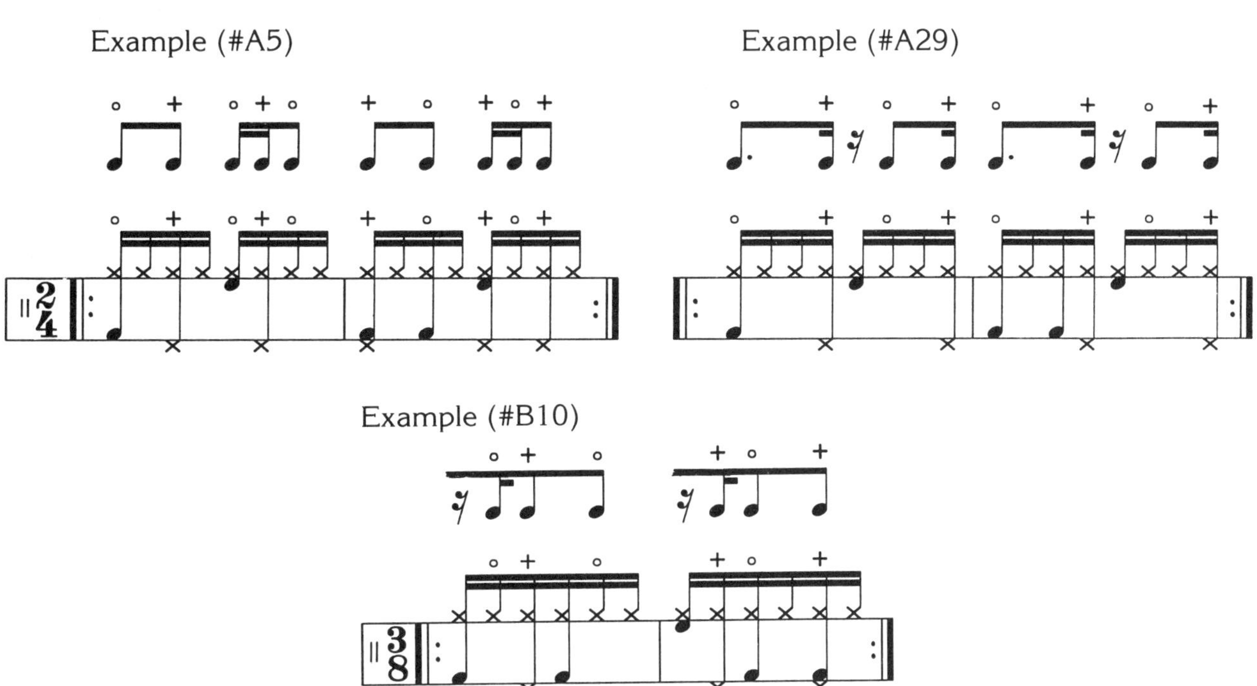

Also try opening the hi-hat on <u>every</u> note of the figures, closing the hi-hat on subsequent subdivisions.

Example (#A5)

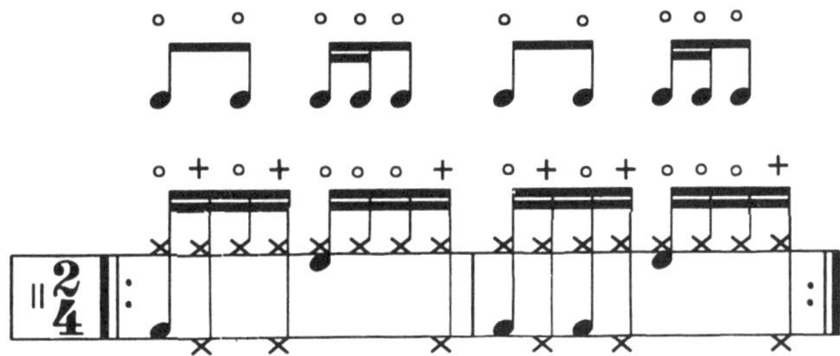

fill context

☐ Play each figure as a fill. Use various surfaces including the bass drum and hi-hat.

☐ Play each figure as a fill on the snare drum, allowing the figure to serve only as an accent pattern in one measure of sixteenth notes. Begin with either hand. Add any appropriate feet pattern (see pp. 150–151). For additional color, add multiple bounce strokes as shown in parentheses in the examples.

Examples (#A24)

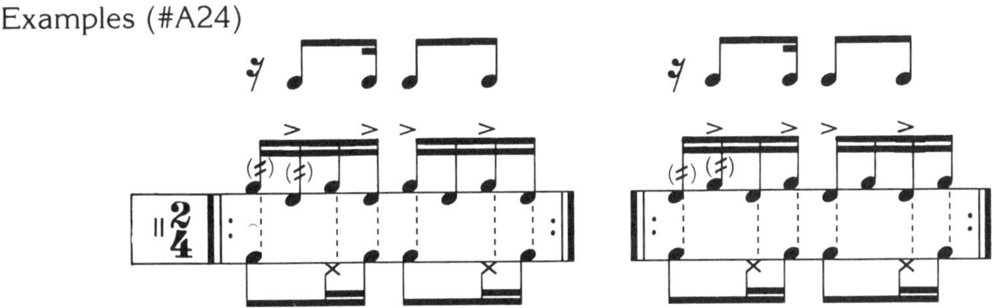

Also try adding multiple bounce strokes on the accented notes only, <u>or</u> on the <u>non</u>-accented notes only.

Following a similar approach as described on the bottom of p. 141, allow the figure to serve as an accent pattern in the closed hi-hat/snare drum sixteenth note pattern shown in the examples. Add any appropriate bass drum pattern (see pp. 150–151). Note: The notes may also be played by the right and left hands on cymbals on the right and left sides of the drum kit.

Examples (#A24)

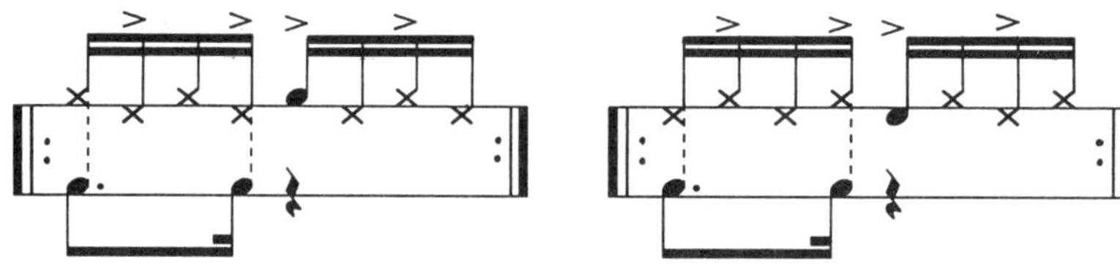

Following a similar approach, play the accented notes on the snare drum and the unaccented notes on the closed hi-hat. Add any appropriate bass drum pattern (see pp. 150–151).

Examples (#A24)

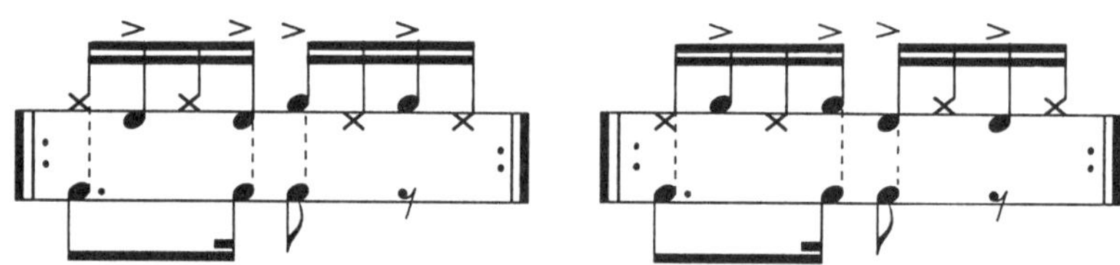

Following a similar approach, play the accented notes on various non-snare surfaces and the non-accented notes on the snare drum. Add any appropriate feet pattern (see pp. 150–151).

Examples (#A24)

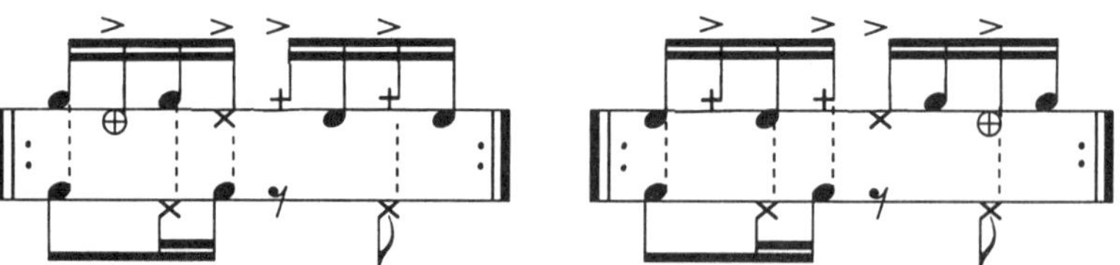

☐ Play each figure on the bass drum. Fill in the remaining sixteenth note subdivisions on the snare drum or toms. Add any appropriate hi-hat pattern (see p. 151).

Example (#B11)

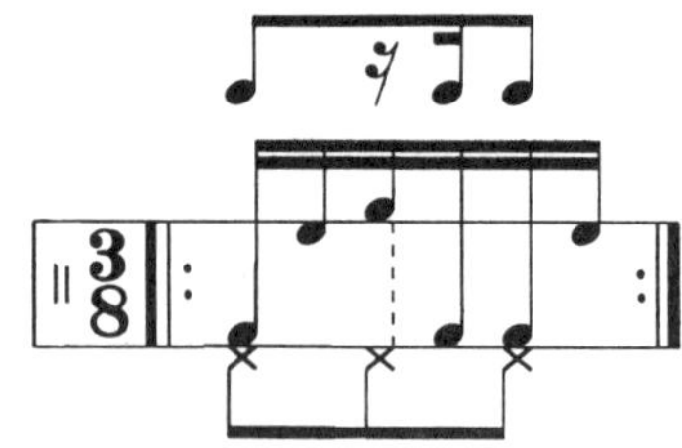

Play the figure on the snare drum or toms. Fill in the remaining sixteenth note subdivisions with the bass drum. Add any appropriate hi-hat pattern (see p. 151).

Example (#B11)

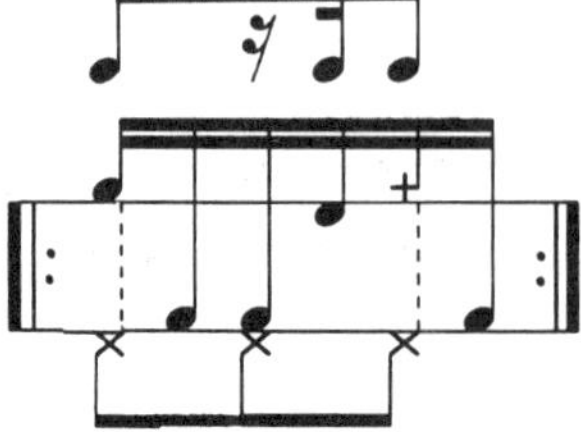

A.
1.
2.
3.
4.
5.
6.
7.
8.
9.
10.
11.
12.
13.
14.
15.
16.
17.
18.
19.
20.
21.
22.
23.
24.
25.
26.
27.
28.
29.
30.
31.
B.
1.
2.
3.
4.
5.
6.
7.
8.
9.
10.
11.
12.
13.
14.
15.

APPENDIX III: *Triplet and Eighth/Sixteenth Note Combination Sticking Patterns*

Beat 1 ("a.") is the same within each section's sticking patterns.

Practice Options

- ☐ Play each pattern repeatedly on snare drum. Once you master the hands alone, add any appropriate feet pattern (see pp. 150–151).
- ☐ Play each pattern on the snare drum as a fill (in the context of time). Add any appropriate feet pattern (see pp. 150–151).
- ☐ Play each pattern on the bass drum and hi-hat. Keep time with the hands.
- ☐ Omit "a." and "d." in each pattern to create $\frac{2}{4}$ patterns. Add any appropriate feet pattern (see p. 151).
- ☐ Omit "b." in each pattern to create $\frac{3}{4}$ patterns. Add any appropriate feet pattern (see p. 151).

Variations

groove context

- ☐ Play the notes above the line in each pattern on a cymbal, cymbal bell, or cowbell. Play notes below the line on the snare drum. Accent the back-beats, and add any appropriate feet pattern (see pp. 150–151).

fill context

- ☐ Play each pattern as a fill using the following surface combinations:
  - — right hand on tom, left hand on snare.
  - — right hand moving from surface to surface, *ad lib.*; left hand stationary on snare.
  - — left hand moving from surface to surface, *ad lib.*; right hand stationary on snare.
  - — both hands moving from surface to surface, *ad lib.*

  Add any appropriate feet pattern (see pp. 150–151).

- ☐ Play each pattern on the snare drum, filling in the remaining triplet or sixteenth note subdivisions with the bass drum. Add any appropriate hi-hat pattern (see p. 151).

Example (#B54)

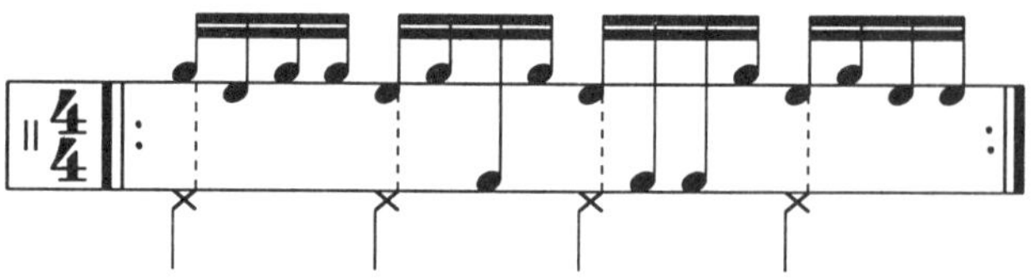

In any of the above Variations:

Replace any "a." with any of the following:

i.  ii.  iii.

Replace any "d." with any of the following:

i.  ii.  iii.

Replace any "b." or "c." with the following:

a.
b.
c.
d.
A.
1.
2.
3.
4.
5.
6.
7.
8.
9.
a.
b.
c.
d.
B.
1.
2.
3.
4.
5.
6.
7.
8.
9.
10.
11.
12.
13.
14.

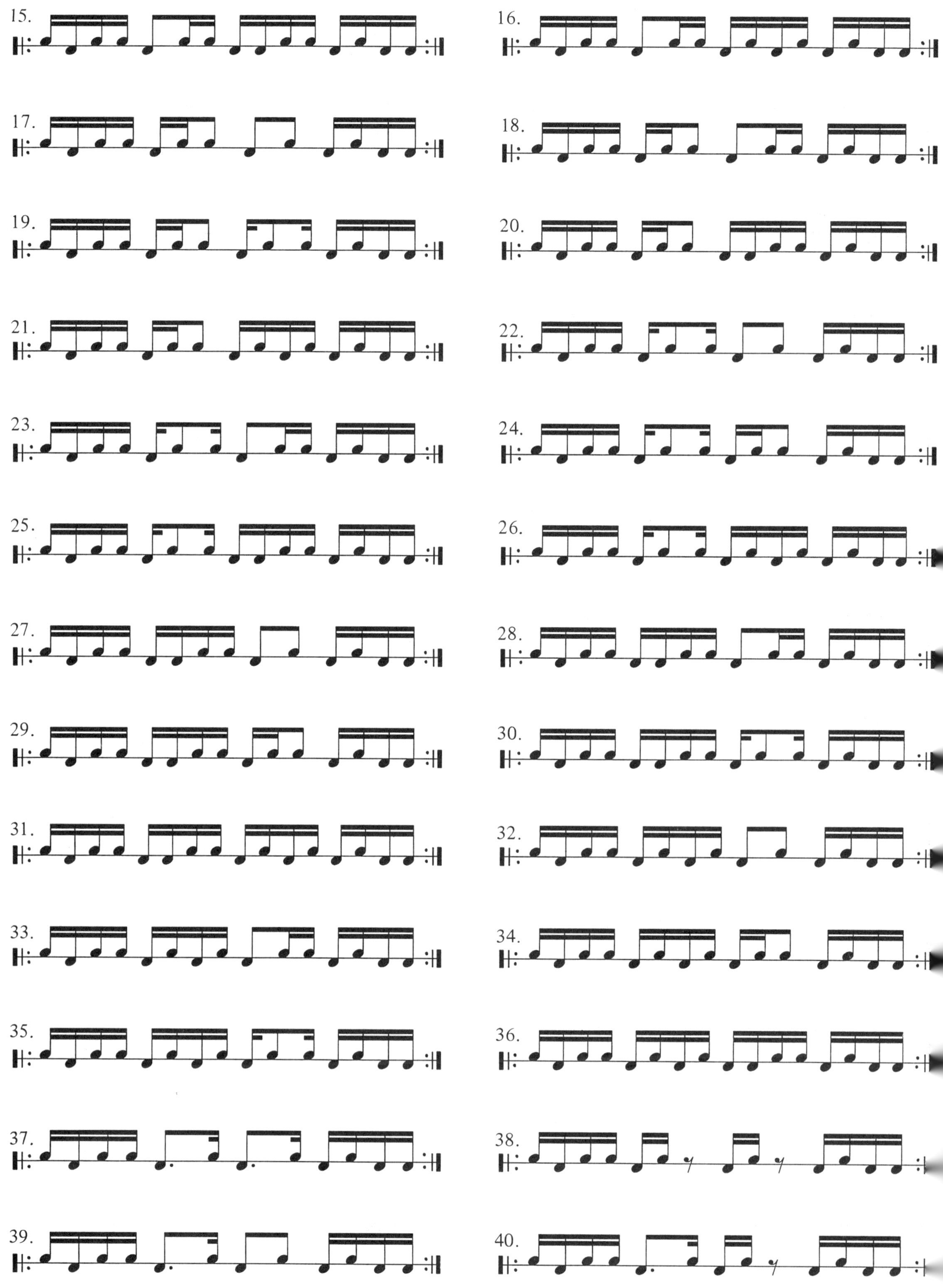
15.
16.
17.
18.
19.
20.
21.
22.
23.
24.
25.
26.
27.
28.
29.
30.
31.
32.
33.
34.
35.
36.
37.
38.
39.
40.

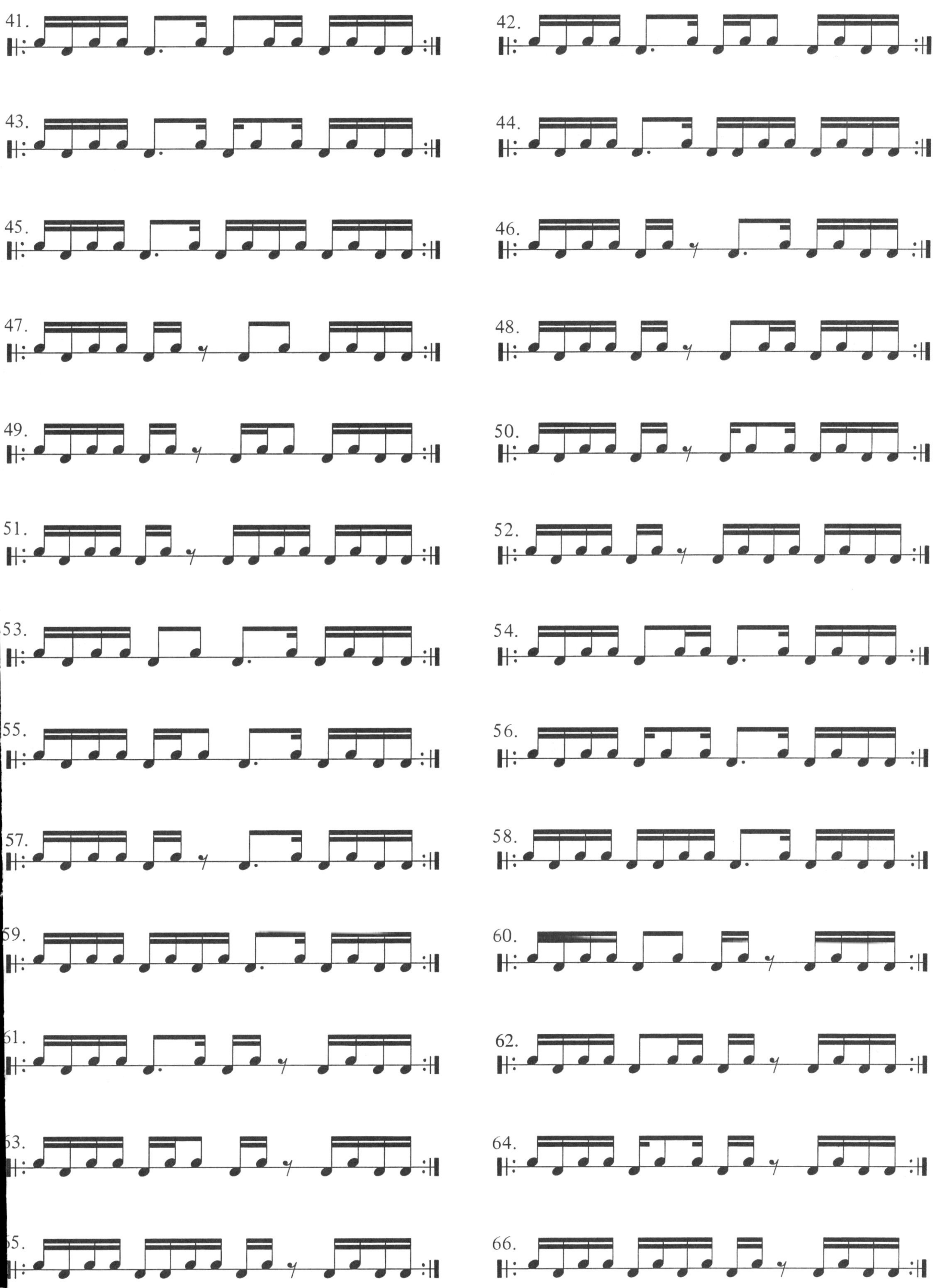
41.
42.
43.
44.
45.
46.
47.
48.
49.
50.
51.
52.
53.
54.
55.
56.
57.
58.
59.
60.
61.
62.
63.
64.
65.
66.

APPENDIX IV: *Constant Rhythm Converters*

The figures on page 149 are designed to replace any constant right hand, left hand, right foot, and/or left foot rhythm in various studies in this book. A few of the many possibilities are shown below. (For ease of use, page 149 may be duplicated.)

Study 3, p. 14; #2 as written:

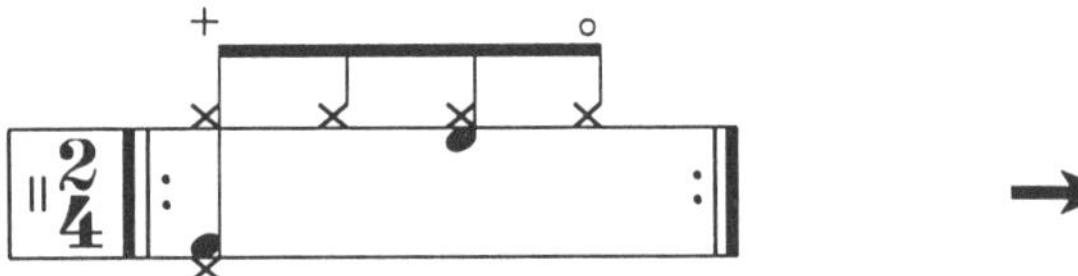

. . . with bass drum rhythm on beat 1 replaced by #A12 from page 149:

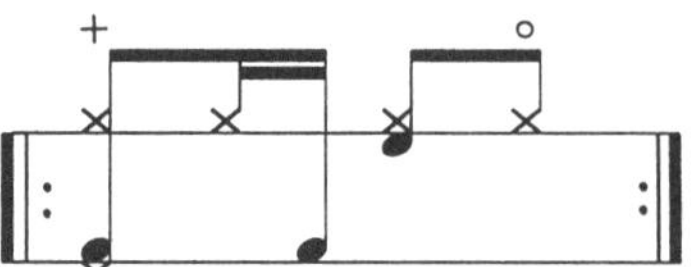

Study 6, p. 18; #8 as written:

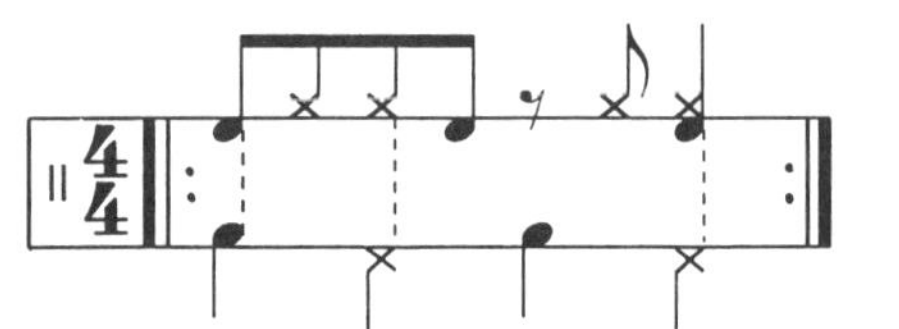

. . . with snare drum rhythm on beat 1 and bass drum rhythm on beat 3 replaced by #A9 from page 149:

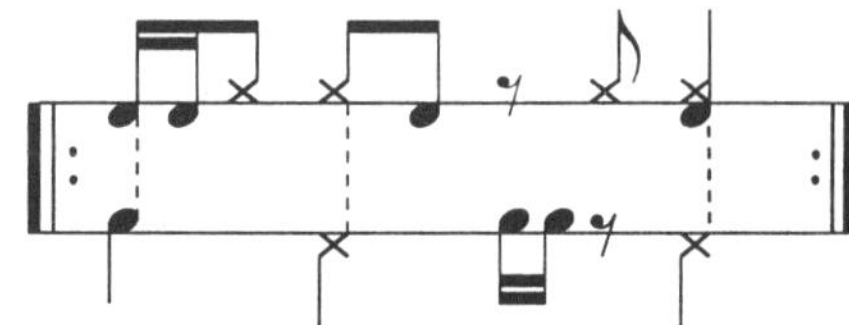

Study 19, p. 40; #12 as written:

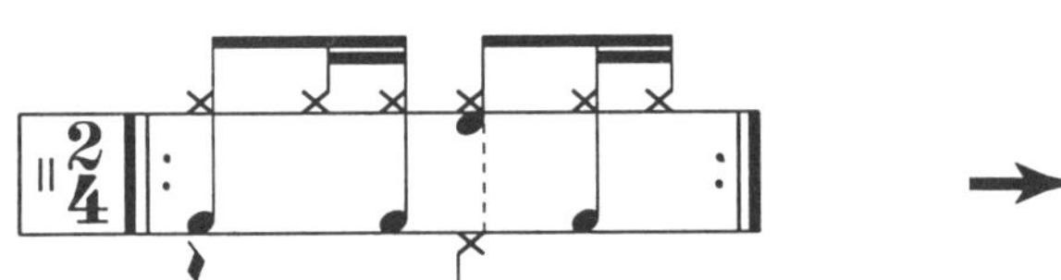

. . . with ride rhythm replaced by #A16 from page 149 on beat 1 and #A12 from page 149 on beat 2:

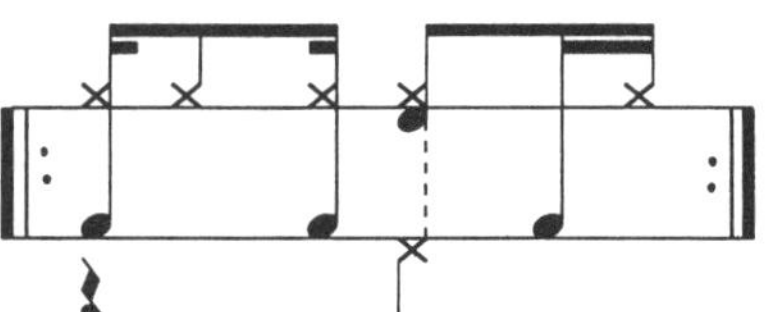

Study 30, p. 63; #C6 as written:

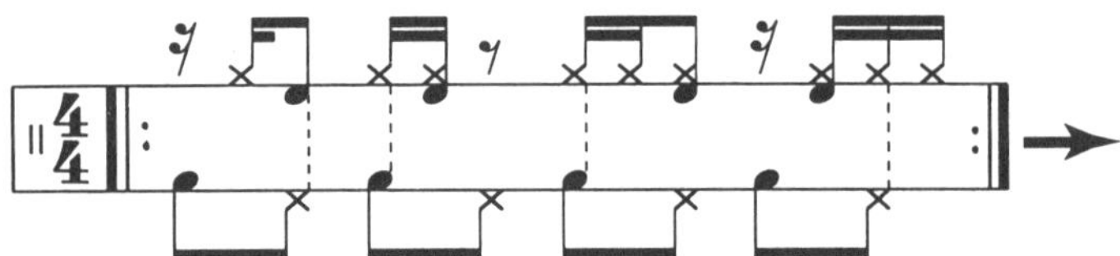

. . . with snare drum rhythm on beats 2 and 4 replaced by #A6 from page 149:

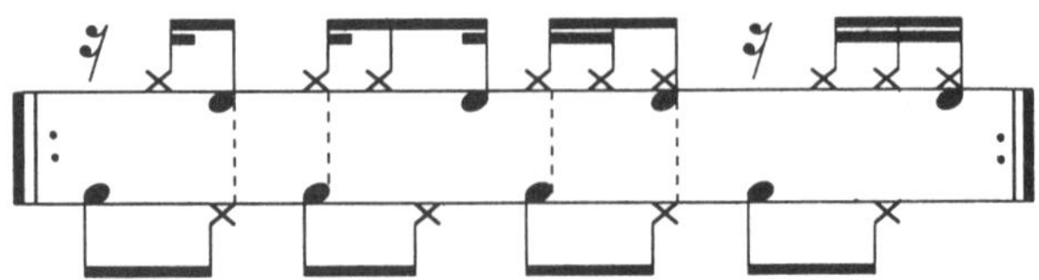

Study 46, p. 85; #B11 as written:

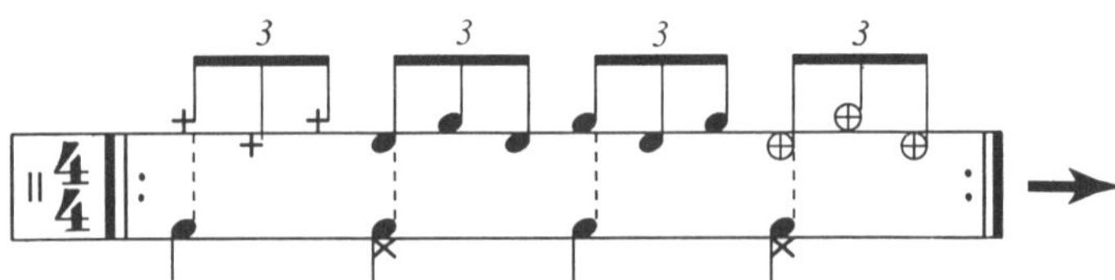

. . . with the hand rhythms on beats 2, 3, and 4 replaced by #B7, B8 and B4 from page 149:

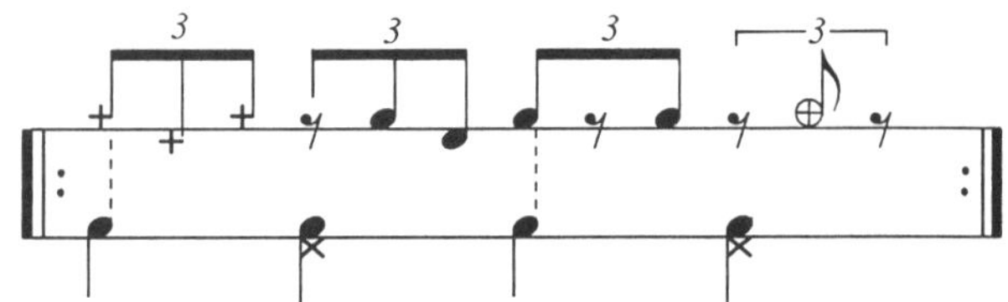

Appendix I, page 139; #A18 as written:

. . . figure played on snare drum, with #A11 from page 149 being played on a closed hi-hat on beats 1, 2, and 4, and #A9 from page 149 being played on the bass drum on beats 1 and 3:

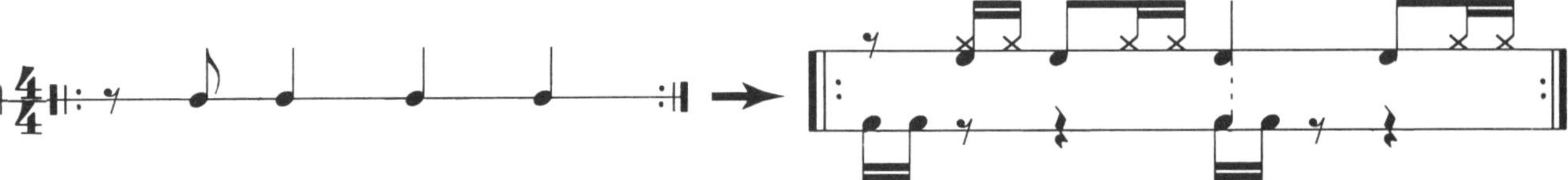

A.
1.
2.
3.
4.
5.
6.
7.
8.
9.
10.
11.
12.
13.
14.
15.
16.
B.
1.
2.
3.
4.
5.
6.
7.
8.

FEET PATTERN LIBRARY

In addition to the patterns shown below, you may create additional $\frac{4}{4}$ feet patterns by combining any two $\frac{2}{4}$ patterns. Likewise, you may divide any $\frac{4}{4}$ feet pattern in half to create two individual $\frac{2}{4}$ patterns, or combine $\frac{2}{4}$, $\frac{3}{4}$, and/or $\frac{4}{4}$ patterns to create patterns in $\frac{5}{4}$, $\frac{7}{4}$, etc.

Bass Drum/Hi-Hat Patterns

$\frac{4}{4}$ PATTERNS

2/4 PATTERNS
1. 2. 3. 4. 5. 6.
7. 8. 9. 10. 11. 12.
13. 14. 15. 16. 17.
18. 19. 20. 21. 22. 23.
24. 25. 26. 27. 28. 29.
3/4 PATTERNS
1. 2. 3. 4. 5.
6. 7. 8. 9. 10. 11.
12. 13. 14. 15. 16.
Hi-Hat Patterns
4/4 PATTERNS
A. B. C.
D. E. F.
2/4 PATTERNS
A. B. C. D.
3/4 PATTERNS
A. B. C. D.

ABOUT THE AUTHOR

Photo by Chuck Keeler, Jr.

Elliot Fine is a noted teacher, author, and performer. His credits include many television, radio, jazz, big band, and classical appearances. As a drum set performer, he has appeared on numerous albums and has backed such acts as Benny Goodman, Judy Garland, Carmen McRae, Liberace, Mary Wells, Dinah Shore, Neil Sedaka, Bobby Vinton, Margaret Whiting, Toots Thielemans, Doc Severinsen, Marvin Hamlisch, Michel Legrand, the Canadian Brass, the Swingle Singers, and the King Singers. As a member of the percussion section of the Minnesota Orchestra, he has performed under such greats as Dorati, Skrowaczewski, Fiedler, Monteux, Szell, Mancini, Stravinsky, Copland, Previn, Whiteman, and most recently, Sir Neville Marriner, Leonard Slatkin, John Williams, and Edo deWaart. His talents may be heard on many Minnesota Orchestra albums, including recent releases of George Gershwin's *Rhapsody in Blue*, and Leonard Bernstein's Symphonic Dances from *West Side Story* and Three Dance Episodes from *On the Town*.

In addition to his frequent performing duties, Mr. Fine is a percussion instructor at the University of Minnesota and Normandale College, and maintains a full load of private students at his studio in Minneapolis, Minnesota. His unique approaches to drum set instruction have resulted in the creation of several landmark percussion publications. These include *Four-Way Coordination*, and *Accents on Accents*, both in collaboration with Marvin Dahlgren. In addition, Mr. Fine has written and published numerous percussion ensembles. His wealth of experience in music disciplines and his versatility as a percussionist are recognized by the countless students who have had the honor of studying with him.